THIS BOOK SHOULD BE RE
DATE SHOWN TO THE LIBI
D0708014
MONTHLY LOAN
11 AUG 1989
15 AUG 2008
SUBJECT TO RECALL
Item on Loan From
QL/P-3 Lancashire
LOAN FROM Z
16 SEP 2008
WITHDRAWN FROM
LANCASHIRE LIBRARIES
Our Ref:
Your Ref:
LOAN FROM Z
16 FEB 1993
- 4 FEB 1993
AUTHOR ELLIS, Ken
CLASS 629.13334
TITLE WRECKS and relics
Lancashire County Council
THE LANCASHIRE LIBRARY.
Library Headquarters,
143, Corporation St.,
PRESTON PRI 2TB.
a30118 037986225b

Eleventh Edition

WRECKS & RELICS

Compiled by Ken Ellis

MIDLAND COUNTIES PUBLICATIONS

Contents

03798622

Cover photographs:

End of an era: Lightning F.3 XR716 minus belly-tank on the dump at RAF Cottesmore, Jan'88. (Ken Ellis, thanks to Sqn Ldr Geoff Roberts, CRO)

'Undercarriage surgery' is applied to Vulcan XL427 to ready it for Machrihanish dump, 1986. ('Pinza')

Brooklands Museum was the venue for the last flight by a civil VC-10. A40-AB at rest in October 1987. (Peter J. Cooper)

Copyright 1988
Ken Ellis and Midland Counties Publications
ISBN 0 904597 71 7

This eleventh edition published by
Midland Counties Publications (Aerophile) Limited
24 The Hollow, Earl Shilton, Leicester, LE9 7NA

Printed in England
by Oxford University Press Printing House

Preface

When the current scribe took the helm of *Wrecks & Relics* way back with the Fourth Edition in 1974 a regular publication cycle was established which clearly was well greeted by the readers. The Eleventh Edition (or perhaps it is just life...) has turned out to have been more problematical and will accordingly 'hit the streets' late. The letters and 'phone calls from concerned followers and the *Mr Angries* have been both pleasing and upping my miffed-factor respectively! To the former I hope that it was all worth waiting for, to the latter can I direct you to the foot of page 222?

While there are no 'new' sections as such, the entire work has been given a rethink and a complete revision. So-called new technology has allowed the book to come *down* in pages but actually *up* in wordage.

This edition also sees the launch of a brother (or is it sister?) in the form of *European Wrecks & Relics* with a very brave Mike Bursell taking on the task of putting it together - further details on page 223.

As ever, a large number of people have given a hand in the compilation of this tome and they are mentioned below and in the following pages. Contributions from readers are vital to *Wrecks & Relics* and will me made most welcome via the publishers, address below.

Coping with slipping deadlines and a slipping, lined and near-dead compiler with great patience and much encouragement have been the following individuals to whom go my many thanks : John Coghill, Trevor Green, Dave Peel and Roger Richards looked after the production-checking phase. .Alan Allen provided much detailed research work and cross-checking. Alan Curry looked after the bulk of the photographic coverage and editorial life-support fluids!. Bev Risdon produced the artwork, despite the fact that the commission was outlined on the back of a bus ticket! Many thanks to Duncan Cubitt and Felicity McAuley of Key Publishing. The publishers, in the form of Neil Lewis and Chris Salter have been not just patient but constantly making inputs and improvements.

This book would not have seen the light of day without the dedication and hard work of Tom Poole who has provided an exceptional amount of cross-checking, refining and research.His personal support and encouragement are gratefully acknowledged.

Finally I must acknowledge *Deep Fraught* the computer who quickly taught me that without him, *anything* is possible!

Gulp, last chance for submissions to *Wrecks & Relics 12* is December 31, 1989.

Ken Ellis
1988

Wrecks & Relics, c/o Midland Counties Publications, 24 The Hollow, Earl Shilton, Leicester, LE9 7NA.

Acknowledgements

As ever, *Wrecks & Relics* is produced with the help of a large number of people and the compiler would like to thank the following specialists for their help with this edition :-

Dave Allport for a vast amount of help on the civilian side and a review of the draft that was longer than the draft!; Peter R Arnold for keeping track of the Spitfire population; Maurice Baalham of NAAG for Norfolk notes; Tim R Badham for his impressive array of photos; John G Chree for northern Scotland; Paul Crellin for constant up-dating and researching 'chestnuts'; Wal Gandy for constant cross-checking of entries; Malcolm Fillmore for much additional information on CAA cancellations; Ian Griffiths for keeping this ex-Merseysider up to date with that neck of the woods; Mark Harris, for RAF Overseas notes; Alan Johnson for the latest news on the UK civil register; Maurice Morgan for handling the Scottish entries; Simon Murdoch for his coverage of East Anglia and Essex; Jeremy Parkin of Alpha Helicopters for much help on all things with a rotor on top; Dave Pope for his extensive notes, particularly on all things Chipmunk and RAF Germany; Paddy Porter for much encouragement and the answer to many a question!; Lloyd P Robinson for up-dates from his many travels; Robert Rudhall for much news on the museums and 'warbirds' front; Dave Wise for coverage of the 'Home Counties'.

Many people within the UK preservation movement have helped and my thanks are recorded below. In answer to enquiries, *every* museum and group receives a questionnaire before each W&R, it therefore follows that the names that are *missing* below couldn't get their act together!

Colin Allen, Down-Bird UK; John Bagley, Science Museum; Philip Baldock, Robertsbridge Aviation Society; Sandy Benzies, Aircraft Preservation Society of Scotland; David Buchanan, Kent Battle of Britain Museum; Ray Burrows, Ulster Aviation Society; Tony Carroll, South Yorkshire Aircraft Museum; Bob Coles, Second World War Aircraft Preservation Society; Joe Collier, Wartime Aircraft Recovery Group; David Cotton, Stratford Aircraft Collection; Major John Cross, Museum of Army Flying; Lewis Deal, Royal Aeronautical Society Medway Branch Preservation Group; Wayne Drurey, Bomber County Aviation Museum; Huby Fairhead, Norfolk & Suffolk Aviation Museum; Ken Fern, Ken Fern Collection; R Ferrand, Scottish Aircraft Collection Trust; Keith Fordyce, Torbay Aircraft Museum; Harry Holmes, British Aerospace Avro Aircraft Restoration Society; Stuart Howe, Mosquito Aircraft Museum; Paul Hunt, North East Aircraft Museum; S/L A Jones, Southampton Hall of Aviation; David King, Booker Aircraft Museum; Leslie Lane, Battle of Britain Memorial Flight Vistor Centre; David Lee, Imperial War Museum; Ray Mackenzie-Blythe, Snowdon Mountain Aviation; Bob Major, Royal Museum of Scotland; Phil Maloney, Military Aircraft Preservation Group; John May, Wessex Aviation Society; Bill Miles, North Weald Restoration Flight; John Moore, Ulster Folk & Transport Museum; Graham Mottram, Fleet Air Arm Museum; Major GG Norton, Airborne Forces Museum; Tony Nuttall, Solway Aviation Society; Dell Paddock, Wellesbourne Aviation Group; Andrew Picton, Vintage Aircraft Team; Nigel Ponsford, Ponsford Collection; Norman Pritchard, British Balloon Museum and Library; Caroline Reed, Royal Engineers Museum; Elfan ap Rees, British Rotorcraft Museum; D Reid, Dumfries & Galloway Aviation Group; Malcolm Reynolds, East Anglian Aviation Society; Gwyn Roberts, Wales Aircraft Museum; Ian Rose, Phoenix Aviation Museum; Mike Russell, Russavia Collection; Ross Sharp, Science Museum and BAPC; Richard Simpson, Royal Air Force Museum; Kelvin Sloper, City of Norwich Aviation Museum; Mick Smith, Newark Air Museum; Peter Smith, Biggin Hill Air Museum; Roger Smith, Midland Air Museum; Mick Skeels, Essex Aviation Group; Graham Sparkes, The Aeroplane Collection; Dave Stansfield, Pennine Aviation Museum; Peter Stoddart, Leicestershire Museums; Peter Symes, Shuttleworth Collection; Steve Thompson, Cotswold Aircraft Restoration Group; Graham Warner, British Aerial Museum; Dave Westacott, Newark Air Museum; Keith Wheeler, Yorkshire Air Museum; Jim Wilkie, Helicopter Museum of Great Britain; Dennis Woodgate, Robertsbridge Aviation Society; Len Woodgate, Aerospace Museum, Cosford; Mike Woodley, Aces High Flying Museum.

And to the many readers who have written in with snippets and observations since W&R10, such reports are the life-blood of the book. My many thanks to :-

Peter Alcock; Martin Barsley; Derek Bailey; John Beacom; D C Bennett; Peter J Bish; Mike Blake; Ellwood and Jake Blues; Paul Brown; Harry Bunn; Ian Burningham; David Burke; Paul Carhart; Peter Castle; Barry Clay; Duncan Curtis; Dent, Arthur Dent; Mark Duffy; Phil Dunnington; John Dyer; Richard Dyett; Andy Edge; Chris Farmer; Paul Flyn; Laurence Goldman; Alan Green; Graham Hall; Martyn Hall; Jim Henderson; Paul Higgins; Chris Hobson; Gawayne Hodgkiss; Nigel Howarth; Steve Hurst; Chrissie Hynde; Sandy Hyslop; Chris Jacewicz; Graham Jackson; Alf Jenks; Mark Kennaway; Paul Kernot; Dave Kinsey; John Marshall; Jason Mather; Chris Michell; Sid Nanson; John Nicholls; Peter Nops; Ian Oliver; Neil Owen; Mike Packham; Richard Parrant; Mick Phillips; *Pinza*; Ian Powell; K R Preen; R J Pritchard; J Probert; Neil Reynolds; Alan Roach; Phil Rogers; M R Rushton; Matt Sharrock; Mark Shortman; Peter Spooner; Martin Standish; Graham Tanner; B Taylor; B V Taylor; Bill Taylor; Graham Taylor; D Thompson; David Thompson; Emma Thompson; Alan Todd; Suzanne Vega; Chris Walkden; Ian Walker; Sigourny Weaver; Michael Westwood; Keith Wilson; John and Ian Wiseman.

Notes

Scope

Wrecks & Relics serves to outline, in as much detail as possible, the status and whereabouts of all known PRESERVED (ie in museum or other collections, under restoration etc); INSTRUCTIONAL (ie static airframes in use for training); and DERELICT (ie out of use for a long period of time, fire dump aircraft, scrapped or damaged etc) aircraft in the United Kingdom and Eire. (The recently-introduced section 'RAF Overseas' follows much the same lines as the main section.) Where information permits all aircraft that fall into these categories are included, with the following exceptions :-
1] airworthy aircraft not part of a specific collection. 2] aircraft that fall into any of the above categories for only a short period of time. 3] aircraft without provision for a human pilot (unless registered in the BAPC system). 4] in general, aircraft will only be considered if they are at least a cockpit/nose section.

Entries

Generally, entries are all dealt with in a standard manner. As *W&R* covers a two year period, in this case 1986-1988, beyond the location header there is a narrative explaining the current status of the entry and outlining any airframes that have moved since the last edition. Airframes moving on are given underlined forwarding references. Thus, if the reader wishes, it is possible to follow the more energetic examples around the book. Any aircraft which fall into any of the four categories above, or are exported, will not have forwarding references and their entry should be considered closed. The LOST! section has been re-introduced to act as a 'safety net' for aircraft that have no determined fate. Entries new to a heading in this edition are marked + after the registration/serial.

Where possible, brief historical details of the aircraft listed are given, in a necessarily abbreviated form. This information varies slightly in presentation, but can mostly be found in column three in the tabulated entries or rarely in brackets behind an entry in the narrative. In each case units etc are listed in *reverse* order, ie first use of an aircraft is listed *last*. Readers should have little trouble with these potted histories, especially with continued reference to the Abbreviations section.

Locations

Directions to the town or village in question are given after each place name. Readers should note that these directions *are to the town or village mentioned and not necessarily to the actual site of the aircraft in question.* Directions are *not* given in the following instances :- 1] where specific directions to the site are not fully known. 2] where the location is a large city or town. 3] where the location is an airfield. It is felt that for the last two points, readers will be able to find their own way around!

Access

Unless otherwise stated, all locations in this work are PRIVATE and access to them is *strictly by prior permission*, if at all. Museum open times are given *as a guide only* and readers are advised to contact the museum in question before setting out on a journey.

Serial and registration presentation

Aircraft are listed in registration/serial sequence. Previous registrations and/or serials are given in the aircraft's history section, if known. In the majority of cases for military aircraft, entries are given using the airframe's serial number (accurate or fictitious) and 'A' or 'M' numbers or similar are given in column three. Incorrect, or fictitious registrations and serials are marked ", eg VZ999" or G-BKEN".

Wrecks & Relics *is put together using the best information available to the compiler. Every effort is made to be as accurate as possible. However, neither the compiler nor the publishers can be held responsible for any errors or changes that may occur in the location or status of aircraft or places listed.*

Part 1

ENGLAND

Avon

BATH

Sea Hawk Restoration Group Dr Bob Poulter has had to put his Sea Hawk restoration project and its 'spares ship' up for sale, but it is believed that work on the Swift F.7 forward fuselage is to continue. Current status of the group itself is unknown.

WM993	Sea Hawk FB.5	A2522, arr by 5/85, ex Corsham, Culdrose, SAH, FRU, 806, 811, 800. Source of spares for WV795.
WV795	Sea Hawk FGA.6	8151M/A2661, ex Cardiff-Wales, Culdrose, Halton, Sydenham, 738, 806, 700.
XF113	Swift F.7	forward fuselage, ex Frome, Farnborough, ETPS, A&AEE, Handling Sqn.

BRISTOL

Bristol City Museum and Art Gallery The Museum still displays the *Magnificent Men* Boxkite replica. Open Monday to Saturday 1000-1700. Address : Queen's Road, Clifton, Bristol BS8 1RL. Tel 0272 299771.

BAPC, 40	Boxkite replica	ex Old Warden, built by Miles at Ford. c/no BM.7281.

Bristol Industrial Museum BIM holds an impressive selection of Bristol aero engines and continues to display the Sycamore. Open Monday-Wednesday & Saturday/Sunday 1000-1300 and 1400-1700. Prince's Wharf, Bristol BS1 4RN. Tel 0272 299771.

XL829	Sycamore HR.14	ex 32, MCS, Khormaksar SAR Flight.

Bristol Plane Preservation Unit The well known 'Miles Duo' continues to operate from an airstrip in the area, under the guidance of Jim Buckingham and team, with the sponsorship of SAC Ltd. They can be seen regularly at air displays. Visits to the strip are not possible. Messenger G-AKBO, mentioned as leaving in W&R10, made its first flight following restoration by Clive du Cros in 1987 at Hullavington.

G-AKBM	Messenger 2A	ex Elsham Hall, Goxhill, Tattershall, Barton. For spares.
G-AKKB	Gemini 1A	SAC logos, airworthy.
RG333"	Messenger 2A	G-AIEK, p/i Miles 'B' Condition U-9, airworthy.

Brunel Technical College Located at Ashley Down, off the A38 north of the city centre, the College had a reshuffle of its instructional airframes in 1987, with an Apache coming in and Whirlwind XK944 moving to Malpas 19/2/87. Other airframes are held at Bristol Airport, which see.

G-ATHA+	Apache 235	ex Aviation West, Bristol Airport. CoA exp 7/6/86, arrived 15/7/87.
G-AWBW	Cessna F.172H	ex Bristol Airport, Compton Abbas. dbr 20/5/73, wfu 23/5/74.
G-AWUK	Cessna F.150H	ex Biggin Hill, crashed 4/9/71.

Winbolt Collection Dr G E Winbolt has a large collection of aircraft radios and associated equipment. A Sea Vixen nose is also held. Visits by prior application only to Dr G E Winbolt, The Cottage, Castle Road, Pucklechurch, near Bristol, Avon.

XN651	Sea Vixen FAW.2	A2616, ex Culdrose, SAH, 766, FAW.1 893. Nose section only.

Others In the locality of Bristol there are now three restoration projects underway. Robs Lamplough's Spitfire VIII continues. Tim Cox is working on a restoration of the former Boston Auster J/1 composite. Finally, Phil Dunnington moved into the area in late 1986, bringing with him his Drone.

G-ADPJ+	BAC Drone II	ex Benson, Thetford, accident Leicester 3/4/55. Under restoration using parts from G-AEKU.
F-BFUT+	J/1N Alpha	ex Fiskerton, Boston, Bodmin, fuselage frame, with wings of J/1N G-AJEI.
MV154	Spitfire VIII	G-BKMI, ex Huntingdon, Duxford, Australia, RAAF A58-671, 82 MU, 6 MU.

BRISTOL AIRPORT

(Also known as Lulsgate). The Brunel Technical College airframes here have not changed. An Apache from here did move to their site in Bristol (see above). Another Apache is in use for spares.

G-ANAP	Dove 6	ex CAFU Stansted. wfu 31/8/73. Brunel.
G-ARJW+	Apache 160	ex Biggin Hill. CoA exp 9/1/82. Arrived by 6/86, spares for G-ARJV.
G-AVFM	Trident 2E	ex BA and BEA. Flew in 13/1/84. Brunel.
G-AVHN	Cessna F.150G	wreck, crashed 28/1/85. First noted 7/85.
G-AVVW	Cessna F.150H	CoA expired 31/5/82. Brunel.
G-BIUO	Commander 112A	ex Staverton, OY-PRH, N1281J. Crashed 12/5/84. On fire dump by 3/87.
WF376	Varsity T.1	ex CFS, CAW, 5 FTS, 151, 201 AFS. Fire service.
WF410	Varsity T.1	ex 6 FTS, 2 ANS, 5 FTS, 2 ANS, RAFC, CNCS, 201 AFS. Brunel.

FILTON

Airfield For a long time a landmark at Filton, the British Airways 'spares-ship' Concorde has had a hangar built for it - it will have 'vanished' from outside eyes by the time these words are read, with its tail fin coming off in the process.

G-BBDG Concorde 100-002 CoA expired 1/3/82. BA spares - see notes above.

Rolls-Royce Technical School Located opposite the airfield, the School still houses its Provost T.1.

XF603 Provost T.1 ex Bristol, 27 MU, CAW, RAFC.

GROVESEND

Whirlwind HAS.7 XN264 which was kept at a private house here was destroyed by fire circa 1986.

KEYNSHAM

(On the A4 south east of Bristol). Mr K Baker continues with his Pup restoration project.

G-EAVX Sopwith Pup ex Dorset and B1807, crashed 21/7/21. PFA project 101-10523.

LOCKING

(On the A371 east of Weston-super-Mare) While the Canberra and Meteor remained in blissful peace, the transfer of a Spitfire to the American Eagle Squadron (see under Halton, Bucks) meant a major shift around of Spitfires during 1986. Locking lost its F.21 LA198 to Leuchars in 1986. After an embarrassing period with a nude plinth inside the camp, a Gnat T.1 arrived from Halton to make the 'gate' all jet.

WH840 Canberra T.4 8350M, ex 19 MU, Geilenkirchen SF, A&AEE, 97, 151, 245, 88, 231 OCU, CFS.
WL360 Meteor T.7 7920M, ex 229 OCU, 1, Wattisham SF, 211 AFS, 210 AFS, 215 AFS. Coded 'G'.
XM708+ Gnat T.1 8573M, ex Halton, 4 FTS, CFS, HS. Arrived by 10/86, Red Arrows colours.

MONKTON FARLEIGH

Avon Aviation Museum (East of the A363, east of Bath) At the former wartime armaments store, the Monkton Farleigh Mines, the Avon Aviation Museum (originally named the Wessex Aviation Museum) have established a base and moved their first aircraft, the former Worcester Javelin in during 7/87. AAM also own the Wessex HAS.3 at Lasham, and this was due on site here as W&R11 went to press. Contact : Paul Brown, 8 Hobbes Close, Malmesbury, Wilts, SN16 0DA.

XH767+ Javelin FAW.9 7955M, ex Worcester, 27 MU, 228 OCU, 11, 25. Arrived 7/87.
XM833+ Wessex HAS.3 ex Lasham, Wroughton. Due to arrive Spring 1988.

WESTON-SUPER-MARE

Woodspring Museum Located in Burlington Street, the Museum displays a gyroplane, on loan from the British Rotorcraft Museum - see below.

G-BAPS Campbell Cougar ex Weston Airport. CoA exp 20/5/74, first flew at Weston 25/4/73.

WESTON-SUPER-MARE AIRPORT

British Rotorcraft Museum Following agreement concerning a permanent site for the Museum, the planned re-opening date is now set at May 1988. In the meantime a £300,000 appeal has been launched to cover the erection of a purpose-built display building. Until an announcement has been made, the helicopter store is not available for inspection and intending visitors should scan the aviation press or make enquiries before setting off on a visit. Contact : BRM, White Acre, 75 Elm Tree Road, Locking, Weston-super-Mare, Avon BS24 8EL. Tel 0934 822524

Meanwhile, BRM has continued its energetic acquisitions policy with several new exhibits coming on to the site. SARO P.531 XN334 moved out by road to Yeovilton on 18/9/87. Other airframes are held at other locations, as follows : Crawley; Middle Wallop; Weston-super-Mare; Wroughton; Yeovilton.

G-ACWM+ Cierva C.30A ex Staverton, AP506, 529, 1448 Flt, 74 Wing, 5 RSS, G-ACWM. Frame only, arrived by 20/12/86.
G-ANFH Whirlwind Srs 1 ex Redhill, Great Yarmouth, Bristow, BEAH. wfu 7/71.
G-ANJV Whirlwind Srs 3 ex Redhill, Bristow and VR-BET.
G-AOUJ Fairey Ultra-Light ex 'Essex', White Waltham, XJ928. CoA exp 29/3/59.
G-ARVN Grasshopper 1 ex Shoreham and Redhill. wfu 5/63. See notes under Shoreham.
G-ASHD Brantly B.2B ex Oxford Airport and area, crashed 15/2/67.
G-ATKV+ Whirlwind Srs 3 ex Redhill, Bristow, VR-BEU, G-ATKV, EP-HAN, G-ATKV.
G-AVKE Gadfly HDW-1 ex Southend, Thruxton. wfu 1971.

G-AVNE+	Wessex 60	ex Bournemouth Airport, Sykes Av, Weston-super-Mare, Bristow, 5N-AJL, G-AVNE, 9M-ASS, VH-BHC, PK-HBQ, G-AVNE. Arrived late 24/11/87.
G-AZYB	Bell 47H-1	ex Thruxton, LN-OQG, SE-HBE, OO-SHW, crashed 21/4/84.
G-48/1+	Sycamore III	ex Duxford, Staverton, G-ALSX, VR-TBS ntu, G-ALSX. Arrived 1987.
BAPC128	Watkinson CG-4-IV	ex Bexhill. Man powered rotorcraft.
BAPC153	Westland WG-33	ex Yeovil. Mock-up ultra-light helicopter/drone
5N-ABW+	Widgeon 2	ex Cuckfield, Shoreham, Bristow, G-AOZE. Arrived 1986.
VZ962+	Dragonfly HR.1	ex Helston, BRNC Dartmouth. Arrived 1987, for spares.
WG719	Dragonfly HR.5	G-BRMA, ex Shawbury, Weston, Yeovilton, Yeovilton SF, 705.
XE521	Rotodyne Type Y	large components, ex Cranfield.
XG452	Belvedere HC.1	G-BRMB/7997M, ex Ternhill, 2 SoTT, Westlands.
XG547	Sycamore HR.14	G-HAPR/8010M, ex CCAS, 5 MU Apprentices, CFS.
XG596	Whirlwind HAS.7	A2651, ex Wroughton, 705, 829, 771, 705, 737.
XM556	Skeeter AOP.12	G-HELI/7870M, with boom of XM529/7979M, ex Connah's Quay, Middle Wallop.
XP165	Scout AH.1	ex HAM Southend, RAE.
XS149+	Wessex HAS.3	ex Wroughton, '661/GL'. Arrived late 1987.
XS463"	Wasp HAS.1	XT431, ex Fleetlands, Lee-on-Solent. Fitted with parts from XS463/A2647.
XT472+	Wessex HU.5	ex Hullavington, Netheravon, Lyneham, Wroughton, 845. Arrived late 1987.

Westlands On 16/9/87 Puma PA-12/ZE449 was roaded out to Sherborne.

Bedfordshire

BEDFORD

Dick Hadlow continues to work on Tiger Moth G-APMM. New here is stored Kite I BGA.400.

G-APMM	Tiger Moth	ex Duxford, DE419, 33 MU, 21 EFTS. CoA expired 31/12/64.
BGA 400+	T.6 Kite 1	ex Bishop's Stortford, VD165. Stored.

BEDFORD AIRFIELD

Royal Aerospace Establishment Bedford (Thurleigh) (Please note, the RAE went very up-market during the final stages of preparation of W&R11, and abandoned good old 'Aircraft' for the much more yuppy 'Aerospace'.) Once a haven for derelict airframes of all shapes and sizes, the RAE's offering of such fodder has fallen in recent years. The Apprentices took delivery of a Hunter F.6 in 1986, but otherwise the story is one of removals. Going back to W&R10, the Newark Air Museum took delivery of the bulk of Sea Vixen XJ560 on 10/8/86 and not as given. Departures have been as follows : Hastings C.1A TG568 was reduced to just a tail section on the dump by 7/87; Canberra B.2 WG789 was sold to a private owner in 'Sussex' during 7/86 - precise destination unknown; Canberra B.6 WH952 left by road 16/4/86 for Woolwich.

BGA1301	L-13 Blanik	G-ATCH, '351', ex Twinwood Farm, dismantled. Not reported for some time.
BGA1459	L-13 Blanik	G-ASKX, wrecked. Not reported for some time.
WH872	Canberra T.17	ex 360, RAE, 249, 32, 202, 15, 10, 40. Dump, in sections by 7/87
XG210+	Hunter F.6	ex BAe Hatfield, CFE, 19, 14. Apprentices, flown in 25/9/86.
XK530	Buccaneer S.2	ex RAE catapult trials and S.1. Open store, poor state.
XM694	Gnat T.1	ex Filton, Dunsfold, A&AEE. Apprentices, last noted 9/86.
XW626	Comet AEW	ex A&AEE, MinTech, G-APDS, BOAC. Open store, last flown 28/8/81.

CARDINGTON

Royal Air Force Museum Restoration and Storage Centre There has been a fairly large influx of airframes into the workshop/store since W&R10, some for storage and others for restoration prior to display. Leaving here, by April 1986, was the superb Bristol F.2b restoration 'E2466'/BAPC.165 for Hendon. Of the arrivals, three are of particular note; the former Yugoslav P-47D coming from Bitteswell as part of the complex Warbirds of Great Britain exchange; and two replicas, Leo Opdycke's Bristol Scout and Don Cashmore's briefly flown Bristol Monoplane. Of the aircraft listed overleaf, the Dolphin and Demon have not been reported for a considerable period of time.

G-AHED	Dragon Rapide	ex Henlow, RL962, DH Witney. In store.
BAPC 28	Wright Flyer rep	ex Finningley. In store.
BAPC180+	Silver Dart rep	arr during 1986, ex Farnborough and Canada. Stored.
BAPC181	BE.2b replica	under construction by John McKenzie, off-site.
F-HMFI	Farman F.40	ex Henlow and Nash Collection.
N5419+	Bristol Scout D	replica, arr by 5/86, built Leo Opdyke, USA. US civil registration.
C4912+"	Bristol M.1C rep	G-BLWM, ex Hucknall, arr 8/87 for fitting of original engine.
D5329	Sopwith Dolphin	almost complete fuselage. In store
K4972+	Hart Trainer	1764M, ex Hendon, St Athan, Carlisle, 2 FTS. Arr 1987 for restoration.
N9899	Southampton I	ex Henlow and Felixstowe. Fuselage only, under restoration.
FE905	Harvard IIB	ex Royston, London Bridge, Southend, LN-BNM, Danish AF 31-329, RAF FE905, 42-12392. Under restoration.
MP425	Oxford I	ex G-AITB, Shawbury, Perth, MP425. Under restoration, 1536 BATF colours.
VX275+	Sedbergh TX.1	8884M, ex St Athan, BGA.572. On charge here.
XE946	Vampire T.11	7473M, fuselage pod only, in store. Ex Henlow, Habbaniya SF, Nicosia SF.
	FE.2b	cockpit nacelle, in store.
	Hawker Demon	fuselage frame only, believed ex Cloughjordan, Eire.
	Horsa	8596M, incomplete fuselage sections.
8417/18	Fokker D.VII/OAW	ex Hendon, Cardington, Hendon, Cardington. Under restoration.
13064+	P-47D-40-RA	ex Bitteswell, Yugoslavia, USAAF 45-49295. Arrived by 6/86.

Airship Industries
Within the giant airship hangars, Skyship 500 G-BIHN is stored, following its accident.

G-BIHN+	Skyship 500	wrecked in gale 27/4/87.

CLAPHAM

(On the A6 north west of Bedford) Andrew Nowicki has acquired a Skeeter which is under restoration.

XL809+	Skeeter AOP.12	G-BLIX, under restoration, ex Shobdon, PH-HOF, (PH-SRE), Moordrecht, 26 Regt, 22F, 654, 652, 654. Arrived during 1986.

CRANFIELD

Cranfield Institute of Technology The Institute uses a small number of airframes for instructional purposes, including the teaching of crash investigation techniques. There has been some expansion of airframes in use of late.

G-AZZT	Cherokee 180D	ex N5302L. Crashed 10/2/80.
G-BBOJ	Aztec 250E	ex 5Y-AOK, N14130. Crashed 3/12/80.
G-BGGY+	AB JetRanger III	Crashed 13/9/84. Arrived by 10/86.
XJ604+	Sea Vixen FAW.2	8222M, ex Halton, Sydenham, 890, '755/VL'. Arrived 23/10/86.
XN979	Buccaneer S.2	ex 801, ditched 9/6/66. Nose section.
XT439+	Wasp HAS.1	ex Wroughton, 829 HQ Flight. Crashed 25/3/86. Arrived by 7/87.
XW272	Harrier T.4	8783M, ex 4, 20. Crashed 29/6/82. Nose section.

Vintage Aircraft Team/Militair As is usual with VAT and their newly established warbird acquisition and overhaul operation, Militair, there is much toing and froing to record here. The team's Vampire T.11 G-VTII/WZ507 and Venom FB.54 G-BLKA/'WR410' are well known at displays, with the Jet Provost slotted to join them during the 1988 season. VAT/Militair undertake specialist work for other operators and frequently visiting jets can be found under maintenance. Pressures of work mean that VAT are not really geared up for visitors, but enquiries can be addressed to : Andrew Picton, 92 Conway Gardens, Grays, Essex RM17 6HG.

Keeping up with the movements in and out of here, particularly on a two-year time span, is almost a full time job! Recapping to W&R10, Vampire FB.5 VZ304 has yet to move from the previous base at Bushey, due to a seized wing bolt. It was due on site at Cranfield by the time these words are read. Vampire T.11 XH330 did *not* come here from Bushey (qv). Instead WZ616 *did* come, although it has since left, see below. Venom FB.54 G-BLSD/J-1758 was not crated up and sent off to the USA as stated. It became N203DM and was ferried by air to North Weald 12/4/86. Provost T.1 WW442 arrived by road from Booker 13/2/86 and left by similar means in 3/87 for Leverstock Green. Hunter T.7 ET-271/G-BNFT arrived by road from Booker 11/1/87 for preparation for crating to the USA where it will be restored to flying condition by Ed Stead as N10271, it left during 3/87. The Meteor WS760 Group continue to restore their aircraft at the VAT compound and are best listed under this heading, although major components have been moved off site.

Other departures have been : Messenger 2A G-AHUI, Messenger 2A G-AJFF, Gemini 1A G-AKER, Gemini 1A G-AKGD and Gemini 1A G-AKHZ all transferred to the Berkshire Aviation Group and moved to Henley during 4/86. Dove G-ANVU was exported to Sweden during 10/86. Terrier G-AYDW moved to Camberley 20/2/88. Vampire T.11 pod WZ616 (see above) was sold in the USA during the summer of 1987 and exported. Vampire T.11 pod XD459 moved during late 1987 to storage near Ware. Venom FB.50 G-GONE/J-1542 made its first flight following restoration on 29/3/86 and was delivered to Phil Meeson at Bournemouth Airport on 12/1/87. Finally, Gunbus replica BAPC.123/'P-641' was acquired by VAT as components only and should be deleted from the listing.

As well as the specialist 'early jets' theme, VAT has a clear fascination with Austers, with still more arriving since W&R10. The Miles Student is a long term restoration project. Lightning F.2A G27-239/G-BNCA has been acquired from Aces High for use in the proposed restoration to flying condition of the former Newton T.5. The latter is now reported to be going to the USA and will be restored by Flight Systems Inc at Mojave, California. Current here are the following :

G-AIBR	J/1 Autocrat	ex Bushey, Duxford, Sywell, Gamston. Crashed 5/9/70. Frame only.
G-AMTK	Tiger Moth	ex Bushey, Rochester, Croydon, N6709, 2 GS, 6 EFTS, 1 EFTS, 34 ERFTS.
G-ANEH	Tiger Moth	ex Leighton Buzzard, Bushey, Didcot, N6797, 11 RFS, 1 RFS, 1 EFTS, 12 RS, 9 EFTS, 9 ERFTS.
G-ARSL	Terrier 2	ex VF581, 664. CoA expired 30/9/85.
G-AVCS	Terrier 1	ex Bushey, Cranfield, Finmere, WJ363, Odiham SF, AAC, 1900F. Crashed 18/10/81. Under restoration.
G-BMSG+	SAAB 32A Lansen	ex Swedish AF, Malmslatt, Fv32028. Flew in 8/9/86.
G-MIOO+	Student 2	ex Duxford, G-APLK, Glasgow, Shoreham, XS941, G-35-4. Crashed 24/8/85. Arrived by 7/86, for restoration.
G-SHOW+	MS.733 Alcyon	ex Booker, F-BMQJ, FAF 125. Arrived 31/10/86, for restoration.
G27-239+	Lightning F.2A	G-BNCA/8346M, ex Warton, Saudi Support Unit, XN734, Rolls-Royce, A&AEE, BAC. Arrived 28/10/87, for spares use.
FT323"	Harvard II	ex Bushey, East Ham, Portuguese AF 1513, SAAF 7426, EX884, 41-33857. Under restoration.
NL985	Tiger Moth	7015M, ex Leighton Buzzard, Bushey, Leamington Spa, Finningley. Frame.
TW467+	Auster 5	G-ANIE, airworthy, lodges with VAT.
WR410"	Venom FB.54	G-BLKA, ex Swiss AF J-1790. 6 Sqn colours, airworthy.
WS760	Meteor NF.14	7964M, ex 'Z-14', Bushey, Duxford, Brampton, Upwood, 1 ANS, 64, 237 OCU. Under restoration by The Meteor WS760 Group.
WV686+	Provost T.1	7621M, ex Camberley, Blackbushe, Ascot, Halton, 2 FTS, CS(A), 8 FTS, 2 FTS. Arrived 20/2/88.
WZ507	Vampire T.11	G-VTII, ex Carlisle, 60 MU, CATCS, 3/4 CAACU, 5 FTS, 8 FTS, 229 OCU, 22 MU. Airworthy.
XF914	Provost T.1	ex Bushey, East Midlands, Barton, Connah's Quay, 27 MU, FTCCF, CFS, G&S UAS, LON UAS.
XH328+	Vampire T.11	ex Hemel Hempstead, Croxley Green, Bushey, Keevil, Exeter, 3 CAACU, 60. Arrived 19/9/87 for restoration to flying condition.
XK416	Auster AOP.9	7855M/G-AYUA, ex Bushey, Luton area, Sibson, Middle Wallop, 651, 19 MU.
XN637	Jet Provost T.3	G-BKOU, ex Bushey, Duxford, Winterbourne Gunner, 1 FTS, RAFC. Nearing flight test, camouflage colour scheme.
XP248+	Auster AOP.9	7822M, ex Wroughton, Marlborough, Old Sarum, Middle Wallop, 651. Arrived by 7/87.
XP283+	Auster AOP.9	7859M, ex Shoreham, Middle Wallop, 654. Frame, arrived by 7/87.
XS451+	Lightning T.5	8503M, ex Newton, St Athan, Binbrook, LTF, 11, 226 OCU, 5, AFDS. Arrived 4/88 - see notes above.
J-1523	Venom FB.50	G-VENI, ex Swiss AF. For D Woods, awaiting restoration.
J-1601	Venom FB.50	G-VIDI, ex Swiss AF.
J-1632	Venom FB.50	G-VNOM, ex Swiss AF.
91007"	Lockheed T-33A	G-TJET, ex Danish AF DT-566, USAF 51-8566. Owned Ipswich Airport Ltd, maintained by VAT. Airworthy.

Autair The helicopter store was wound down by mid 1987. JetRanger RP-C1797/G-BKUB was sold in Australia as VH-JWF. Bell 205 5X-UWA/G-BKGH was sold in Canada as C-GEAT. Bell 212 LN-OQS/G-GLEN moved to Panshanger. The two former Saudi Agusta-Bell 205As 1401 and 1403 were built into G-BLXK, but the present whereabouts of this hybrid and of JetRanger 5X-UVV are not known.

Others To go back to W&R10 for a moment, parts of Sea Fury FB.11 WH589/G-AGHB certainly went to the USA for use in Lloyd Hamilton's *corncob* conversion N4434P (and it uses that identity for its paperwork), but the bulk of the wreck went to far less exotic Milton Keynes. Meteor NF.14 WS760 has been refiled under VAT, see above. There have been a couple of additions in this section ;

G-AJIW+	Auster J/1N Alpha	ex Panshanger. Under rebuild in Rogers hangar. CoA expired 16/10/82.
G-AVGU+	Cessna F.150G	Crashed 25/5/83, wreck, thought in use for spares.
G-AWZN	Trident 3B-101	ex BA, BEA. Used for airfield rescue training.
G-BDUX+	T.31B Motor Cadet	stored in trailer. CoA expired 23/2/84.

DUNSTABLE

The Pawnee frame mentioned in W&R10 is still present, along with a stored Weihe.

	Pawnee	frame only, stored, Farmair titles.
BGA 448	DFS Weihe	ex G-ALJW. Stored, damaged condition, here since circa 1979.

EATON BRAY

(3 miles west of Dunstable) P & D Underwood, of the Russavia Collection (see under Bishop's Stortford), is working on two gliders at their workshop, and keep an airworthy example. At the airstrip, the derelict Cessna 182 turned out to be the prospective G-JOON. It had gone by 7/87, perhaps to the USA as it was cancelled as sold there as long ago as 4/84!

BGA 493	Dagling	BAPC.81, ex Dunstable, Duxford, Warton. Under restoration.
BGA 833	T.8 Tutor	ex Lytham St Annes and VW535. Under restoration.
BGA1754+	Grunau Baby III	CRU, ex RAFGSA, airworthy.

HATCH

(Off the B658, south west of Sandy) Skysport Engineering lost the very talented Cathy O'Brien when she was tragically killed in an air crash 2/8/87. Sopwith Pup replica G-BIAT/N6160 was written off during its first test flight at Old Warden on 2/7/86. Harry Fox's Comper Swift was completed during 1987 and moved to Booker to be based. Mew Gull G-AEXF came here from its accident at Redhill on 6/5/85 for rebuild on behalf of Desmond Penrose by 2/86. By early 1988 it was completed and moved to Old Warden. Major project here is the creation of a Westland Wallace replica for a film. During late 1987, Skysport received the forward fuselage and centre section of a Beaufighter, from Henlow, for possible rebuild to flying condition.

G-AGOY	Messenger 3	ex Southill, Castletown, EI-AGE, HB-EIP, G-AGOY, U-0247. Under rebuild.
+	Wallace	replica, under construction.
+	Beaufighter TF.X	ex Henlow, Halton. Arrived 12/87. See notes above.

HENLOW

Royal Air Force Museum Storage Site There has been a considerable out-pouring of airframes from here and it is belived that the store must vacate the airfield. Several aircraft are not accounted for, and only aircraft noted within 1987 are listed below. Disposals from here have been as follows ; G-AJLR Consul airfreighted out to Singapore via Manchester in an SIA 747 4/11/86; G-ALAH Messenger reported as "returned to owner's custody", which was TAC - current location unknown; HH379 Hostspur rear end and the centre section of Hamilcar NX836, really too small for W&R listing, but for completeness both to the Museum of Army Flying at Middle Wallop; XK699 Comet C.2 by road to Lyneham 17/10/86; Beaufighter TF.10 forward fuselage and engines last used as a test bed at Halton, plus the former Portuguese fuselage sections to Skysport at Hatch ; Avro 504 replica BAPC.177/G1381 left by road to Brooklands 29/1/87; Vampire T.11 XE920 to Scampton; the anonymous 'He 111' forward fuselage was reported sold to a private owner during 1987; Demoiselle replica (previously not known as being here) also by road to Brooklands 29/1/87.

The following were not present during two visits in 1987 and are unaccounted for ; Argus II G-AIZE; Swordfish IV HS503/BAPC.108; Vampire FB.5 VX461; Canberra B.2 WJ573 believed scrapped, sections certainly having appeared on the dump at Marham; Sycamore HR.12 WV783; Venom NF.3 WX905; Valiant BK.1 nose XD816; 8469M Fa 330; the remains of the Ayr and Kingston flying boats; Fi 103 BAPC.92; BGA.679/BAPC.109 Cadet; Avro 504K replica BAPC.178/E373. That leaves the following as confirmed residents of the store :-

H2311	Avro 504K	ex G-ABAA and Nash Collection.
DG590	Hawk Major	8379M, ex Ternhill, G-ADMW.
VX595	Dragonfly HR.1	'29', ex Fleetlands.

XF785	Bristol 173	7648M, ex G-ALBN.
6130	Ventura II	ex SAAF Museum, AJ469. No RAF service, delivered direct.
+	Belvedere HC.1	forward fuselage. First noted 1986.

Others The Hunter remains on the gate and the Vampire is within the camp on a plinth. The ATC have gained an EoN Primary which is kept with the based Ventures.

BGA 580+	EoN Primary	ex Twinwood Farm, G-ALPS. Arrived by 7/86. Stored in VGS hangar.
WT612	Hunter F.1	7496M, ex Halton, Credenhill, Hawkers, A&AEE. Gate guardian.
XH278	Vampire T.11	7866M/8595M, ex Upwood, 27 MU, RAFC. On display on a plinth.

Henlow Area Lee Mullins continues to work on his Terrier and the ATC still have their Pup.

G-ASDK	Terrier 2	ex Sutton Bridge, Terrington St Clement, Galashiels, G-ARLM (2), G-ARLP, VF631, 654, 652, 656. CoA exp 28/3/74. Under restoration.
HB-NAV	Pup 150	fuselage only, ATC unit, ex Redhill, G-AZCM.

LUTON

Derek Hunt's Autocrat continues its rebuild here.

G-AJDW	J/1 Autocrat	under restoration, CoA expired 17/11/77.

LUTON AIRPORT

The W&R situation here is very static. F-280 N581H wreck is thought to have been scrapped. Otherwise, both the Britannia and the Navajo are very much long-termers.

G-AOVS	Britannia 312	ex Redcoat, 'G-BRAC', Lloyd, BOAC. Fuselage only.
G-TAXY	Navajo (Turbo)	ex LN-PAD, LN-NPB, SE-EZK. *Memphis Belle*. CoA exp 17/3/83.

MEPPERSHALL

On 22/10/86 magnificent Queen Bee LF858/G-BLUZ flew for the first time following its restoration at the hands of Brinkley Light Aircraft Services. Since then there have been no long term W&R-type inmates.

OLD WARDEN

The Shuttleworth Collection Shuttleworth offers a unique atmosphere as museums go. It is an excellent static collection of historic aircraft and vehicles giving the visitor the ability to watch at close quarters restoration work going on. At regular intervals during the summer, including two popular *Twilight* evening stagings, the collection comes 'alive' with a series of themed air displays, using visiting as well as based aircraft. (Please note that there are higher entrance fees for flying days.) The Collection is open every day except Mondays March 1 to December 21. During the summer months it is open Monday to Sunday. Times are 1030 to 1730 or dusk if later. Further details of opening times and the flying displays are available upon receipt of an SAE. The Collection is fortunate for the support of the Shuttleworth Veteran Aeroplane Society, members of which can take advantage of special facilities at Old Warden. Details of membership of the SVAS can be had from David Reader, 151 Marshalswick Lane, St Albans, Herts AL1 4UX.

Major achievement since W&R10 was the first flight since 1939 of the DH.88 Comet G-ACSS, achieved at Hatfield on 17/5/87. Sadly the aircraft ground looped at Hatfield on 4/7/87 and is currently under restoration again there. New with the collection are Desmond Penrose's Mew Gull replica G-AEXF and Dragon Rapide G-AHGD on loan from Mike Astor. A whole series of major restorations are underway, including both aircraft being produced by Northern Aeroplane Workshops. Shuttleworth Aircraft can also be found under the following headings in W&R : Dewsbury (Triplane and the Bristol Museum's M.1 replica); Duxford (Sea Hurricane); Flixton (Provost T.1); Hatfield (DH.88); Loughborough (Jet Provost); Yeovilton (Sea Gladiator).

The Jean Batten Gull Six G-ADPR moved to Salisbury during late 1987 for completion of its restoration, in the hands of Cliff Lovell. Bill Sayer's Voisin replica G-BJHV to Brooklands during 1987. Fi 103 (V-1) replica BAPC.36 returned from loan to the IWM Duxford and moved via Old Warden to Hawkinge. The fate of Jupiter MPA BAPC.127 is unknown at present. Toucan MPA BAPC.146 moved initially to Hitchin in 1985 and then to London Colney. The Collection accordingly currently stands at :-

G-EACN	BAT Bantam	ex Watton, Old Warden, K-123, F1654. Components, in store.
G-EBHX	Humming Bird	ex Lympne No 8. *L'Oiseau Mouche*. CoA exp 11/6/81.
G-EBIR	DH.51	ex VP-KAA, G-KAA, G-EBIR. *Miss Kenya*.
G-EBJO	ANEC II	dismantled, stored.
G-EBWD	DH.60X Moth	airworthy.
G-AAIN	Parnall Elf II	airworthy.
G-AANG	Bleriot XI	No 14/BAPC.3, ex Ampthill, Hendon. Under restoration.

G-AANH	Deperdussin	No 43/BAPC.4, ex Ampthill. Airworthy.
G-AANI	Blackburn Mono D	No 9/BAPC.5, ex Wittering. Airworthy.
G-AAPZ	Desoutter I	ex Higher Blagdon. CoA expired 3/3/39. Under restoration by SVAS.
G-AAYX	Southern Martlet	ex Woodford. CoA expired 12/4/49. Under restoration.
G-ABAG	DH.60 Moth	airworthy.
G-ABVE	Arrow Active II	airworthy. On loan from Desmond Penrose.
G-ABXL	Archaeopteryx	airworthy. CoA expired 22/9/82.
G-ADND	Hornet Moth	ex Hawarden, W9385, St Athan SF, 3 CPF, G-ADND.
G-AEBB	HM.14 Pou du Ciel	ex Southampton. Taxiable.
G-AEOA	Puss Moth	ex ES921, G-AEOA, YU-PAX, UN-PAX. Loan from P & A Wood, airworthy.
G-AEXF+	Mew Gull	ex Hatch, Redhill, ZS-AHM. On loan from Desmond Penrose, arrived by 12/87 for flight test.
G-AFCL	BA Swallow II	airworthy. On loan from A Dowson.
G-ARSG	Roe Triplane rep	BAPC. 1. Hampshire Aero Club built. Airworthy.
G-ASPP	Boxkite replica	BAPC. 2. Miles built. Airworthy.
BAPC 8	Dixon Ornithopter	in store.
BAPC11	EE Wren	No 4. Composite with G-EBNV. Airworthy.
BAPC37	Blake Bluetit	ex Winchester. Under restoration by SVAS.
D8096	Bristol F.2b	G-AEPH, ex Filton, Watford, D8096, 208. Airworthy.
H5199	Avro 504K	G-ACNB, ex 'E3404' and Avro 504N. Airworthy.
F904	SE.5A	G-EBIA, ex 'D7000', Farnborough. Airworthy.
K1786	Tomtit	G-AFTA, ex 5 GCF, 23 GCF, 3 FTS. Under restoration.
K3215	Tutor	G-AHSA, ex HSA, RAFC. Airworthy.
K4235	Cierva C.30A	G-AHMJ, ex Middle Wallop, 529, 1448 Flt, SAC. Static.
K5414"	Hind (Afghan)	G-AENP/BAPC.78, ex 'K5457', Kabul. Airworthy.
L8032	Gladiator I	G-AMRK, ex 'L8032', Glosters, Hamble, 8 MU, 61 OTU, 1624F, 2 AACU. Airworthy.
N5180	Sopwith Pup	G-EBKY, Built as Sopwith Dove. Airworthy.
P6382	Magister I	G-AJRS, very complex composite airframe. Airworthy.
T6818	Tiger Moth II	G-ANKT, ex Aston Down, 21 EFTS. Airworthy.
Z7258"	Dragon Rapide	G-AHGD, ex NR786. On loan from Mike Astor. *Women of the Empire*. Airworthy
AR501	Spitfire V	G-AWII, 'NN-D', ex Duxford, Henlow, Loughborough, CGS, 61 OTU, 1 TEU, 58 58 OTU, 422, 312, 504, 310. Airworthy.
WB588	Chipmunk T.10	G-AOTD, ex Chessington, 22 RFS. Airworthy.
7198/18	LVG C.VI	G-AANJ, ex Stanmore, Colerne, Fulbeck. Airworthy.

STANBRIDGE

(3 miles south of Leighton Buzzard) The Hunter still guards the gate of the Staff College.

WP190	Hunter F.5	8473M/7582M, ex Upwood, Finningley, Bircham Newton, Nicosia, 1, 41.

Berkshire

ARBORFIELD

Princess Marina College (On the A327 south of Reading) There has been some change in the instructional airframe fleet at this Army apprentice college. The entry is further extended by the re-introduction of the two Jet Provost fuselages which are more substantial than W&R10 would have the reader believe. Two of the inmates have not been noted for some time, but will remain in the listing for at least this edition. There are two departures to note, Scout AH.1 XP190 moving by road to Wroughton 8/12/86 and Sioux AH.1 XT548 to Middle Wallop.

XM379	Jet Provost T.3	ex Shawbury, 3 FTS, 6 FTS, 2 FTS. Fuselage only, see notes above.
XM413	Jet Provost T.3	ex Shawbury, 2 FTS, 7 FTS, CFS. Fuselage only, see notes above.
XP244	Auster AOP.9	7864M, 'M7922'. Fuselage only, engine test bed.
XP886+	Scout AH.1	ex Wroughton. First noted 10/86.

XP899	Scout AH.1	ex Middle Wallop. 'D'.
XR601	Scout AH.1	ex 657.
XT827	Sioux AH.1	ex 654 'D'. Last noted 6/85.
XV139+	Scout AH.1	ex Wroughton. First noted 10/86.
XV141	Scout AH.1	ex Wroughton. Last noted 6/85.
+	Gazelle TAD	Possibly TAU.3/WA.67 which was here during 1985. First noted 10/86.

BINFIELD

(North of the B3034, north west of Bracknell) Here a small workshop specialises in helicopter rebuilds and has two Robinsons in hand. The one-off Airmaster helicopter, last noted at Blackbushe in 1980, has also appeared here and may be the basis of a new project. All a new since W&R10.

G-ASXF+	Brantly 305	ex Thruxton, Biggin Hill. CoA expired 16/2/79. First noted 1986.
G-AYNS+	Airmaster H2/B1	ex Blackbushe, Redhill. CoA expired 13/2/73. First noted 1986.
G-BKXH+	Robinson R-22	ex Luton, Stapleford, SE-HOF. Crashed 23/7/85. Arr by 12/85, for rebuild.
G-BLMD+	Robinson R-22	ex Luton, N90623. Crashed 8/4/85. Arrived by 5/85.

BRACKNELL

RAF Bracknell The Staff College continues to exhibit its Hunter within the grounds.

XG196	Hunter F.6A	8702M, ex Kemble, 1 TWU, TWU, 229 OCU, 19.

John & Maureen Woods The restoration of Harvard III G-BMJW is underway in the area.

EZ259	Harvard III	G-BMJW, ex Tattershall, Oxford, Sandhurst, EZ259, 42-84182.

FINCHAMPSTEAD RIDGES

(On the B3016 south of Wokingham) The Staravia yard here continues to hold several Jet Provost T.4 airframes and the lonely Vampire T.11. There is a possibility that the yeard will close during 1988. The famous Jet Provost dropped off the tower in the film *Spies Like Us* (see under Bournemouth Airport in W&R10) is now thought almost certainly to have been XP683 from this yard and is still to be found at Pinewood. Listed here in previous editions, XP681 is now believed never to have come here and is best deleted. Current contents are as follows :

XH362	Vampire T.11	ex Shawbury, CATCS, CNCS, 8 FTS, 7 FTS, 1 FTS, DH.
XP586	Jet Provost T.4	ex Lasham, Shawbury, RAFC. Fuselage.
XP642	Jet Provost T.4	ex Lasham, Shawbury, 2 FTS, CFS. Fuselage.
XP669	Jet Provost T.4	ex Lasham, Shawbury, 2 FTS. Fuselage.
XP685	Jet Provost T.4	ex Lasham, Shawbury, 2 FTS, 7 FTS.

HAMPSTEAD MARSHALL

(Off the B4009, north of the M4) With no evidence to the contrary, the Tiger is thought still here.

G-ANEM	Tiger Moth	ex Bristol, EI-AGN, Weston, G-ANEM, R5042, 14 RFS, 3 RFS, 6 EFTS. UK CoA expired 13/11/54. Stored.

HUNGERFORD

Newbury Aeroplane Company Now flying and a familiar sight at rallies is the lovely Aeronca C-3 G-ADYS, a tribute to the workmanship of Ben Cooper. Work on Fox Moth G-ACEJ continues slowly, but new inmates are two aircraft previously at Strathallan and the newly-imported BA Eagle. Omitted from W&R10, Tiger Moth G-AOIM is also here.

G-ACEJ	Fox Moth	ex Old Warden. Remains only, written off 17/7/82.
G-ADPS+	BA Swallow II	ex Dorchester, Strathallan, Sandown. CoA expired 28/11/80. Under restoration for Brian Woodford/Wessex Aviation & Transport.
G-AFAX+	BA Eagle	ex VH-ACN. Arrived 2/88 for restoration to flying condition.
G-ANTS+	Tiger Moth	ex Lower Upham, Strathallan, Mintlaw, N6532, BCCF, Wyton CF, 22 RFS, 22 EFTS, 30 ERFTS. Under restoration.
G-AOIM	Tiger Moth	ex Elstree, T7109, RAE, Eindhoven, Honiley SF, 24 EFTS, 19 EFTS. Crashed 25/5/69.

MEMBURY

Southern Sailplanes Some of the short term inmates have been turned around here, although the Dragon Rapide and the two Tigers continue to be long termers. Super Cub G-APZJ completed another metamorphosis during 1986 and was flying again, although the original fuselage frame remains here. The hulk of Mooney G-BAFB has not been noted for some time and is thought scrapped. Robin DR.400 G-BJUD (the former PH-SRM) was flying by 1986. A Tiger Moth has arrived for repair.

G-AHAG	Dragon Rapide	ex Blandford Forum, Ford, Whitney, RL944. CoA exp 15/7/73.
G-AHVV	Tiger Moth	ex Lympne, EM929. Crashed 12/12/71.
G-AJHU+	Tiger Moth	ex T7471, 83 GSU, 132, 65, 116. Crashed 4/6/86.
G-AMIU	Tiger Moth	ex Booker, T5495, 16 EFTS, 54 OTU, Church Fenton SF. Crashed 15/10/69/
G-APZJ	Super Cub 150	original fuselage frame - see notes above. Crashed 12/6/83.
G-BAVA	Super Cub 150	ex D-EFKC, ALAT 18-5391. Crashed 20/11/77. Frame only.

NEWBURY

British Balloon Museum and Library Exhibits for future display by BBML continue to be stored at various locations centred upon Newbury. Occasionally items are inflated, there is a small display in Newbury District Museum and a newly-established reference library at Newbury College (open during normal college hours). Readers should note that it is not possible to visit the stored items. General enquiries can be made to : The Secretary, BBML, 75 Albany Road, Old Windsor, Berkshire SL4 2QD.

G-ATGN	Thorn Coal Gas	ex Newcastle. Envelope and basket. *Eccles.*
G-AVTL	HAG Free HAB	Envelope only. *Bristol Belle.*
G-AWOK	Sussex Free Gas	Envelope only, never flew. *Sardine.*
G-AXVU+	Omega 84 HAB	Envelope only. *Henry VIII.*
G-AXXP	Bradshaw Free HAB	Envelope and basket. *Ignis Volens.*
G-AYAL	Omega 56 HAB	Envelope and basket. *Nimble II.*
G-AZSP	Cameron O-84 HAB	Envelope. *Esso.*
G-AZUV	Cameron O-65 HAB	Envelope and basket. *Icarus.*
G-BAMK	Cameron D-96 HAB	Original airship control car. *Isibidbi.*
G-BBGZ	Cambridge HAB	Envelope and basket. *Phlogiston.*
G-BCAR+	Thunder Ax7-77	Envelope only. *Marie Antoinette.*
G-BCFD	West HAB	Envelope. *Hellfire.*
G-BCFZ	Cameron O-500 HAB	Basket only - but a double-decker 31 'seater'. *Gerard A Heineken.*
G-BETF+	Cameron SS HAB	Envelope only, spark-plug shape. *Champion.*
G-BETH+	Thunder Ax6-56 HAB	Envelope only. *Debenhams I*
G-BHKR	Colt 14A HAB	Envelope and harness/burner. *Green Ice 5.*
G-BIGT+	Colt 77A	Envelope only, fire damaged. *Big T.*
G-ICES+	Thunder Ax6-56 HAB	Envelope only, ice cream cone shaped. *Fiesta.*
G-PNUT+	Cameron SS HAB	Envelope only, peanut shaped. *Mr Peanut.*
EI-BAY	Cameron Ax8 HAB	ex G-AYJZ. Original envelope. *Godolphin.*
F-BTVO+	Cameron A-140 HAB	Envelope only. *Cumulonimbus.*

READING

Ben Borsberry Ben's Tiger Moth 'fleet' has been rationalised somewhat. G-ANRM moved to Southampton and is now airworthy. G-ASXB was sold in the USA during 1987. The remains of VP-YOJ did not come here, staying in Malawi. The other Malawi example is now confirmed and the fuselage of G-ANLX has arrived.

G-ANDE	Tiger Moth	ex Stapleford, EM726, complex composite. Crashed 22/7/84.
G-ANLX+	Tiger Moth	ex Luton, T7792, Dyce SF, 18 RFS, 8 RFS, 10 FIS, 26 EFTS. Crashed 31/12/55. Frame only, arrived by 7/87.
7Q-YMY	Tiger Moth	ex Malawi, VP-YMY, ZS-DLB, SAAF 4606, DE671.

Dave Pope Dave's small collection of airframes is now based here and the identity of his initial Chipmunk is now confirmed. Chipmunk cockpit section WD355/8099M arrived by road from Ruislip 13/12/86 for use as spares for WP784. With all usable spares salvaged, the hulk was scrapped 10/87. Tobago fuselage G-BGTB arrived by road from Firbeck on 30/1/88.

WP784+	Chipmunk T.10 PAX	ex Benson, Abingdon, 6 AEF, Bicester, LEE UAS, ABN UAS, 8 FTS, MAN UAS, QUB UAS, Air Attache Paris, 5 RFS, 17 RFS.
G-BGTB+	TB-10 Tobago	ex Firbeck, Sherburn, F-ODKE. Crashed 8/6/80. Fuselage, arrived 30/1/88.

Others 2287 Squadron ATC's Vampire T.11 XD536 moved to Southall by 9/86. Joe Iliffe's Thruxton Jackaroo is still believed to be in the area, as are the two stored Provost T.1s.

G-ANZT	Jackaroo	ex Thruxton, T7798, Wunstorf SF, 19 RFS, 5 RFS, 28 EFTS. CoA exp 15/3/68.
WV486	Provost T.1	7694M, 'N-D', ex Halton, 6 FTS. Stored.
WW447	Provost T.1	ex Exeter, CATCS, CNCS, RAFC. Stored.

SANDHURST

Piper J3C-65 Cub G-ASPS was airworthy by 4/86.

SHAWDENE

(To the north of Newbury, on the old A34) Tiger Moth G-BALX was flying again by late 1986. The current status of CEA DR.1050 G-ATIC is unconfirmed, but a Horizon has arrived for rebuild.

G-ASZS+	Horizon 160	ex Stapleford. Damaged 10/10/86. Arrived by 4/87.
G-ATIC	CEA DR.1050	ex F-BJCJ. CoA expired 1/6/81.

SLOUGH

Chipmunk 22 G-AORF did indeed come to the Berkshire Fire Service station here, but was in the form of parts only and these were scrapped by 1984.

TWYFORD

Peter Woods' Seafire restoration makes progress here.

SX336	Seafire XVII	A2055, ex Newark, Warrington, Stretton, Bramcote. Rear fuselage of LA546.

WHITE WALTHAM

The PAX Chipmunk, long lost here, is now known to be at <u>Welling</u>. There has been an expansion in civilian W&R material here.

G-AJPI+	Argus III	ex Booker, HB614, 43-14887. CoA expired 6/12/84.
G-ARMC+	Chipmunk 22A	ex WB703, 613, 9 AFTS, LEE UAS, 25 RFS. CoA expired 22/7/85.
G-ARNG	Colt 108	CoA expired 12/10/73. For spares.

WINDSOR

Gordon King took delivery of a Harvard IIB frame from North Weald during 2/88 and is using this as the basis for a static Harvard.

B-163+	Harvard IIB	ex North Weald, Amsterdam, Dutch AF, FE930, 42-12417. See above.

WOODLANDS PARK

(South of the A423M, south of Maidenhead) Joe Austin carries on with his rebuild of the Chilton.

G-AFGI	Chilton DW.1	ex Booker. CoA expired 10/5/83. Under restoration.

WOODLEY

<u>Berkshire Aviation Group</u> Great strides have been made by BAG towards their goal of establishing a museum on this, the former Miles airfield. A hangar and site have now been earmarked, and as such BAG can be listed under here instead of the previous 'Wallingford'. W&R10 recorded BAG's major airframe project as the long term Miles Master composite, based upon the wings of AZ361 and DL906, plus other parts. This project continues, but major airframes have since been acquired. All of the Vintage Aircraft Team Miles collection is now with BAG and currently held in store at Henley - which see. On site at Woodley is Graham Johnson's superb Magister restoration, which was donated to BAG in July 1987. Airframes are not currently available for inspection. General enquiries can be made to : Secretary, BAG, 45 Malvern Way, Twyford, Reading, Berkshire RG10 9PY.

L6906+"	Magister I	BAPC.44, ex Wroughton, Frenchay, G-AKKY, T9841, 11 EFTS, 16 EFTS.

<u>Others</u> Work continues on Bob Ogden's Moth Major and Barry Welford's Moth Minor remains stored.

G-ABZB	Moth Major	ex Sweden, SE-AIA, G-ABZB. Under restoration.
G-AFNI	Moth Minor Coupe	ex W7972, 100 GCF, Foulsham SF, 241, G-AFNI. CoA expired 26/5/67.

Buckinghamshire

AYLESBURY

1365 Squadron ATC keep a Hunter nose section at their headquarters. It was acquired in 1978.

XF522+	Hunter F.6	ex Bucks Ambulance Service, Aylesbury, Aylesbury Fire Service, Halton, 92, 66, 92. Nose section.

BOOKER AIRFIELD

(Or Wycombe Air Park) Booker Aircraft Museum There have been a few airframe changes at BAM. As well as the aircraft, BAM have assembled an excellent internal display of items of all sizes and are currently assembling material to portray the history of Booker itself. BAM is open Saturdays, Sundays and Bank Holidays 1030 to 1730 and parties can be arranged by appointment. Contact : David King, Chairman, Booker Aircraft Museum, 3 Spearing Road, High Wycombe, Buckinghamshire HP12 3JP.

Noralpha G-BAYV was returned to the Friends of Biggin Hill 10/87, going to Sevenoaks. Ed Stead acquired loaned Hunter T.7 ET-271 and it moved by road to Cranfield 11/1/87 for onward shipment to the USA. As predicted in W&R10, the nose of Dakota G-AMSM returned to Brenzett. BAM's Harvard, on loan from Barry Parkhouse, is a composite, the starboard wing coming from FX360 and the port wing from a former Dutch Air Force example. BAM still hold Alan Allen's C-10A Jetstream nose mock-up. W&R10 reported the arrival of Harvard cockpit section KF423, this did not transpire.

KF435+	Harvard IIB	ex Camerley, Sandhurst, RAFC. Arrived 1/3/87 - see notes above.
WV495	Provost T.1	7697M, ex St Merryn, Tattershall Thorpe, Strensall, Halton, 6 FTS.
WZ550	Vampire T.11	7902M, ex Slough, Ewyas Harrold, CATCS, CFS, 8 FTS, 7 FTS, 202 AFS.
XA571+	Javelin FAW.1	7722M/7663M, ex Sibson, Aylesbury, Halton, 87, 46. Nose, arrived 7/6/86.
XM665	Whirlwind HAS.7	ex Chelsfield, Chertsey, Wroughton, Fleetlands, 829, 847, 848, 846, 737, 700H Flight. On loan.

Hon Patrick Lindsay Collection Under the care of Personal Plane Services the collection of the late Patrick Lindsay has remained largely intact. Sopwith Triplane G-BHEW, which had been sold to Kermit Weeks in Florida, was finally crated up and left 10/87. 'Storch' G-AZMH was acquired by Brian Woodford and is now based at Dorchester. The aircraft in this collection can occasionally be seen at air shows, but otherwise are not available for public inspection. The Hawker Fury replica is still at Land's End - which see.

G-BBII	Fiat G.46-3B	ex I-AEHU, MM52801. Italian World War Two colours, airworthy.
G-BIIZ	Great Lakes 2T-1A	ex N603K, NC603K. CoA expired 3/4/86.
B4863"	SE-5E	G-BLXT, ex Orlando, N4488, USAAC 22-296. Airworthy.
AR213	Spitfire IA	G-AIST, ex Old Warden, *Battle of Britain*, Allen Wheeler, 8 MU, 53 OTU, 57 OTU. 'QG-A'. Airworthy.
45	SNCAN SV-4C	G-BHFG, ex F-BJDN, French military. *Aeronavale* c/s. Airworthy.
120	SNCAN SV-4C	G-AZGC, ex F-BCGE. French AF colours. Airworthy.
1076	MS.230	G-AVEB, ex F-BGJT, FRench AF. Recently painted and modified to look like the Ryan NYP *Spirit of St Louis* for a commercial.

Others Of the aircraft listed under this heading in W&R10 there have been many removals, and a goodly number of new candidates have arrived. Of these, at least one of the two C.3605s is bound for Kermit Weeks in Florida. Lysander IIIA G-BCWL/V3718 made its first test flight following restoration on 18/9/87 and is expected to join the rest of the Wessex Aviation and Transport collection at Dorchester. Alcyon G-SHOW was acquired by the Vintage Aircraft Team and moved by road to Cranfield 31/10/86. Kermit Week's Mosquito TT.35 N35MK/RS712 flew off for endurance tests to Benson and then departed from there on its trans-Atlantic ferry flight on 29/9/87. Provost T.1 WW442 also joined VAT and moved to Cranfield 13/2/86. Provost T.1 XF898 expired on the dump by late 1986 and was replaced by a Tomahawk - someone exhibiting taste at last! Stampe G-AZNF moved initially to Kingsclere before settling upon Shoreham. Stephen Grey's MS.230 G-BJCL was restored here to French Air Force colours and upon completion was crated for export to the USA in 10/87. Strangest departure of all was that of Dornier Do 27A-4 fuselage 3497/G-BMFH which was whisked away in the dead of night during 12/87 by person or persons unknown!

G-AYCK	SNCAN SV-4C	ex Tattershall Thorpe, F-BANE. Crashed 4/10/80, for spares.
G-AZIO	SNCAN SV-4C Coupe	ex Redhill, Billingshurst, Croydon, F-BACB. Under conversion to SV-4L.
G-BDBL+	Chipmunk 22	ex WK621, Oxf UAS, Lon UAS, 6 AEF, Lon UAS, Biggin Hill SF, Lon UAS, Oxf UAS, Bri UAS, 22 RFS. Crashed 21/1/84. Cockpit, first noted 1/87.
G-BJAL	CASA 1-131	ex Audley End, Spanish AF E3B-114. Under rebuild.
G-KENS+	Cherokee Six 300	ex Bodmin, N2209U. Crashed 16/9/79. Hulk to fire dump 18/6/87.
BAPC103	Pilcher Hawk rep	built by PPS. In store.
C-GVXN+	Tomahawk 115	arrived 31/10/86, stripped and placed on fire dump 4/1/87.
3460	Dornier Do 27A-4	G-BMFG, ex Martlesham Heath, Portuguese AF, Luftwaffe AC+955. Stored.
C-499+	EKW C-3605	ex Lodrino, Swiss AF. Arrived 4/88.
C-558+	EKW C-3605	ex Lodrino, Swiss AF. Arrived 4/88.
+	Yak C-11	ex La Ferte Alais (?), Egyptian AF. c/n 172623. Stripped frame.

DENHAM

All of the interest here stems from the rebuild of at least one Cessna 310. The hulk of G-ATCR arrived from Swanton Novers by 4/87 but was quickly stripped and departed to a local scrappie 10/87.

G-OITD+	Cessna 310F	ex G-AROK, N5848X. spares for G-XITD.
G-XITD+	Cessna 310G	ex G-ASYV, HB-LBY, N8948Z. Under rebuild, using tail of G-OITD.

FINMERE

An Auster is in store at the airfield. Meanwhile off site the Shield Xyla is under rebuild.

G-AIGD+	J/1N Alpha	CoA expired 20/12/83. Stored. First noted 1985.
G-AWPN	Shield Xyla	Crashed 16/8/80. Under restoration, off site.

HALTON

1 School of Technical Training Halton's vast instructional airframe fleet is always in a state of flux, but it is true to say that in recent years there has been a lot more stability with some very long term residents clocking up a small lifetime of service here. The major news is the advent of the Jaguar in strength at last, although they are reported to be under a special maintenance category whereby they can go operational again in a short period of time. The Sea Vixens finally left during 1986, engine a sixteen year association with the School. Several Gnats were removed to other establishments, and others offered for tender.

Departures since W&R10 have been as follows : Sea Vixen FAW.2 XJ604/8222M by road to Cranfield 23/10/86; Sea Vixen FAW.2 XN699/8224M to North Luffenham; Sea Vixen FAW.2 XP921/8226M to Hereford 20/11/86; Jet Provost T.3 XN458/8234M to St Athan by 11/85; Gnat T.1s XR535/8569M and XR951/8603M were out on the field and dismantled by 8/86, leaving shortly afterwards and are likely candidates for the two noted at Bitteswell; Gnat T.1 XM708/8573M moved to the gate at Locking; Gnats XP538/8607M, XS102/8624M and XP533/8632M all moved to Cosford by 6/87; Whirlwind HAR.10 XP395/8674M was put up for tender 10/86 and moved to Tattershall Thorpe by 5/87; Hunter F.6 XF527/8680M joined the gate and is now listed under 'Others' below; Hunter F.6 XG209/8709M moved to Cranwell; Hunter F.6 XG290/8711M to Bentley Priory by 5/87; Hawk T.1 hulk XX257 moved to Chivenor 8/5/87.

In this edition the compiler gives in to considerable bullying by listing the airframes in serial order and not by 'M' number. Halton codes, if worn, are given at the end of each potted history.

G-ASWJ	Beagle 206 Srs 1	8449M,	ex Rolls-Royce. wfu 8/75.
WT746	Hunter F.4	7770M,	ex St Athan, AFDS. 'A'.
WV276	Hunter F.4	7847M,	ex Horsham St Faith, A&AEE, Rolls-Royce. 'D'.
XD165	Whirlwind HAR.10	8673M,	ex SARTS, 202, 228, 22, 225, 155, Navy loan. 'B'.
XE597+	Hunter FGA.9	8874M,	ex Bentley Priory, Brawdy, 1 TWU, 2 TWU, TWU, 229 OCU, West Raynham SF, 1, 54, MoA, 208, 56, 63, 66. Arrived by 5/87.
XE656	Hunter F.6	8678M,	ex 1 TWU, 229 OCU, DFLS, 92, 65. '35'.
XF319	Hunter F.4	7849M,	ex 229 OCU, 112, 66. 'B'.
XF974	Hunter F.4	7949M,	ex St Athan, 26, 3. 'C'.
XG164	Hunter F.6	8681M,	ex Kemble, West Raynham SF, 74, 111. '31'.
XG274	Hunter F.6	8710M,	ex 4 FTS, 229 OCU, 66, 14.
XJ435	Whirlwind HAR.10	8671M,	ex 2 FTS, CFS, 1563 Flt, 22.
XJ727	Whirlwind HAR.10	8661M,	ex 2 FTS, CFS, 1310 Flt, 228, 22.
XM355	Jet Provost T.3	8229M,	ex Shawbury, 1 FTS, 7 FTS, CFS. 'D'.
XM362	Jet Provost T.3	8230M,	ex Kemble, Shawbury, 3 FTS, 2 FTS. Sectioned and camouflaged.
XM369	Jet Provost T.3	8084M,	ex Shawbury, 2 FTS. '07'.
XM375	Jet Provost T.3	8231M,	ex Shawbury, RAFC, 3 FTS, 2 FTS. 'B'.
XM381	Jet Provost T.3	8232M,	ex Kemble, Shawbury, RAFC, 2 FTS. 'O'.
XM386	Jet Provost T.3	8076M,	ex Shawbury, 2 FTS, CFS, Huntings, Luton. '08'.
XM402	Jet Provost T.3	8055AM,	ex Newton, Shawbury, 6 FTS, 2 FTS. 'J'.
XM404	Jet Provost T.3	8055BM,	ex Newton, Shawbury, 3 FTS, 2 FTS.
XM408	Jet Provost T.3	8333M,	ex Kemble, Shawbury, MoA, 2 FTS. Marked as '8233M'. 'P'.
XM409	Jet Provost T.3	8082M,	ex Shawbury, 2 FTS. 'A'.
XM410	Jet Provost T.3	8054AM,	ex Shawbury, RAFC, 7 FTS, 2 FTS. 'C'.
XM411	Jet Provost T.3	8434M,	ex St Athan, Shawbury, Kemble, CFS. 'L'.
XM417	Jet Provost T.3	8054BM,	ex Shawbury, 6 FTS, 7 FTS, 2 FTS. 'D'.
XM467	Jet Provost T.3	8085M,	ex Shawbury, 6 FTS, 1 FTS, RAFC. '06'.
XM468	Jet Provost T.3	8081M,	ex Shawbury, 6 FTS, RAFC. 'B'.
XM480	Jet Provost T.3	8080M,	ex 6 FTS, 1 FTS. '02'.

XM706	Gnat T.1	8572M,	ex 4 FTS, CFS.
XM709	Gnat T.1	8617M,	ex 4 FTS, CFS. '67'.
XN126	Whirlwind HAR.10	8655M,	ex 2 FTS, Queens Flt.
XN467	Jet Provost T.3	8559M,	ex Kemble, Shawbury, CFS, A&AEE, Huntings, Luton. 'F'.
XN512	Jet Provost T.3	8435M,	ex St Athan, Shawbury, CFS.
XN549	Jet Provost T.3	8335M,	ex Shawbury, 1 FTS, CFS. Marked as '8235M'. 'R'.
XN554	Jet Provost T.3	8436M,	ex St Athan, Shawbury, CFS. 'K'.
XP354	Whirlwind HAR.10	8721M,	ex 22, 202.
XP405	Whirlwind HAR.10	8656M,	ex 2 FTS, CFS, 228.
XP442	Argosy T.2	8454M,	ex Kemble, Benson SF, 114, Benson Wing, 114, MoA, 114. '10'.
XP503	Gnat T.1	8568M,	ex 4 FTS.
XP504	Gnat T.1	8618M,	ex 4 FTS, CFS, 4 FTS. '68'.
XP511	Gnat T.1	8619M,	ex 4 FTS, CFS, 4 FTS. '65'.
XP530	Gnat T.1	8606M,	ex 4 FTS, CFS.
XP534	Gnat T.1	8620M,	ex 4 FTS, CFS, 4 FTS, CFS, 4 FTS. '64'.
XP540	Gnat T.1	8608M,	ex 4 FTS. '62'.
XP557	Jet Provost T.4	8494M,	ex 6 FTS, RAFC.
XP567	Jet Provost T.4	8510M,	ex CATCS, 6 FTS, RAFC. '23'.
XP573	Jet Provost T.4	8336M,	ex Kemble, Shawbury, Rolls-Royce, 1 FTS, CFS. Marked '8236M'.
XP585	Jet Provost T.4	8407M,	ex St Athan, RAFC, 6 FTS, RAFC. '24'.
XP640	Jet Provost T.4	8501M,	ex CATCS, 6 FTS, CAW, CFS, 3 FTS. 'E'.
XP672	Jet Provost T.4	8458M,	ex SoRF, CAW, CATCS, CAW, 2 FTS. '27'.
XP686	Jet Provost T.4	8502M,	ex 8401M, CATCS, 6 FTS, CAW, CATCS, CAW, 3 FTS. 'G'.
XR140	Argosy E.1	8579M,	ex 115, 114, 242 OCU, 114.
XR458	Whirlwind HAR.10	8662M,	ex 2 FTS, CFS, 28, 110, 103.
XR538	Gnat T.1	8621M,	ex 4 FTS. '69'.
XR569	Gnat T.1	8560M,	ex 4 FTS, CFS, 4 FTS, CFS.
XR574	Gnat T.1	8631M,	ex Cosford, Kemble, 4 FTS. '72'.
XR643	Jet Provost T.4	8516M,	ex Kemble hack, 3 CAACU, RAFC, 6 FTS. '26'.
XR650	Jet Provost T.4	8459M,	ex SoRF, CAW, CATCS, 3 FTS, CAW, 7 FTS. '28'.
XR651	Jet Provost T.4	8431M,	ex SoRF, CAW, CATCS, 3 FTS, 7 FTS. 'A'.
XR662	Jet Provost T.4	8410M,	ex SoRF, CAW, CATCS, RAFC, CAW, 6 FTS, 7 FTS. '25'.
XR669	Jet Provost T.4	8062M,	ex Shawbury, BAC Warton, Huntings, Luton.
XR670	Jet Provost T.4	8498M,	ex SoRF, CATCS, 3 FTS, 1 FTS, 2 FTS, 7 FTS, CFS.
XR672	Jet Provost T.4	8495M,	ex SoRF, 6 FTS, CAW, CATCS, 3 FTS, 1 FTS. 'C'.
XR704	Jet Provost T.4	8506M,	ex St Athan hack, CAW, CFS. '30'.
XR953	Gnat T.1	8609M,	ex 4 FTS. '63'.
XR954	Gnat T.1	8570M,	ex 4 FTS, CFS, 4FTS. Dismantled on field by 8/86, still 6/87.
XR980	Gnat T.1	8622M,	ex 4 FTS, CFS, 4 FTS, CFS, 4 FTS. '70'.
XR984	Gnat T.1	8571M,	ex 4 FTS.
XR998	Gnat T.1	8623M,	ex 4 FTS. '71'.
XS100	Gnat T.1	8561M,	ex 4 FTS. Dismantled on field by 8/86, still present 6/87.
XS109	Gnat T.1	8626M,	ex Cosford, Kemble, 4 FTS, Red Arrows, CFS, 4 FTS. '75'.
XS110	Gnat T.1	8562M,	ex 4 FTS, CFS, 4 FTS, CFS, 4 FTS.
XS176	Jet Provost T.4	8514M,	ex CATCS, 3 FTS, 2 FTS. 'N'.
XS179	Jet Provost T.4	8337M,	ex Kemble, Shawbury, CAW, RAFC. Marked as '8237M'. '20'.
XS180	Jet Provost T.4	8338M,	ex Kemble, CAW, 6 FTS. Marked as '8238M'. '21'.
XS186	Jet Provost T.4	8408M,	ex St Athan, Kemble, Shawbury, CAW. 'M'.
XS209	Jet Provost T.4	8409M,	ex St Athan, Kemble, Shawbury, CAW. '24'.
XS210	Jet Provost T.4	8339M,	ex Kemble, CAW. Marked '8239M'. '22'.
XS215	Jet Provost T.4	8507M,	ex CAW. '17'.
XS218	Jet Provost T.4	8508M,	ex Shawbury hack, 3 FTS. '18'.
XT257	Wessex HAS.3	8719M,	ex A&AEE.
XX110"	Jaguar GR.1 rig	- ,	BAPC.169, engine systems rig, made of GRP.
XX118	Jaguar GR.1	8815M,	ex Shawbury, Indian AF JI018, G-27-318, XX118. Centre section. Corrects W&R10.
XX726+	Jaguar GR.1	8947M,	ex Shawbury, 6. Arrived 1/88.
XX739+	Jaguar GR.1	8902M,	ex Shawbury, Gibraltar Det. Arrived by 7/86.
XX743+	Jaguar GR.1	8949M,	ex Shawbury. Arrived by 4/88.

XX746+ Jaguar GR.1A 8895M, ex 226 OCU. Arrived by 8/86.
XX747+ Jaguar GR.1 8903M, ex Gibraltar Det. Arrived by 6/87.
XX757+ Jaguar GR.1 8948M, ex Shawbury, 20. Arrived 1/88.
XX818+ Jaguar GR.1 8945M, ex Shawbury. Arrived by 4/88.
XX956+ Jaguar GR.1 8950M, ex Hawbury. Arrived by 4/88.
XX966+ Jaguar GR.1A 8904M, ex Shawbury, 6. Arrived by 12/86.
XX975+ Jaguar GR.1 8905M, ex 226 OCU. Arrived by 6/87.
XX976+ Jaguar GR.1 8906M, ex Shawbury, 17. Arrived by 12/86.
XZ382+ Jaguar GR.1 8908M, ex Shawbury, 14. Arrived by 12/86.
XZ389+ Jaguar GR.1 8946M, ex Shawbury, 17. Arrived 1/88.

Others During 1986 former Bentley Priory Spitfire XVI SL574 arrived and it is being prepared by the Appentices for display atop a pole at the San Diego Air and Space Museum. A P-51 Mustang will come the other way for the RAF Museum. Work on SL574 is to airworthiness standards, although it is doubted if it will fly. During 5/86 former 1 SoTT Hunter XF527 was mounted on the gate and is consequently listed below. The oft-reported Vampire pod is still present near the woods and is now identified. W&R10 mentioned resident Kittiwake G-AWGM. This first flew after restoration 15/7/85, but was damaged 18/1/86 and left by road 3/4/86 for Hanworth.

SL574+ Spitfire XVI 8391M, ex Bentley Priory, *Battle of Britain*, 11 GCF, North Weald SF, Biggin Hill SF, 3 CAACU, 103 FRS, CGS, EAAS. See above.
WZ559 Vampire T.11 7736M, ex Oakington, 5 FTS, 94, 145. Gutted pod - see above.
XF527 Hunter F.6 8680M, ex 1 SoTT, Laarbruch SF, 4 FTS, CFE, 19, Church Fenton SF, Linton SF. Gate guardian - see notes above.

MILTON KEYNES

The hulk of Sea Fury FB.11 G-FURY was joined here by the centre fuselage and other parts of G-AGHB/WH589 by 1/87 from Cranfield. However, both had moved by 7/87. The two Tempest cockpit sections held in this area are now thought to be from a scrapyard in Gloucestershire.

NEWPORT PAGNELL

Spitfire historian Peter R Arnold is restoring his superb Seafire in the locality.

LA564 Seafire F.46 ex Redbourn, Newark, Southend, Charnock Richard, Carlisle, Anthorn, 738, 767, A&AEE and cancelled Spitfire F.22 PV585.

PINEWOOD

The film studios took on the fuselage of Jet Provost T.4 XP683 during 1986 for filming and still hang on it it. Also noted here during 1/88 was a Hunter nose.

XP683+ Jet Provost T.4 ex Finchampstead Ridges, Lasham, Bicester, 1 FTS, 6 FTS. Fuselage.
+ Hunter nose section.

WORMINGHALL

(North of the A40 east of Oxford) The hulk of Beverley C.1 XB288 continues to lie in the yard of Fred Ford (corrects W&R10). There are also significant bits from another Bev here, possibly from XB285.

XB288 Beverley C.1 ex Bicester, 47, 53. SOC 8/1/69. Section.

Cambridgeshire

ALCONBURY

Major construction work at the base, including the inevitable HASs, has literally put paid to the old fire dump and the two aircraft on it, F-100D 42204 and F-100F 63935 had gone by 5/87. Of these 63935 turned up at Molesworth. The BDR airframes gained two Phantoms and a U-2 during 1986 but lost T-33A FT-37 to the disposal dump at Molesworth. The U-2 came in with a little help from a C-5B flight into Mildenhall on 21/2/88 and with the already resident F-101 makes the BDR airframes here decidedly tasty. The plastic F-5E still guards the main entrance.

01534	F-5E Tiger II	mock up, pole mounted on gate, 527 TFTAS colours.
60312	F-101B-80-MC	ex MASDC Davis Monthan, Kentucky ANG. BDRT.
63419+	F-4C-15-MC	ex Texas ANG. Arrived early 1986 for BDRT.
66692+	U-2CT-LO	ex 5 SRTS/9 SRW, Beale. See notes above.
153008+	F-4N-MC	ex VF-154/USS *Coral Sea*. Arrived early 1986 for BDRT.

BASSINGBOURN

Allenbrooke Barracks Displayed within the former airfield is a Canberra as a reminder of the days when pairs of Avons were the main noise here, not the churning of battle tanks!

WJ821	Canberra PR.7	8668M, ex RAE Bedford, 13, 58, 82.

East Anglian Aviation Society EAAS completed their excellent restoration of Dragon Rapide G-AJHO and, painted as 'G-ADDD' of the King's Flight, it made its first flight from a strip near here on 20/5/87. After a short series of appearances, it was sold early in 1988 to DH collector Victor Gauntlett. EAAS hope to find a smaller aircraft to do a similar restoration project on. EAAS also run the control tower at the airfield as a museum dedicated to the 91st Bomb Group USAAF and the RAF units 11 OTU and 231 OCU. Visits can be made by prior arrangement : M Reynolds, Secretary EAAS, 8 Pingle Lane, Northborough, Peterborough, PE6 9BW.

BOURN

At the airfield, the operations of the Rural Flying Corps and the Rural Naval Air Service have come to a halt. The Sea Prince is now in open store and the Provost T.1 XF877/G-AWVF moved to Compton Abbas. A battered Robin has arrived for spares use. At the heliport side, the horrors of trying to record those devices with rotating wings and high-mobile booms continue to rear themselves! Enstrom F-28A G-BACH mentioned in W&R10 should be deleted, believed to have been confused with G-DMCH which was in on a 'major'. Hiller UH-12E G-BBBA listed in W&R10 was a boom only, the rest of the device (with another boom!) continuing to fly until an accident on 26/9/86. The exact identity of the Bolkow 105C that is kept here on rebuild/store is open to hot dispute and this edition will take the easy route out by declaring it to be either D-HMUT (c/no S.047) or G-BGKP (ex D-HDGC)!

WP321	Sea Prince T.1	G-BRFC, ex Kemble, 750, 744, Stretton. See notes above.
G-BBJT+	Robin HR.200-100	ex Rochester, F-WUQK. Damaged 14/1/87. Arrived by 6/87 for spares.
	Bolkow Bo 105C	Soviet markings as '06' - see notes above.

CAMBRIDGE

It is assumed that both the Chipmunk and the Airedale continue to be stored locally, the former for Vintage Aircraft Team and the latter for Skycraft Services.

G-ASRK	Airedale	ex Oakington area. CoA expired 29/7/84.
WD356	Chipmunk T.10	7625M, ex Bushey, Nostell Priory, Aldergrove, QUB UAS.

CAMBRIDGE AIRPORT

(Or Teversham) Always an interesting airfield, but the only item of W&R interest continues to be the dumped Canberra nose section on the Church End side.

WJ863	Canberra T.4	ex 231 OCU, 360, Akrotiri SF, 231 OCU, Honington SF, Cottesmore SF. Nose.

CHATTERIS

(On the A141 south of March) The store here is still intact, both aircraft living on in 'limbo'.

G-ARNH	Colt 108	ex Elstree. Damaged 1/9/72. Dismantled.
G-AXNY	Fixter Pixie	ex Crowland area. Fuselage only, poor state.

DUXFORD

Imperial War Museum The now massive complex at Duxford Airfield is the venue for many a pilgrimage by enthusiasts from all over the country. There have been continued improvements and enlargements to the facilities, the most notable being the decision to open all year round - although during the winter season only the impressive *Superhangar* is open. Special events and flying days are also staged. There is much news, some sad, concerning aircraft here, and the narrative will give further details under appropriate headings below.

Part of the magic of Duxford is that it is a working site, with the public always able to view restoration in progress. The other appealing element is the number of 'co-operative' operations that are contained within the 'Duxford' banner, ranging from the warbird operations of the Old Flying Machine Company and The Fighter Collection to the aviation archaeology domain of the Essex Aviation Society.

Cornerstone of the IWM operation at Duxford is the superb support of the Duxford Aviation Society, which has now amassed, in its own right, an airliner collection second to none. DAS are always looking for new members, be they far-flung enthusiasts who wish to support the work at Duxford, or more local people who would like to lend a hand in some capacity. Membership enquiries can be made to :- Duxford Aviation Society, Duxford Airfield, Duxford, Cambridge, CB2 4QR. Tel 0223 835594.

Duxford's main season is mid-March to the end of October, 1030 to 1730, with the winter season November to mid-March, 10.30 to 15.45. Please note that admission charges vary on flying days. An SAE to the IWM at the address below will bring the latest information on opening times and special events. Contact : Imperial War Museum, Duxford Airfield, Duxford, Cambridge, CB2 4QR. Tel 0223 833963.

All aircraft based at Duxford are technically on loan to the Imperial War Museum, but to give the main 'inner' operations their full credit, aircraft are given owner-codes so that readers can assess the position of any particular 'fleet'. These codes are given alongside the names of the major operators listed below.

Imperial War Museum (IWM) Major influx with the IWM aircraft here was the arrival of many of the aircraft previously on display at Duxford's 'parent', the IWM at South Lambeth. Development work at Lambeth has made them welcome refugees here, but most will return eventually. The Fw 190 has entered a major restoration programme during its stay at Duxford. The Skyfame Collection is now wholly owned by the IWM, but is retained as a collection as a tribute to the pioneering work of Peter Thomas. Hunter F.4 WN904 is due to move to Waterbeach some time during 1988, to take the place of Whirlwind XG577 on the gate. Major IWM acquisition was the arrival of the former Warbirds of Great Britain Lancaster G-LANC, which is already under a restoration programme. Some aircraft at Duxford are stored off main site and are not available for public inspection. Aircraft that have left since W&R10 have been : CASA 352L G-BFHG flew to North Weald 7/12/85; Miles Student G-MIOO was acquired by the Vintage Aircraft Team and moved to Cranfield by 6/86; T-33A G-TJET flew out to North Weald 7/12/85 but stayed only briefly, settling upon Cranfield; Sycamore III G-48/1 to the BRM at Weston-super-Mare; Beech C-45G N75WB to North Weald by road for Aces High during 2/86; Mitchell N9089Z (omitted from W&R10) out by road to North Weald for Aces High in late 1987; Whirlwind HAS.7 XG577 to Waterbeach via a repaint at Wyton; SPAD XIII N2727V moved to Benington for restoration to flying condition; former Norwegian He 111 components should be deleted from the W&R10 listing as they are too small for our coverage; V-1 replica BAPC.36 was returned to the Shutleworth Collection at Old Warden briefly, before moving on to Hawkinge; Spitfire IX replica BAPC.184 was acquired by Aces High following the demise of Specialised Mouldings and moved to North Weald by 8/87.

Duxford Aviation Society (DAS) Through the kindness of Dan-Air, the DAS airliner collection took a major step forward with the arrival of York G-ANTK on 23/5/86 and unique Ambassador G-ALZO on 16/10/86, both from Lasham. The latter has been reassembled while the former is stripped down on a major restoration programme. The loan of Bristol 170 G-BISU is also much appreciated, but may well be only very temporary as it was put up for sale as W&R11 went to press.

B-17 Preservation Ltd (B-17) *Sally B* continues to operate from Duxford thanks to the care and drive of its air and ground crews and the backing of its very active supporter's club. *Friends of Sally B* always welcome new members, offering plenty of activities and a first-rate members' magazine. Contact : B-17 Preservation Ltd, PO Box 34, Horley, Surrey RH6 9RQ. Tel 0342 716031.

British Aerial Museum (BAM) Within the space of just less than a month, the dedicated craftsmen at BAM reached the height of their Blenheim restoration project with the first flight, at the hands of John Larcombe, on 22/5/87. At Denham on 21/6/87, with another pilot in command, the most ambitious restoration project ever undertaken by a largely part-time group was written off after a touch-and-go went badly wrong. Thankfully nobody was killed. Out of the bad came the good with a massive influx of support and encouragement and another airframe arrived by road on 21/1/88 for the determined team to have another go. Additionally, the Blenheim Society has been formed to support the project and to bring former Blenheim air and ground crews together. Enquiries concerning BAM and the Blenheim Society can be addressed via the IWM.

Essex Aviation Group An excellent display of aviation archaeology artefacts and other exhibits is maintained in one of the out-buildings by EAG. This is viewable on Sundays. Enquiries to : Essex Aviation Group, Mick Skeels, 142 Leigham Court Drive, Leigh-on-Sea, Essex SS9 1PU.

The Old Flying Machine Company (OFMC) The activities of Ray and Mark Hanna and friends have been consolidated under this name and all operations are staged out of Duxford. Well known airshow performers, OFMC is also heavily involved in film work. During 1988 the 'fleet' was swollen with a

Vought Corsair, a Fokker D.VII and a Grumman Avenger was expected as W&R11 went to press. The former Italian T-6G Texan is here on a short term basis, and will move to Rochester for restoration, along with another, currently transitting Lyneham. Enquiries regarding OFMC should be made via the IWM.

Russavia Collection (RC) On the same day that the Blenheim crashed (21/6/87), the Russavia 'flagship' Dragon Rapide G-AGTM/NF875 suffered an accident at Duxford. In a very bitter blow, this has led to the withdrawal of the Russavia pleasure flying concession at Duxford and as we go to press has brought the entire collection into jeopardy. Pleasure flying will never be the same again at Duxford as it seems certain that 'tin' will take over. Clearly, the situation regarding Russavia is in great flux and a more extensive reference will be found under the Bishop's Stortford heading. The restoration of Dragon Rapide G-AGJG will continue at Duxford, but no longer under the Russavia banner. As W&R11 goes to press, both the DH.2 replica and the Tiger Moth are being allowed to stay, but their future must also be in doubt. Dragon Rapide G-AGTM moved to Audley End 2/88 for initial storage, pending a decision on its future. The other Russavia aircraft have also left, whereabouts uncertain as we go to press : Dron G-AEDB, Chipmunk G-BCIW and ASW.20 BGA.2848.

The Fighter Collection (TFC) During 1987 Stephen Grey's magnificent collection of World War Two aircraft was given a more formal identity and based in the T2 hangar on the site. There has been considerable expansion, with much former Bitteswell material coming to Duxford. TFC have several Spitfires under restoration with the view to using them for trade, and the first of these, G-CDAN, is to be exported to New Zealand during 1988. Also arriving have been the Corsair, Kingcobra and Mitchell, with a P-38 Lightning under restoration at Chino also for the collection. Staging through Duxford briefly was B-17G N900RW *Thunderbird*, coming in from repaint at Southend on 16/7/87. The former Bitteswell based G-FORT. This started its ferry flight to Texas on 13/7/87. Enquiries about TFC should be made via the IWM.

G-ACUU	Cierva C.30A	ex Staverton, HM580, 529, 1448 Flt, G-ACUU. CoA exp 30/4/60. IWM.
G-AFBS	Magister I	ex Staverton, G-AKKU ntu, BB661, G-AFBS. CoA exp 25/2/63. IWM.
G-AGJG	Dragon Rapide	ex X7344, 1 Cam Flt. CoA expired 15/5/74. Under rebuild, see notes.
G-AGTO	J/1 Autocrat	airworthy. DAS.
G-ALDG	Hermes 4	ex Gatwick, cabin trainer, Silver City/Britavia, Falcon, Airwork, BOAC. Fuselage only. DAS.
G-ALFU	Dove 6	ex CAFU Stansted. CoA expired 4/6/71. DAS.
G-ALWF	Viscount 701	ex Liverpool Airport, Cambrian, British Eagle, BEA. DAS.
G-ALZO+	Ambassador	ex Lasham, Dan-Air, Handley Page, Jordan AF 108, BEA. Arr 16/10/86. DAS.
G-ANTK+	York	ex Lasham, Dan-Air, MW232, Fairey Aviation, 511, 242. Arrived 23/5/86. Under restoration. DAS.
G-AOVT	Britannia 312	ex Monarch, British Eagle, BOAC. DAS.
G-APDB	Comet 4	ex Dan-Air, MSA 9M-AOB, BOAC G-APDB. DAS.
G-APWJ	Herald 201	ex Norwich, Air UK, BIA, BUIA. DAS.
G-ASGC	Super VC-10 1151	ex BA, BOAC. DAS.
G-AVFB	Trident 2E	ex BA, Cyprus 5B-DAC, BEA. DAS.
G-AVXV+	Bleriot XI	BAPC.104, ex St Athan, Colerne. Arrived by 9/86. IWM.
G-AXDN	Concorde 01	ex BAC/Aerospatiale. DAS.
G-BFPL+	Fokker D.VII rep	ex Lower Upham, Sandown, Land's End, Chertsey, D-EAWM. Arr by 4/88. OFMC.
G-BISU+	B.170 Srs 31M	ex Air Atlantic/Instone, ZK-EPH, RNZAF NZ5912, ZK-BVI, NZ5912, G-18-194. Flew in 22/11/87. On loan DAS from Jeremy Instone.
G-CDAN	Spitfire XVI	TB863, ex Booker, Southam, Duxford, Southend, Henlow, Pinewood, Kenley, 3 CAACU, 17, 691, 183, 453, 84 GSU. Under restoration, to go to New Zealand. TFC.
G-HURI+	Hurricane IIB	ex Coningsby, Coventry, Canada. Nearing completion. TFC. Arrived 30/1/88.
G-PSID+	P-51D-20-NA	ex Bitteswell, Blackbushe, N166G, N3350, N335J, N6171C, USAAF 44-63788. Flew in 3/3/87. Airworthy. TFC. Cancelled as sold in France 2/88.
G-36-1	SB.4 SHERPA	ex Staverton, Bristol, Cranfield, G-14-1 and SB.1 glider. Stored. IWM.
BAPC90	Colditz Cock rep	ex Higher Blagdon. Arrived during 1987. Stored.
BAPC93	Fi 103 (V-1)	8583M, ex Cosford. IWM.
CF-EQS	Boeing A75N-1	ex Canada, USAAF 41-8169. Stored. IWM.
CF-KCG	TBM-3E Avenger	ex Canada, Conair, RCN 326, USN 69327. Under restoration. IWM.
F-BCDG	MS.502 Criquet	ex USA, EI-AUY, F-BCDG, ALAT. Stored. IWM.

N47DD	P-47D-30-RA	ex Chino, USA, Peru AF FAP.119, USAAF 45-49192. Major restoration project, including parts from other airframes. IWM.
N240CA+	F4U Corsair	ex USA. Arrived via Felixstowe Docks 4/88. OFMC.
NC88ZK+	Boeing A75N-1	ex USA. Arrived crated 6/86. Airworthy. OFMC.
NX700H	F8F-2P Bearcat	ex N1YY, N4995V, US Navy 121714. Airworthy, 'S/100'. TFC.
N7614C	B-25J-30-NC	ex Shoreham, Dublin, Prestwick, Luton, USAF 44-31171. Restoration. IWM
N8297+	FG-1D Corsair	ex N9154Z, USN 88297. Arr 6/86. Airworthy. TFC.
N62822+	P-63C-5-BE	ex 44-4393. Arrived 6/1/88. Will fly in Soviet c/s. TFC.
N88972+	B-25D-30-ND	ex KL161, USAAF 44-43-3318. Flew in 8/11/87. TFC.
N94466	P-40E Kittyhawk I	ex USA, RCAF 1057, AK933. Airworthy, 'SU-E'. *Sneak Attack*. OFMC.
2699	RAF BE.2c	ex South Lambeth, 192, 51, 50. IWM.
5964"	DH.2 replica	G-BFVH, ex *Gunbus*, Lands End, Chertsey. RC.
E2581	Bristol F.2b	ex South Lambeth, 2 GCF, 30 TS, HQ Flt SEa Area, 1 Com Sqn. IWM.
F3556	RAF RE.8	ex South Lambeth. *A Paddy Bird from Ceylon*. IWM.
K2567"	Tiger Moth	G-MOTH, complex composite, airworthy. RC.
N4877	Anson I	ex Staverton, G-AMDA Derby Airways, Watchfield SF, 3 FP, ATA, 3 FPP. 'VX-F'. IWM.
R3950+	Battle I	ex Sandown, Strathallan, Canada, RCAF 1899. Arr by 10/87. On loan to IWM from Charles Church.
V3388	Oxford I	G-AHTW, ex Staverton, Boulton Paul, V3388. CoA exp 15/12/60. IWM.
V6028"	Bolingbroke IVT	G-MKIV, ex G-BLHM ntu, RCAF 10038. First flown 22/5/87, crashed 21/6/87. For component salvage for 2nd restoration project. See notes above. BAM.
V9300	Lysander III	G-LIZY, ex 'Y1351', Canada, RCAF 1558, V9300. For restoration. BAM.
Z2033	Firefly I	ex Staverton, G-ASTL, SE-BRD, Z2033. IWM.
Z7015	Sea Hurricane I	G-BKTH, ex Staverton, Old Warden, Loughborough, Yeovilton, 759, 880. Under restoration. IWM/Shuttleworth Trust.
FR870"	P-40N Kittyhawk	NL1009N, ex Wright Patterson, RCAF 877, 43-23484. Airworthy, 'GA-S'. TFC
JV928+	PBY-5A Catalina	G-BLSC, ex Barkston Heath, South Africa, C-FMIR, N608FF, CF-MIR, N10023, USN 46633. Based from 6/87. Airworthy. Plane Sailing.
KB889+	Lancaster X	G-LANC, ex Bitteswell, Blackbushe, Niagara Falls, RCAF 107 MRU, 428. Arrived 14/5/86. Under restoration. IWM.
LZ766	Proctor III	ex Staverton, G-ALCK, Tamworth, HQ Bomber Command, 21 EFTS. IWM.
MH434	Spitfire IX	G-ASJV, ex Booker, COGEA OO-ARA, Belgian AF SM-41, Fokker B-13, Netherlands H-68, and H-105 322, MH434 349, 84 GSU, 222, 350, 222. Airworthy. 'AC-S'. OFMC.
ML417	Spitfire IX	G-BJSG, ex Booker, USA, Indian AF Tr.IX HS543, G-5-11, ML417, High Ercall, 411, 442, 443. '21-T'. Airworthy. TFC.
ML796	Sunderland MR.5	ex La Baule, Maisden-le-Riviere, *Aeronavale* 27F, 7FE, RAF 230, 4 OTU, 228. Under restoration. IWM.
MV293+	Spitfire XIV	G-SPIT, ex Sleaford, Blackbushe, G-BGHB ntu, Bangalore, Indian inst T20, Indian AF, ACSEA, 215 MU, 33 MU. Arr by 11/86. Under restoration. TFC.
NF370+	Swordfish II	ex South Lambeth, Stretton, RAF charge. Arrived early 1986. IWM.
NH799+	Spitfire XIV	ex Bitteswell, Blackbushe, Indian AF instructional, 9, ACSEA, 215 MU, 9 MU. Arrived by 9/86. Under restoration. TFC.
PN323+	Halifax A.VII	ex South Lambeth, Duxford, Staverton, Radlett, Standard Telephones, SOC 28/5/48, HP test fleet. Nose section. IWM.
SM832+	Spitfire XIV	G-WWII, ex Bitteswell, Blackbushe, Indian Air Force, Dehra Dun gate, RAF SM832, ACSEA, 222 MU, 29 MU. Under restoration. TFC.
TA719	Mosquito TT.35	ex Staverton, G-ASKC, Shawbury, 3/4 CAACU, 4 CAACU, Shawbury. Under restoration. IWM.
TG263	SARO SR.A.1	ex Staverton, Cranfield, G-12-1, TG263. IWM.
TG528	Hastings C.1A	ex Staverton, 24, 24/36, 242 OCU, 53/99, 47. IWM.
TX226	Anson C.19	7865M, ex Little Staughton, East Dereham, Colerne, Shawbury, FTCCF, OCTU Jurby, 187, Hemswell SF, Coningsby CF, CBE. Stored. IWM.
VT260	Meteor F.4	8813M, ex Winterbourne Gunner, 49 MU, 12 FTS, 209 AFS, 203 AFS, 226 OCU, 203 AFS. Under restoration. IWM.
WD686	Meteor NF.11(mod)	ex RAE Bedford, Wroughton, TRE Defford. IWM.
WF425	Varsity T.1	ex RAE Met Flt, RAE, CFS, 1 ANS, 2 ANS. IWM.
WG752	Dragonfly HR.3	ex Dulwich, Fleetlands, Britannia Flt, 727, Culdrose SF, 705. '911'. IWM.

WH725	Canberra B.2	ex Wroughton, 50, 44. IWM
WJ288+	Sea Fury FB.11	G-SALY, ex Lympne, Southend, Biggin Hill, Dunsfold, FRU, Lossiemouth, Anthorn, Donibristle. On loan to IWM.
WJ945	Varsity T.1	G-BEDV, ex CFS, 5 FTS, AE&AEOS, CFS, 115, 116, 527. Badly damaged in 10/87 gales. DAS.
WK991	Meteor F.8	7825M, ex Kemble, 56, 46, 13 GCF, NSF. IWM.
WM969	Sea Hawk FB.5	A2530, ex Culdrose 'SAH-5', FRU, 806, 811, 898. IWM.
WN904	Hunter F.2	7544M, ex Newton, 257. IWM. See notes above.
WZ515	Vampire T.11	ex Staverton, Woodford, Chester, St Athan, 4 FTS, 8 FTS, 56, 253, 16. Stored. IWM.
WZ590	Vampire T.11	ex Woodford, Chester, St Athan, 8 FTS, 5 FTS, 228 OCU. IWM.
XE627+	Hunter F.6A	ex Brawdy, 1 TWU, TWU, 229 OCU, 1, 229 OCU, 54, 1, 54, Horsham St Faith SF, 54, 229 OCU, 65, 92. Arrived 14/11/86. IWM.
XF708	Shackleton MR.3/3	ex Kemble, 203, 120, 201. Under restoration. IWM.
XG613	Sea Venom FAW.21	ex Old Warden, 766, 809. IWM.
XG743	Sea Vampire T.22	ex Brawdy SF, 736, 764. '597/BY'. IWM.
XG797	Gannet ECM.6	ex Arbroath, 831, 700, 810. '766/BY'. IWM.
XH648	Victor BK.1A	ex 57, 55, 57, 15. IWM.
XH897	Javelin FAW.9	ex A&AEE, 5, 33, 25. IWM.
XJ824	Vulcan B.2A	ex 101, 9/35, 9, 230 OCU, 27. IWM.
XK695	Comet C.2(RCM)	ex Wyton, 51, 216, G-AMXH. IWM.
XK884+	Pembroke C.1	G-BNPG, ex Shawbury, 60, 21, 207, SCS, 70, MECS, Nicosia SF, MECS. Flew in 7/7/87. John Allison and Mike Searle.
XK936	Whirlwind HAS.7	ex Wroughton, 705, 847, 848, 701, 820, 845. IWM.
XM135	Lightning F.1A	ex Leconfield, 60 MU, Leuchars TFF, 226 OCU, 74, A&AEE, AFDS. IWM
XN239+	Cadet TX.3	8889M, arrived by 7/86. IWM.
XP281	Auster AOP.9	ex AFWF, Middle Wallop. IWM.
XR222	TSR-2 XO-4	ex Cranfield, Weybridge. Unflown. IWM.
XR241	Auster AOP.9	G-AXRR, ex Shuttleworth, St Athan, 1 Wing HQ, 654, Middle Wallop. Dismantled, awaiting restoration. CoA expired 30/9/86. BAM.
XS576	Sea Vixen FAW.2	ex Sydenham, 899, Brawdy. '125/E'. IWM
XS863	Wessex HAS.1	ex A&AEE. IWM.
+	Typhoon	ex South Lambeth. Cockpit section. Arrived early 1986. IWM.
A-549	FMA Pucara	ZD487 ntu, ex Boscombe Down, Yeovilton, Stanley, FAA. IWM.
671+"	Chipmunk 22	G-BNZC, ex Hampton, G-ROYS, 7438M, WP905, CFS, 664, RAFC. Arr 8/87, due to fly Spring 1988. John Romain/BAM.
9893	Bolingbroke IVT	ex Canada. Held in store - will be used for spares in the restoration of the second BAM Blenheim. IWM.
10201+	Bolingbroke IVT	ex Strathallan, Canada, RCAF. Arrived 28/1/88, for restoration. BAM
18393	CF.100 Mk IV	G-BCYK, ex Cranfield, RCAF. IWM.
57	Mystere IVA	ex Sculthorpe, FAF 8 Esc, 321 GI, 5 Esc. '8-MT'. IWM.
92	Broussard	G-BJGW, ex F-BMMP, ALAT, AIA, GAM.50. Moroccan c/s. BAM.
100143	Fa 330A-1	IWM.
120235+	He 162A-1	AM.68, ex South Lambeth, Cranwell, 6 MU, Farnborough, JG.1 Leck. Arrived early 1986. IWM
191660	Me 163B-1	AM.214, ex South Lambeth, Cranwell, 6 MU, RAE. IWM.
733682+	Fw 190A-8	AM.75, ex South Lambeth, Biggin Hill, Cranwell, 6 MU, Farnborough. Arrived early 1986. Under restoration. IWM.
"	Amiot AAC.1	ex Portuguese AF 6316. *Luftwaffe* c/s, 'IZ+NK'. IWM.
MM54099+	T-6G Texan	ex Lyneham, Decimomannu, Italian AF 'RR-56'. Arr 31/10/87. Due to move to Rochester for restoration. OFMC.
35075	SAAB J35A Draken	ex RSwAF F16. '40'. IWM.
164"	Beech 18 3TM	G-BKGL, ex Prestwick, CF-QPD, RCAF 1564. USN c/s, airworthy. BAM.
592"	Mustang Mk 22	G-HAEC, ex Stansted, Gatwick, Hong Kong, VR-HIU, PI-C-651, VH-FCB, A68-192. *Missy Wong from Hong Kong*. Airworthy. OFMC
14286	T-33A-1-LO	ex Sculthorpe, FAF CIFAS 328. 'WK'. IWM.
17899	VT-29B-CO	ex 513 TAW, Mildenhall, USAF. IWM.
42165	F-100D-11-NA	ex Sculthorpe, FAF Esc 2/11, Esc 1/3, USAF. '11-ML'. IWM.
60689	B-52D-40-BW	ex 7 BW Carswell and others, USAF. IWM.

226671"	P-47D/N	NX47DD, composite, *No Guts, No Glory*, Airworthy, f/f 24/2/86, TFC,
231965"	B-17G-95-DL	ex IGN F-BDRS, N68629, USAAF 44-83735, *Mary Alice*, 401 BG c/s, IWM,
315509	C-47A-85-DL	ex Aces High G-BHUB, *Airline* 'G-AGIV', 'FD988' and 'KG418', Spanish AF T3-29, N51V, N9985F, SAS SE-BBH, 43-15509, 9th AF colours, IWM,
461748	TB-29A-45-BN	G-BHDK, ex China Lake, 307th BG, Okinawa, *Hawg Wild*, IWM,
463221"	P-51D-25-NA	N51JJ, ex N6340T, RCAF 9568, USAAF 44-73149, *Candyman/Moose*, 'G4-S', Airworthy, TFC,
472258"	P-51D-25-NA	ex RCAF 9246, USAAF 44-73979, Under restoration, 78th FG colours, IWM,
485784	B-17G-105-VE	G-BEDF, ex N17TE, IGN F-BGSR, USAAF 44-85784, *Sally B*, Airworthy, B-17,
133722	F4U-7 Corsair	NX1337A, Aeronavale c/s, airworthy, Lindsey Walton,
C-551+	EKW C-3605	ex Lodrino, Swiss AF, Arrived by 4/88, TFC?
J-1605	Venom FB,50	G-BLID, ex Swiss Air Force, Aces High,
J-1616	Venom FB,50	G-BLIF/N202DM, ex Swiss Air Force, Aces High, to move during 1988,
+	Mitsubishi A6M	ex South Lambeth, Cockpit section Arrived early 1986, IWM,

Locally Not too far away, the Nord continues its storage,

G-NORD	SNCAC NC,854	ex Fowlmere, F-BFIS, CoA expired 27/5/82, Stored,

ELY

In the grounds of the RAF Hospital, the Meteor still watches over the inmates,

WS774	Meteor NF,14	7959M, ex Upwood, Kemble, 1 ANS, 2 ANS,

EVERSDEN

(On the A603 west of Cambridge) There has been little change with the long term airframes at Brian Mills' workshop, Cessna F,150L G-BAXV has moved to Bredhurst, Otherwise ;

G-ADJJ	Tiger Moth	ex BB819, G-ADJJ, CoA expired 20/3/75, Stored,
G-ATEV	CEA DR,1050	ex F-BJHL, CoA expired 13/8/71, Stored,
G-AYBV	YC-12 Tourbillon	unfinished homebuild project, Stored,
G-AZDY	Tiger Moth	ex F-BGDJ, French AF, PG650, CoA expired 25/6/82, Stored,
G-BKKS	Mercury Dart	unfinished homebuild project, Stored,
F-GAIP	WA,81 Piranha	G-BKOT, Unflown in UK markings, Stored,

HUNTINGDON

The current status of Peter Jackson's two rebuild projects is unconfirmed with the demise of Specialised Mouldings here, G-ANME, listed in W&R10, is components only and should be deleted,

G-AMNN	Tiger Moth	ex Redhill, NM137, Crashed 27/5/64, See above and also under Shoreham,
G-BPAJ	Tiger Moth	ex Jackaroo G-AOIX and Tiger T7087, Henlow CF, 6 FTS, 3 EFTS, ACC CF, 170, 20 EFTS, 12 EFTS, Under restoration,

KIMBOLTON

(On the A45 north west of St Neots) The CCF at Kimbolton School still have their Meteor nose in an out building, At the airfield, the hulk of Cessna G-ARRG still holds on to a tenuous existence,

G-ARRG	Cessna 175B	ex Great Yarmouth, N8299T, Crashed 3/11/70, Hulk,
VZ477	Meteor F,8	7741M, ex APS, 245, Nose only,

KINGSTON

(On the B1046 west of Cambridge) Laurie Taylor's Magister restoration suffered a set-back here on 4/7/87 when Cessna G-AYPH ran amok and ploughed into it, Full extent of the damage is not known,

G-AKPF	Magister	ex Bassingbourn, Duxford, Burnaston, Composite, fuselage G-ANLT, ex N3788, 169, 2 FIS, 2 FTS, 5 EFTS, 8 EFTS, 27 ERFTS, Wings from G-AKPF, ex V1075, See notes above,

LITTLE GRANSDEN

(On the B1046 west of Cambridge) At the airstrip Tiger Moth G-AIRI has been out of use for some time, It was joined by an Aztec during 1985,

G-AIRI+	Tiger Moth	ex N5488, 29 EFTS, 14 EFTS, 20 ERFTS, CoA expired 9/11/81, Stored,
G-AWDI+	Aztec 250C	ex Air Foyle, N6520Y, CoA expired 21/6/85, Stored,

LITTLE STAUGHTON

By 11/86 Widgeon G-ANLW/MD497 had arrived here from Tattershall Thorpe. During 1987 it moved on, this time to Wellingborough. By 4/87, a Skeeter AOP.12 was noted in store here. It is most likely XL735 from Tattershall Thorpe, but could be XL765 from Leamington Spa.

MOLESWORTH

While Ronnie and Mikhail are busy making sure that the current plans for this base are already obsolete, it would seem that another role has been carried out here for a considerable time. A compound at the base is used for storing USAFE scrap and then offering it for tender. Last noted user was former 527 TFTAS F-5E Tiger 01555, first noted 6/79 and left (for Faygate) by 11/80. The aircraft listed below are all new to the location and are substantial. There are also plenty of bits from A-10s to note here.

FT-37+	T-33A-1-LO	ex Alconbury, Belgian AF, USAF 55-3082. Arrived by mid 1986.
10"+	Mystere IVA	97, ex Mildenhall, Lakenheath, Sculthorpe, Chateaudun, French AF. First noted 8/87.
63935+	F-100F-16-NA	ex Alconbury, Sculthorpe, French AF. Arrived by mid 1986.
660014+	F-111A-CF	ex 366 TFW 'MO'. First noted 4/87.
702375+	F-111F-CF	ex 48 TFW 'LN'. Crashed 28/7/87. First noted 1/88.
702418+	F-111F-CF	ex 48 TFW 'LN'. Crashed 23/2/87. First noted 4/87.
720142+	RF-4C-51-MC	ex 10 TRW/1 TRS, 'AR'. Crashed 24/7/86. First noted 10/87.

OAKINGTON

Work on the Provost is thought to continue. The Varsity nose is still on the airfield.

G-BKFW	Provost T.1	ex Connah's Quay, XF597, Shawbury, CAW, RAFC.
	Varsity T.1	nose section. With local ATC.

SIBSON

(Or Peterborough Sport Airfield) Nene Valley Aviation Society fell foul of planning permission here and the aircraft museum had a tenure of only two years. All of the aircraft were put up for disposal during 1986 and moved on as follows ; Auster G-AGXT did not return to TAC and is reported to have moved into 'Lincolnshire'; Javelin nose XA571 to Booker 7/6/86; Vampire T.11 XE935 to Firbeck; Whirlwind HAR.10 XJ726 to Caernarfon; Whirlwind HAS.7 XL840 to Norwich 4/86; and Luton Minor BAPC.97 back to NEAM at Sunderland. NVAS is still in being and welcomes members from the general area. Contact : R M Houghton, 166 Sywell Road, Overstone, Northants.

The airfield itself has taken on several more W&R inmates. Cessna 150 G-ARAU moved to Willingham for further storage. Current here are :-

G-ARRS	Menavia CP.301A	ex F-BIMA. CoA expired 21/4/78. Stored.
G-BDFJ+	Cessna F.150M	ex Coventry. Crashed 13/4/86. Wreck, arrived 12/86.
G-BFWF+	Cessna 421B	ex Staverton, ZS-JCA, N1567G. CoA expired 15/5/80. Stored.
N620GS	Cessna 310B	ex SABENA OO-SEF, N5420A. Arrived during 1986. Stored.
WF372	Varsity T.1	ex 6 FTS, 1 ANS, RAFC, 201 AFS. 'T'. External store.
WW444+	Provost T.1	ex Coventry, Bitteswell, St Athan, 6 FTS. Arrived by 10/86.

WATERBEACH

At the former airfield, the gate is guarded by a former Duxford Whirlwind. This will be replaced during 1988 with the more appropriate Hunter F.4 from Duxford - which see.

XG577+	Whirlwind HAS.7	A2571, ex Duxford, East Midlands, Duxford, Lee-on-Solent, Arbroath, 705, 737, 815, 705, 701, Albion Ship's Flt. Arrived by 11/86.

WHITTLESEY

(On the A605 east of Peterborough) ABH Aviation still keep their Alpine here.

G-AOGV	J/5R Alpine	CoA expired 17/7/72. Stored. (Correcting W&R10)

WILLINGHAM

(South of the A1123, east of Huntingdon) Cessna 150 G-ARAU is now stored in this area.

G-ARAU+	Cessna 150	ex Sibson, N6494T. CoA expired 14/9/84. Stored.

WITTERING

There has been quite a throughput of airframes to talk of since W&R10. Harrier GR.3 XV778 became the base's first gate guardian proper (ie at the gate, the Spitfire is shown off from the corner of the 1 Squadron hangar) during 3/88. The Varsity lives on at the fire dump (located at the Collyweston end of the airfield and visible from the A47) but P.1127 hulk XP976 went to Faygate by 8/87 and Harrier GR.1 hulk XV788 were cleared from it by 10/86. Wrecked GR.3 XW916 (crashed 17/6/86) appeared on the dump by 3/87 but stayed for only a short time before moving on, or perishing. The Spitfire is displayed outside 1 Squadron's hangar in good weather. There have been some additions ;-

LA255	Spitfire F.21	6490M, ex West Raynham, Cardington, Tangmere, 1. 'JX-U'.
WJ902	Varsity T.1	ex 5 FTS, CAW, 5 FTS, 2 ANS, 11 FTS, 201 AFS.
XF383	Hunter F.6	8706M, ex Kemble, 12, 216, 237 OCU, 4 FTS, 229 OCU, 65, 111, 263. BDR.
XV279	Harrier GR.1	8566M, ex Farnborough, Culdrose, A&AEE. Weapons loading trainer.
XV281+	Harrier GR.1	ex Filton, Rolls-Royce, A&AEE, BSE Filton, Dunsfold. Arrived 5/10/87.
XV778+	Harrier GR.3	8931M, ex 1 See notes above.
XW923	Harrier GR.3	8724M, ex 1417 Flt, 1, 233 OCU, 1. Nose section, rescue training.

WYTON

Another Canberra joined the dump during 1986 and two Canberra noses were 'rediscovered', but the remainder of the W&R Canberra population remains unchanged. The former Air Scouts Comet C.2R was declared unsafe and was threatened with the axe during the summer of 1987. Mosquito Aircraft Museum stepped in to salvage whatever they could, but were halted by MoD's urge to have it declared through the bid system. As W&R11 went to press it was sectioned and awaiting a scrapman.

WH773	Canberra PR.7	8696M, ex 13, 58, 80, 31, 82, 540. Gate guardian, with 2331 Sqn ATC.
WJ817	Canberra PR.7	8695M, ex 13, 58, 80, 17, 58. 'FO'. BDR.
WJ977	Canberra T.17	8761M, ex 360, 139, 9, Binbrook SF, 139, 21, 57, 15. Dump, poor state.
WK162+	Canberra B.2	8887M, Marham, ex 100, 85, 98, 245, 527. 'CA'. Crashed 8/8/85. On dump, in sections, first noted 11/86.
WT305	Canberra B.6(mod)	8511M, ex RAE, RRE, 51, 192. Gate guardian.
XH170	Canberra PR.9	8739M, ex 39, RAE, 58. Gate guardian.
XK697	Comet C.2R	ex Air Scouts, 51, 216, G-AMXJ. See notes above.
+	Canberra T.4	nose section, on dump, escape training. First noted 11/86.
+	Canberra T.4	nose section, on trolley, marked '160 CSC'. First noted 11/86.

Cheshire

ALDERLEY EDGE

Colin Fray completed restoration of his Aiglet Trainer G-AMTO and by 8/87 it had moved to Manchester Airport for flight testing.

CHESTER

Neil Owen and Elizabeth Shanklin still keep their Vampire T.11 here, with restoration work continuing.

XH312	Vampire T.11	ex Knutsford, Woodford, Hawarden, St Athan, 8 FTS.

CONGLETON

Mike Abbott's Leopard Moth restoration is a more complicated arrangement than given in W&R10. G-ACUS, currently flying from Panshanger used some parts from this airframe and the Leopard that will be completed here is best described as being based upon the mortal remains of HB-OXO.

G-ACOL	Leopard Moth	ex HB-OXO, CH-368. Under restoration.

HANDFORTH

395 Sqn ATC maintain their Chipmunk T.10 PAX Trainer here. It is 'parented' by Shawbury.

WZ869	Chipmunk T.10 PAX	8019M, ex 1 FTS, RAFC, Dishforth SF, Benson SF, OXF UAS, DUR UAS, 64 GCF, Colerne SF. Crashed 20/5/68.

MACCLESFIELD

Lovaux Ltd Main base for the support and spares operations of Lovaux is Bournemouth Airport, but the large stores and refurbishing unit here continues to be very busy, working on Canberra, Hunter and Jet Provost/Strikemaster contracts. Several airframes have moved down to Bournemouth Airport however ; the nose of Hunter FGA.9 XG195 was combined with the rear fuselage and wings of XJ690 and moved during 1987; Hunter F.51 E-402 also made the journey by late 1987. Coming the other way by 4/87 was the fuselage of Jet Provost T.4 XR654 and the now reunited ET-272. Being without its nose, the centre section of Canberra B.2 WT212, mentioned in W&R10, should be deleted as beyond the scope of the tome. Substantial airframes current here are as follows :-

WJ722	Canberra B.2	ex St Athan, 98, 85, 98, CAW, 50, 21. Dismantled.
XE584	Hunter FGA.9	ex Bitteswell, G-9-450, 208, 8, 1. Sections, dismantled.
XJ690	Hunter FGA.9	ex Bitteswell, G-9-451, 20, 14. With the rear end of T.7 ET-271.
XR654+	Jet Provost T.4	ex Hunter One Bournemouth Airport, Coventry, Puckeridge, Hatfield, 27 MU, CAW, 3 FTS, 6 FTS. Fuselage only, arr by 4/87. Dark blue colours, marked '201 Sqn ATC'.
ET-273	Hunter T.53	ex Hatfield, Dunsfold, G-9-431, Danish AF, Aalborg store, ESK.724. Dismantled.

Macclesfield College of Further Education Located in Park Street, the College still have their instructional airframe.

XD624	Vampire T.11	ex CATCS, CNCS, Church Fenton SF, 19.

MALPAS

(East of the A41 north west of Whitchurch) 617 Sqn ATC at Malpas School took delivery of a Whirlwind HAS.7 during 3/87.

XK944+	Whirlwind HAS.7	A2607, ex Brunel Tech Bristol, Lee-on-Solent, Fleetlands, Arbroath, Fleetlands, Lossiemouth SF, Fleetlands, Yeovilton, 824, Ark Royal Flight.

WARMINGHAM

(South of Middlewich in between the A530 and the A533) The Aeroplane Collection TAC continue to base their activities at the craft centre here and have adopted an overall theme of light aviation, as can be seen from their recent additions. TAC also have a long term store at Wigan and of course are heavily involved in the Greater Manchester Museum of Science and Technology - both of which see. TAC aircraft are also to be found at East Fortune and Henlow - but see note under the latter heading.

As well as the aircraft TAC have a large range of engines and other displays at the Warmingham Craft Centre, The Old Mill. The Craft Centre is open 1000 to 1700 weekdays and 1000 to 1800 at weekends. TAC can be contacted at : 7, Mayfield Avenue, Stretford, Manchester M32 9ML. (061 865 0665)

Contrary to W&R10 Luton Minor G-AFIU and HM.14 Pou du Ciel BAPC.13 did not come here, but instead went to store at Wigan. Ken Fern's Vampire T.11 XE998 arrived here from Wigan 14/10/86 but stayed only until 20/12/86 when it moved on again to Biggin Hill. TAC's Emeraude G-BLHL was due here from East Kirkby by the time W&R11 went to press. Current here are as follows :-

G-AFIN	Chrislea Airguard	ex Wigan, Finningley. Complete, fuselage replica built at Finningley, wings, tail etc original. The Airguard is due to go to Ken Fern at Stoke.
G-AJEB	J/1N Alpha	ex Brize Norton, Wigan, Cosford. Withdrawn 1969.
G-BLHL+	CP.301A Emeraude	ex Wigan, East Kirkby, Tattershall, Chinnor, Booker, F-BLHL, F-OBLM. Crashed 4/8/81. Due here spring 1988. Engineless.
BAPC 15	Addyman STG	ex Wigan, Harrogate. Restoration complete.
BAPC192+	Weedhopper JC-24	complete, but unflown. Arrived during 1987.
BAPC193+	Hovey Whing Ding	fuselage and one wing, uncompleted homebuild project.
+	Chrislea Skyjeep	ex Bristol area, fuselage frame only. Arrived 1987.
WB624	Chipmunk T.10	ex East Midlands, Wigan, DUR UAS, ABN UAS, Henlow, St Athan, 22 GCF, Debden, Jurby SF, 8 FTS, 18 RFS. Fuselage.
XL811	Skeeter AOP.12	ex Southend, 9/12 Lancers, 17F, 652, 651.

WARRINGTON

Used as a travelling exhibit and seen at many north western events during 1987 was 1330 Sqn ATC's Jet Provost T.3 nose. The unit keeps the nose in a container when it is not out and about. The nose is 'parented' by Shawbury. Last heard of at Shrewsbury, it may have been here since 1984.

XM474+	Jet Provost T.3	8121M, ex Shrewsbury, Shawbury, MinTech, 6 FTS, MoA, 6 FTS, CFS. Nose.

WILMSLOW

By 9/86 the unfortunate Meta-Sokol G-APVU had arrived at a private house here.

G-APVU+	L.40 Meta-Sokol	ex Manchester Airport, OK-NMI. Accident 12/9/78.

WINSFORD

(On the A54 south of Northwich) It is thought the Musketeer hulk can still be found at Ash Croft Farm.

G-ASFB	Musketeer 23	crashed 23/5/81. Remains only.

Cleveland

MIDDLESBOROUGH

Briefly, from October 1986, the docklands here became a place of pilgrimage for many an enthusiast. A cache of fourteen Polish-built and operated MiG 15s arrived in crates, in superb condition. The aircraft did not stay long, being largely snapped up by Classics in America Inc of Reno, Nevada and being onward crated to the USA. Just prior to this 01120 was donated to the RAF Museum and was roaded to Hendon on 10/11/86. First aircraft to depart to the USA was 01016 in mid November and by the following February the remainder had gone and the docks could return to normality.

For completeness the transitory aircraft were as follows, including the US civil registration allocated to them : MiG 15bis (NATO - *Faggot*; Polish = LIM-2) 00822/N822LM, 01013/N13KM, 01016, 01205/N205JM, 01416/N416JM, 01606/N606BM, 01614/N614BM, 01621/N621BM, 01629/N629BM. MiG 15UTI (NATO - *Midget*; Polish SBLim-1) 06038/N38BM, 06040/N40BM, 08017/N17MK, 242271/N271JM. 242271 is thought to have been built as a MiG 15bisR and then converted to UTI status. 01016 is as yet unregistered in the USA. As it left decidedly earlier than the others, it is thought to have gone to a separate destination.

TEES-SIDE AIRPORT

(Or Middleton St George) Main interest here still centres on the Civil Aviation Authority Fire School. The school has gained two more Tridents since W&R10, although some of the older inmates are now in poor condition. Also coming the school's way have been two of the former BMA Viscounts and a passing Aztec. Of the BMA Viscount store, the four former South African ones were traded in to British Aerospace as part of the ATP deal with G-AZNB and G-AZNC being broken up during 1987 and the other two joining the fire school. Series 814 G-AYOX left by road on 4/9/86 for Southend. Accordingly, all the airframes of note to W&R are currently with the CAA Fire School.

G-ARPD	Trident 1C	ex British Airways, del 27/ 8/81. Poor state.
G-ARPO	Trident 1C	ex British Airways, del 12/12/83. Whole.
G-ARPR	Trident 1C	ex British Airways, del 16/ 9/81. Poor state.
G-ARPW	Trident 1C	ex British Airways, del 26/ 3/82. Whole.
G-AVFJ	Trident 2E	ex British Airways, del 24/ 6/82. Whole.
G-AWZR*	Trident 3B-101	ex British Airways, del 19/ 3/86. Whole.
G-AWZS*	Trident 3B-101	ex British Airways, del 12/ 3/86. Whole.
G-AZLP	Viscount 813	ex BMA, SAA ZS-CDT, del 7/11/83. Whole.
G-AZLS	Viscount 813	ex BMA, SAA ZS-CDV, del 1/11/82. Whole.
D-IOMI*	Aztec 250	wreck, first noted 8/87.
XP330	Whirlwind HAR.10	ex Stansted, 21, 32, 230, 110, 225. Gutted.

Others

Noel Robinson's rebuild of former Israeli P-51D-20-NA Mustang 41/44-72028 is thought to have moved from this locality to 'North Yorkshire'. Further details awaited.

THORNABY-ON-TEES

No sooner had we consigned the Fewsdale Gyroplane G-ATLH to the LOST! section than it was seen again in store here in 11/86, so back it comes into the fold...

G-ATLH	Fewsdale Gyro	accident 7/78, stored. wfu 10/2/82.

Cornwall

BODMIN

Bill Hosie's rebuild of Supermarine S.5 G-BDFF/N220 took the the air again in late 1986. It was destroyed in a crash on 23/5/87, tragically killing Bill. Prior to his death, Bill had acquired the DH.88 Comet G-ACSP *Black Magic* restoration project from Chirk. It was brought here and put up for sale /87. Safaya and Nick Hemming purchased it and it moved to Gloucester/Cheltenham Airport 3/88.

CHACEWATER

(East of the A30, north east of Redruth) It is thought that the wrecked Mooney and stored VP-2 can still be found here.

G-ARWY	Mooney M.20A	ex Bodmin, N1079B. CoA expired 6/8/80. Wreck.
G-BTSC	Evans VP-2	CoA expired 18/7/84. *Spirit of Truro*. Stored.

CULDROSE

With the School of Aircraft Handling (SAH) here at HMS *Sea Hawk* all of the Gnats have gone, giving way to Hunter GA.11s for use on the dummy deck, training ground crew (seacrew?) how to handle aircraft on a carrier. With SAH is the Naval Air Command Driving School (NACDS), teaching tug and crane drivers how to change gear and roll with the swell at the same moment. The fire pits have had quite a clear out.

Disposals since W&R10 have been as follows :- Gnat T.1 A2676/XR572 left by road for Leavesden 28/10/87; Gnat T.1 A2677/XR993 was crated and left for Canada (USA eventually?) 2/87; Gnat T.1 A2678/XR955 left by road 29/10/87, destination unknown; Gnat T.1 A2679/XP535 left by road for Leavesden 3/11/87; Wessex HAS.1 A2690/XS887 was trundled not too far to Helston 9/87; Gnat T.1 A2708/XR540 left as per XR993; Gnat T.1 A2709/XR991 left by road for Leavesden 11/11/87; the hulk of Sea King HAS.5 ZD635 had moved to Predannack by 3/86; Wasp HAS.1 XT441 moved out to Predannack by 8/86. On the dump the following airframes had given up the ghost by 1987, Whirlwind HAR.9 XN384, Wessex HAS.1 XP117 and Wessex HAS.1 XP155. Finally, the forward fuselage of Hunter GA.11 XE682 arrived from Shawbury by 6/86 for spares recovery. Suitably denuded, it joined the fire pits 11/86 and expired shortly afterwards.

As with elsewhere in this tome, the listing here will go all conformist and be listed in serial order, not by 'A' number, as has been the fashion for the last couple of editions. 'SAH' numbers seem to be out of vogue, with 'DD' (Dummy Deck) codes coming in. Current inmates are as follows :-

WF225	Sea Hawk F.1	A2645, ex FRU, 738, 802. Gate guard.
WT711	Hunter GA.11	ex Shawbury, FRADU, 14, 54. 'DD833'. SAH.
WT804	Hunter GA.11	ex Shawbury, FRADU, Lossiemouth, 247. 'DD831'. SAH.
WV267+	Hunter GA.11	ex FRADU, 738, 98, 93, 14. Arrived by 6/86. 'DD836'. SAH.
WW654+	Hunter GA.11	ex FRADU, 738, 229 OCU, 98, 4, 98. With rear fuselage of XF368. Arrived 11/2/87. 'DD834' SAH.
XE668	Hunter GA.11	ex Yeovilton, FRADU, 738, 26, 4. 'DD832' SAH.
XM328	Wessex HAS.3	ex Wroughton. SAH.
XM874	Wessex HAS.1	A2689, ex Wroughton, 771. SAH.
XN953	Buccaneer S.1	A2655/8182M, 'SAH-23', ex St Athan, Lossiemouth, 736. Out of use since 6/86. Parked near the fire pits.
XP158	Wessex HAS.1	A2688, ex Wroughton, 771. NACDS.
XP160	Wessex HAS.1	A2650, ex fire pits, NACDS, SAH-24, 771. NACDS.
XP980	Hawker P.1127	A2700, ex Tarrant Rushton, RAE Bedford, Cranwell. SAH.
XS695	Kestrel FGA.1	A2619, ex Manadon, Tri-Partite Evaluation Squadron, A&AEE, RAE. SAH.
XS877	Wessex HAS.1	A2687, ex Wroughton, 771. SAH.
XS885	Wessex HAS.1	A2668, ex 772. SAH.
XT762+	Wessex HU.5	ex Wroughton. Arrived 28/7/87. SAH.
XV588	Phantom FG.1	nose section only.
XV669	Sea King HAS.1	A2659, ex Lee-on-Solent, 820. Engineering Training School. *Mr Walter* §.
XX466+	Hunter T.7	ex Shawbury, FRADU, 1 TWU, Jordan AF, RSaudi AF 70-616, HSA, XL620, 74, 66. Arrived 14/5/86. 'DD830' SAH.

§ *Mr Walter* = Mechanical Radio Weapons and Electrical Training Engineering Rig!

HAYLE

There have been no recent sightings of the 1907 Squadron ATC Cherokee. The unit is located at the Old Drill Hall in Hayles Terrace on the B3301.

G-AVXZ	Cherokee 180C	crashed 8/9/73. Dismantled.

HELSTON

Flambards Triple Theme Park, *nee* Cornwall Aero Park, has continued to expand and restore its aircraft content, and, as the new name suggests, offers plenty of other attractions for visiting families who can remember obscure TV series! Open every day Easter to October 1000 to 1700, further details from Flambards Triple Theme Park, Clodgey Lane, Helston, Cornwall, TR13 0GA. Tel 03265 3404.

Dragonfly HR.5 VZ962 moved to the British Rotorcraft Museum at Weston-super-Mare during 1987.

G-APTW	Widgeon	ex Southend, Westlands. Registration cancelled 26/9/75.
G-BDDX	MW.2B Excalibur	Only flight 1/7/76, built Bodmin.
BAPC116	Demoiselle rep	ex *Flambards*, Wysall.
BAPC129	Blackburn 1911	ex *Flambards*, stored.
BAPC130	Blackburn 1912	ex *Flambards*, stored.
F5459"	SE.5A replica	BAPC142, ex Trevanen Bal. 'Y'.
WF122	Sea Prince T.1	A2673, ex Culdrose, 750, Sydenham SF, Arbroath SF, Lossiemouth SF, 700Z Flt, Lossiemouth SF, FOFT, 750, Eglinton SF, 744.
WF299	Sea Hawk FB.3	A2662/A2509/8164M, ex St Agnes, Topcliffe, Catterick, Lee-on-Solent, Culdrose SAH-8, 802, 738, 736. Under rebuild, including parts of WN105 (ex Culdrose dump, Abbotsinch, 736). Will represent WN105 upon completion.
WG511	Shackleton T.4	ex Colerne, St Mawgan, MOTU, Kinloss Wing, MOTU, 120, 42. Nose only.
WG725+	Dragonfly HR.5	N9987Q/7703M, ex Southend, Middle Wallop, Odiham, Colerne, Weeton, RAE. Arrived 21/9/86. Will be restored as WG754:912/CU.
WN464	Gannet ECM.6	A2540, Culdrose SAH-9, 831, 820, 737.
WV106	Skyraider AEW.1	ex Culdrose, 849, Donibristle, Abbotsinch, USN 124086. '427/CU'.
XA870	Whirlwind HAS.1	A2543, ex Predannack, Lee-on-Solent, *Protector* Flt, 705, *Protector* Flt, 155, 848. Sectioned.
XD332	Scimitar F.1	A2574, ex Culdrose SAH-19, Lee-on-Solent, 764B, 736, 807, 804. '616'.
XE368	Sea Hawk FGA.6	A2534, ex Culdrose SAH-3, Shotley. 897 colours '200/J'.
XG691	Sea Venom FAW.22	ex Chilton Cantelo, Yeovilton, FRU, 891, 894. '737/VL'.
XG831	Gannet ECM.6	A2539, ex Culdrose SAH-8, 831. '396'.
XJ575	Sea Vixen FAW.2	A2611, ex Culdrose SAH-13, 766.
XJ584	Sea Vixen FAW.2	A2621, ex Culdrose SAH-16, 899.
XJ917	Sycamore HR.14	ex Wroughton, CFS, 275. 'S-H'.
XN258	Whirlwind HAR.9	ex Culdrose SF, *Endurance* Flt, Culdrose SF, *Hermes* Flt. '589/CU'.
XN647	Sea Vixen FAW.2	A2610, ex Culdrose SAH-10, 766, 899.
XN967	Buccaneer S.1	A2627, ex Culdrose SAH-20, Lossiemouth.
XP350	Whirlwind HAR.10	ex Chivenor, 22, 225.
XS887+	Wessex HAS.1	A2690, ex Culdrose, Wroughton, 771. Arrived by 9/87. '514/PO'.
XT427+	Wasp HAS.1	ex Yeovilton, Wroughton. Arrived 23/9/86. '606'.

LAND'S END AIRPORT

(Or St Just) A much reduced entry for this lovely airfield this time. The Patrick Lindsay Collection Hawker Fury replica is still kept here. (See under Booker for the remainder of the 'fleet'.) The Leisure Sport Sopwith Camel replica B7270/G-BFCZ was made airworthy for the Christie's Sale at Bournemouth 10/87 (see under Chertsey), but is still to be found here. Tri-Pacer G-ARDU was noted dumped outside 12/84 and has not been seen since - presumed scrapped. Volmer Sportsman G-BAME was restored and flying again by 11/85. Viv Bellamy finished Albacore N4172 and it moved to Yeovilton by 4/87. Also going to Yeovilton (this time 18/9/86) was SPAD XII 3398/G-BFYO. The remains of Barracuda II DP872 did not come here, despite what you might read in W&R10, its turn for restoration still awaited. Finally, the hulk of Airtourer G-AYMF lives on here and is reintroduced to the list.

G-AHAP	J/1 Autocrat	CoA expired 8/2/74. Engine test bed.
G-ARZD	Cessna 175C	ex N1689Y. Crashed 28/5/77. Wreck.
G-AYMF	Airtourer	Crashed 9/6/72. Wreck. See notes above.
G-AZTN	Airtourer	ex Exeter. Crashed 27/6/77. Wreck.
B7270"	Sopwith Camel rep	G-BFCZ, ex Duxford, Chertsey. See notes above.
K1930"	Hawker Fury rep	G-BKBB - see notes above.

ELANT

On the A3074 south of St Ives) Pete Channon stores his Swift here.

-ABTC+ Comper Swift CoA expired 18/7/84. *Spirit of Butler*.

ERRANPORTH

ocally stored Cessna 150 G-ARRF was flying again by 1987. However, the gliding site has made a aliant effort to keep this location within the tome. An unidentified Olympia is stored along with two ompletely unidentified gliders.

Olympia stored, due to glue failure. First noted 7/86.

REDANNACK

he fire school here has lost some airframes to the wear and tear of the job, but has had an incredible nflux of new candidates. Expired by 11/86 were the following : Wessex HAS.1 XM842; Wessex HAS.3 P118; Wessex HAS.3 XP139 and Wessex HAS.3 XS127. The hulk of Sea King HAS.5 ZD635 arrived from uldrose by 3/86, but had perished by 11/86.

F125	Sea Prince T.1	A2674, ex 750, Brawdy SF, 750, Lossiemouth SF, Brawdy SF, Yeovilton SF, Lossiemouth SF, 700Z Flt, 750.
L836	Whirlwind HAS.7	A2642, ex Fleetlands, Wroughton, 705, 848, 847, 848.
L846+	Whirlwind HAS.7	A2625, ex Yeovilton, Lee-on-Solent, Lossiemouth SF, Brawdy SF, 705, 820, 824. Arrived 19/2/86.
L899	Whirlwind HAR.9	ex Wroughton, Culdrose SF, Wroughton, A&AEE, *Protector* Flt, 847, 848.
M329+	Wessex HAS.1	A2609, ex Lee-on-Solent, Arbroath, 771. Arrived by 11/86.
M331+	Wessex HAS.3	ex Lee-on-Solent, Fleetlands. Arrived during 1986. Poor state.
M667+	Whirlwind HAS.7	A2629, ex Lee-on-Solent, Wroughton, Lee-on-Solent, 705, 846, 825, 824. Arrived 11/9/86.
M838+	Wessex HAS.1	ex Lee-on-Solent, Wroughton, 737. Arrived 20/11/86.
M841	Wessex HAS.1	ex Wroughton. forward fuselage, poor state.
N314	Whirlwind HAS.7	A2614, ex Lee-on-Solent, Wroughton, Fleetlands, 781, Yeovilton SF, Culdrose SF, Brawdy SF, Lossiemouth SF, 781, Alvis, 846, 719, A&AEE.
N635	Jet Provost T.3	ex Culdrose, Predannack, Culdrose, Aldergrove, 3 FTS, RAFC. Nose only. Identity now confirmed.
N934	Buccaneer S.1	A2600, ex Culdrose, Lee-on-Solent, 736.
P107+	Wessex HAS.1	A2527, ex Lee-on-Solent, Fleetlands, 845. Arr 11/9/86.
P149+	Wessex HAS.1	A2669, ex Lee-on-Solent, Manadon. Arrived 2/5/86.
S119+	Wessex HAS.3	ex Lee-on-Solent, Wroughton, 737. Arrived during 1986.
S125+	Wessex HAS.1	A2648, ex Yeovilton, Lee-on-Solent, 771. Arrived 21/2/86.
S873+	Wessex HAS.1	A2686, ex Lee-on-Solent, Wroughton, 771. Arrived 9/12/86.
T441+	Wasp HAS.1	A2703, ex Culdrose, Wroughton, 829. Arrived by 7/87.
T450	Wessex HU.5	ex 845 'V'.
T757+	Wessex HU.5	A2722, ex Lee-on-Solent, Wroughton, 845. Arrived 15/10/86.

T MAWGAN

ad arrival here was the unique Short SC-9 XH132 on 24/9/86 for BDR use. Pity a museum couldn't have aken it. Canberra B.2 WJ635 was removed from the dump 2/86 and broken up. Two static external eplicas previously held at St Athan are now based here for travelling display purposes.

1742+"	Bristol Scout SER	BAPC38, ex St Athan, Colerne, Weeton. See notes above.
3419+"	Sopwith Camel SER	BAPC59, ex F1921", St Athan, Colerne. See notes above.
J870	Canberra T.4	8683M, ex Marham, 231 OCU, 100, 231 OCU, Bruggen SF, 213, Ahlhorn SF, Laarbruch SF, 31, 102. BDR.
L795	Shackleton AEW.2	8753M, ex 8, 205, 38, 204, 210, 269, 204. For the gate.
H132+	Short SC-9	8915M, ex RAE Bedford. Flew in 24/9/86. BDR.

T MERRYN

he para-trainer continues to be used and a Stampe is under rebuild. For the record the two Firefly orward fuselages that were here, VT409 and VT475 were sold in the USA.

-MLAS	Cessna 182E	ex Bodmin, OO-HPE, D-EGPE, N2826Y. CoA exp 20/10/82. Para-trainer.
-STMP+	SNCAN SV-4A	ex F-BCKB. Under rebuild.

Cumbria

APPLEBY

(On the A66 south east of Penrith) 2192 Squadron's Vampire T.11, kept at the Grammar School, was put up for tender 7/87. Its current status is unknown - but may have been exported to Canada.

WZ576	Vampire T.11	8174M, ex Shawbury, CFS, 10 FTS, 208 AFS. See notes above.

CARK

The parachute club are still thought to have their para-trainer at the airfield.

G-AWMZ	Cessna F.172H	ex Blackpool Airport. Crashed 18/1/76. Para-trainer.

CARLISLE

(Kingstown, on the A7 north of the City) Airframes at RAF Carlisle are unchanged.

WS792	Meteor NF.14	7965M, ex Cosford, Kemble, 1 ANS, 2 ANS. 'K'. Gate guardian.
WT660	Hunter F.1	7421M, ex 229 OCU, DFLS. 43 Squadron colours, 'C'. Gate guardian.
XT255	Wessex HAS.3	8751M, ex ETPS. BDR within the camp.

CARLISLE AIRPORT

(Or Crosby-on-Eden) The helicopters that dominated this entry in W&R10 have moved on, in one form or another. Gazelle G-BLAN was rebuilt as G-RIFF during 1987; Gazelle G-BLAO was rebuilt during 1986 and was sold as 4X-BHG; JetRanger hulk G-ICRU moved out to Thruxton; Gazelle G-SFTA to Sunderland for NEAM 11/86. The bent Cessna 310 was given to the local firemen by 9/86. The Solway Aviation Society's Meteor and their newly-arrived Canberra are kept on the airfield and is available for inspection uponapplication to : 27 St Martin's Drive, Brampton, Cumbria CA8 1TQ. David Hutchinson and Tom Stoddart's Vulcan is open to inspection most Sundays 1300 to 1700.

G-BAYY	Cessna 310C	ex Hinton-in-the-Hedges, N1782H. CoA expired 6/12/85. Fire crews.
WE188+	Canberra T.4	ex Samlesbury, 231 OCU, 360, 231 OCU, 360, 100, 56, 231 OCU, Upwood SF, 231 OCU, Upwood SF, Waddington SF, Hemswell SF. Arrived 4/88.
WS832	Meteor NF.14	ex RRE Pershore, Llanbedr, 12 MU, 8 MU. 'W'.
XJ823	Vulcan B.2A	ex 50, Wadd Wing, 35, 27, 9/35, Wadd Wing, 230 OCU, MoA.

SPADEADAM

(North of the B6318, north east of Carlisle) On what used to be the Bluestreak test area, has developed the Electronic Warfare Site, teaching aircraft how to avoid the pitfalls of attacking a well defended airbase. A mixture of T-33As and Mystere IVs are used to make the place look more effective. Several aircraft are located around the huge concrete creations put together for the UK's brief flirtation with spaceflight. Two T-33As are much further out on the ranges and used as actual targets so their presence during a visit in early 1987 is more assumed than confirmed! Going back to earlier times, the delivery of Gnat T.1 XP506 recorded as taking place here on 6/4/78 is now though to to have been to Otterburn - which see. (Although, certainly from an airspace point of view, the two ranges are united.)

There are no less than *eight* Mystere IVAs here, of which only five are identified (although the remaining three are *thought* to be 184, 207 & 262). Both the T-33As and the Mysteres are coded with red, Soviet-like, nose numbers. For further fun they carry different codes on each side of the fuselage! The T-33As have been tracked down, but the Mysteres have proved impossible to correlate. For the record the eight Mystere IVAs are coded : '39/18', '63', '69/36', '83/20', '84/18', '84/71', '87/81', '89/91'. Inmates are as follows :-

FT-01	T-33A-1-LO	ex Prestwick, Belgian AF, USAF 51-4041. Range target.
FT-02	T-33A-1-LO	ex Prestwick, Belgian AF, USAF 51-4043. '10/77'.
FT-06	T-33A-1-LO	ex Prestwick, Belgian AF, Neth AF M-44, USAF 51-4231. '11/15'.
FT-07	T-33A-1-LO	ex Prestwick, Belgian AF, Neth AF M-45, USAF 51-4233. '70'.
FT-10	T-33A-1-LO	ex Prestwick, Belgian AF, USAF 51-6664. '14/77'.
FT-11	T-33A-1-LO	ex Prestwick, Belgian AF, Neth AF M-47, USAF 51-6661. '80/01'.
FT-29	T-33A-1-LO	ex Prestwick, Belgian AF, USAF 53-5753. Range target.
61	Mystere IVA	ex Sculthorpe, FAF.)
64	Mystere IVA	ex Sculthorpe, FAF.)
81	Mystere IVA	ex Sculthorpe, FAF.) See notes above.
139	Mystere IVA	ex Sculthorpe, FAF.)
180	Mystere IVA	ex Sculthorpe, FAF.)

+ Mystere IVA)
+ Mystere IVA) all first noted 4/86. See notes above.
+ Mystere IVA)

WINDERMERE

In Rayrigg Road the Windermere Steamboat Museum would be worth a visit, even if it didn't have a flying boat glider on show! Open Easter to October, Monday to Saturday 1000 to 1800 and 1400 to 1800 on Sundays. Windermere Steamboat Museum, Rayrigg Road, Windermere, Cumbria LA23 1BN. Tel 096 62 5565.
BGA.266 T.1 Falcon Modified by T C Pattison 1943 and flown from the lake.

Derbyshire

HADFIELD

(On the A621 east of Greater Manchester) Within Hadfield Industrial Estate is a thriving community of aircraft restorers. Military Aircraft Preservation Group have established an impressive workshop here and are currently hard at work on Vampire T.11 pod XD534 which will be turned into an operating ("simulator-like") display. The former Iraqi Vampire pod is also here and is being restored to original condition. MAPG are also working on smaller sub-assemblies and would like to take on similar work for other groups. Visits to the workshop are by prior permission only, contact ; Phil Maloney, 51 Leak Hey Road, Peel Hall, Wythenshawe, Manchester M22 5FS.
XD534+ Vampire T.11 ex Wythenshawe, Cheadle Hulme, Woodford, Chester, Shawbury, 7 FTS, CFS, 9 FTS, 10 FTS. Pod only, see notes above.
333+ Vampire T.55 ex Dukinfield, New Brighton, Chester, Iraqi Air Force. Pod only.
Others Queen Bee BAPC.186 was exchanged with the Mosquito Aircraft Museum for Tiger Moth G-ANFC on 13/4/86 with the former travelling to London Colney. This aircraft is now under restoration by Malcolm Moosey using the former Malawian components listed in W&R10 for spares. Also here under rework is the nose section of TAC's Anson C.19.
G-ANFC+ Tiger Moth ex London Colney, Dunstable, DE363. Arrived 13/4/86. Original airframe.
TP519+ Anson C.19/2 G-AVVR, ex Stockport, Peel Green, Cosford, Wigan, Irlam, Shawbury, FCCS, 11 GCF, MCS, 31, Malta CF, TCDU. Nose section.

ILKESTON

Britannia Park was a short lived, and expensive, exercise. The three aircraft taken on for display all departed by late 1986, as follows :- Sea Vixen FAW.1 XJ481 to Southampton; Whirlwind HAR.10 XK988 to Middle Wallop and Beaver AL.1 XP817 to Shawbury.

RIPLEY

By 3/87 Auster AOP.9 G-BWKK/XP279 had moved to Shoreham and was flying shortly afterwards.

SHARDLOW

(On the A6 south east of Derby) The Griffiths GH.4 gyroplane remains in store here.
G-ATGZ Griffiths GH.4 stored. Unflown.

Devon

BABBACOMBE

Ian Jones sold Dragon Rapide G-AEML during 1986 and it moved to Walney Island.

BRANDIS CORNER

Hiller UH-12B G-ATKG, which had been here, has been tracked down to Goff's Oak.

EAST BUDLEIGH

(North east of Exmouth) During 6/87 a garage here received a Navajo Chieftain for reduction to spares.

G-BASU+	Navajo 350	ex N7693L. Crashed 12/5/87. Arrived 29/6/87. For spares.

CHIVENOR

Major achievement here W&R-wise came on 26/3/87 when Hunter GA.11 WT806 flew in and was refurbished and painted in 63 Squadron colours with the aim to keep it flying as a tribute to the Hunter and the days when Chivenor and Hunters were always included in the same sentence. Apart from the addition of a Hawk hulk for BDR, little else has changed.

WJ629	Canberra TT.18	8747M, ex FRADU, 7, 6, 32, 40. BDR.
WJ635	Canberra B.2	ex St Mawgan, 7, 98, 245, 35, 50, 100. Nose section only.
WT806+	Hunter GA.11	ex FRADU, CFS, 14. Flew in 26/3/87 - see notes above.
XD186	Whirlwind HAR.10	8730M, ex 22, 202, 228, CFS, 155. On display inside the camp.
XF509	Hunter F.6A	8708M, ex Thurleigh, 4 FTS, MoA, AFDS, 54. Gate guardian.
XL567	Hunter T.7	8723M, ex Kemble, 1, Laarbruch SF, 4 FTS, 19, 229 OCU. Dump.
XX257+	Hawk T.1	ex Halton, Red Arrows. Crashed 31/8/84. Hulk for BDR. Arr 8/5/87.

EXETER

W&R10 placed the famous Bertram Arden collection some distance from Devon, but it is now clear it onl moved from Heavitree to the general Exeter area and is still intact.

G-AALP	Surrey AL.1	CoA expired 17/5/40. Stored.
G-AFGC	BA Swallow II	ex BK893, G-AFGC. CoA expired 20/3/51. Stored.
G-AFHC	BA Swallow II	CoA expired 20/3/50. Stored.

EXETER AIRPORT

There has been considerable turnaround in the W&R material here with a lot of departures and a lot o arrivals. Before charting these, the long talked of Hunter N-315, rumoured to have come here whe Staravia imported PH-NLH, has been tracked down - in Batley! The following airframes have moved o since W&R10 ; Argosy 102 G-APRM was scrapped; Dove 6 G-APZU left by road on 12/12/85 for destructiv film use in the Netherlands; Dove 8 G-ARYM believed scrapped; Viscount 814 G-BAPG flew out 30/12/87 Gemini 1A OO-RLD was flying again during mid 1987 and is due to return to Belgium. Sikorsky S-61N G LINK flew in here 28/5/86 for storage, before moving to Coventry 6/1/87 and thence to Brazil as PT-HTT Of the new material, some constitute 'catching up', but all represent a fine cross section of types.

G-AHAT	J/1N Alpha	ex Taunton, Old Sarum, HB-EOK ntu. Crashed 31/8/74. Stored.
G-AMZY	Dove 8XC	with fire crews, poor state.
G-ANAF+	Dakota 3	ex Air Luton, Air Atlantique, Duxford, KP220, USAAF 44-77104. Open storage, pending export to the USA as N170GP.
G-ANUO+	Heron 2D	ex Topflight. CoA expired 12/9/86. Open storage.
G-AOTI+	Heron 2D	ex Topflight, G-5-19. CoA expired 24/6/87. Open storage.
G-ASRX	Queen Air A80	CoA expired 30/4/84. Spares use.
G-AYTC	Aztec 250C	ex East Midlands, 5Y-ABL, 5X-UUZ, 5Y-ABL. CoA exp 16/11/79. Spares use.
G-BBRN+	Kittiwake 1	ex Yeovilton, XW784. Damaged 16/7/78. Under rebuild. Here since 4/84.
C-FHNH+	PBY-5A Catalina	ex East Midlands. Flew in 5/86. Open storage.
N500LN+	Howard 500	ex N381RD, USN 34670. Open store from early 1987.
PH-NLH	Hunter T.7	ex NLR Amsterdam, Neth AF N-320, XM126 ntu. Stored.
VH-BLF+	Debonair	ex Dunkeswell, VH-MIL. Wreck. First noted 7/87.

EXMOUTH

There have been no further reports on the Vampire T.11 pod with an ATC unit at Phear Park.

HIGHER BLAGDON

(Off the A385 west of Paignton) Torbay Aircraft Museum (including the Torbay Model Railway and Kenneth More Gardens) Located amid beautiful scenery, the Museum's 'fleet' remains largely unchanged, with restoration programmes underway on several aircraft. As usual, there is always a wide variety of supporting displays to see. The Colditz Cock replica BAPC.90 went back to the IWM and was placed into storage at Duxford during 1987. The portable Pitts S-2A 'G-RKSF'/BAPC.134 was returned to Rothmans and is now thought to be the one travelling the country as 'G-CARS'. The Museum is open daily from 1000 to 1800 April 1 to October 31. Contact ; Torbay Aircraft Museum, Higher Blagdon, near Paignton, Devon TQ3 3TG. Tel 0803 553540.

G-ALFT	Dove 6	ex CAFU, Stansted. CoA expired 13/6/73.
BAPC 69	Spitfire replica	ex Stoneleigh.
BAPC 74	'Bf 109' replica	'6'.
BAPC167	SE.5A replica	under construction.
L1592"	Hurricane replica	BAPC.63. 'KW-Z'.
NP184	Proctor IV	ex Brooklands, G-ANYP, Thruxton, Andover, Yatesbury.
RG333"	Messenger 2A	ex Bristol Airport, G-AKEZ. CoA expired 15/11/68.
TX235	Anson C.19	ex Andover, Shawbury, SCS, FCCS, CTFU, OCTU, 64 GCS, 2 GCS.
WB758	Chipmunk T.10	7729M, ex Bicester, Sheldon, OXF UAS, TCCF, 14 RFS.
WF877	Meteor T.7(hybrid)	ex Tarrant Rushton, Chilbolton, 96, 11.
WM961	Sea Hawk FB.5	A2517, ex Culdrose SAH-6, FRU, 802, 811.
WN499	Dragonfly HR.3	ex Blackbushe, Culdrose SF.
WV679	Provost T.1	7615M, ex 1 SoTT, 2 FTS. 'O-J'.
WV843	Sea Hawk FGA.4	nose section only.
XE995	Vampire T.11	ex Woodford, St Athan, 8 FTS, 5 FTS, 32. '53'.
XG544	Sycamore HR.14	ex 32, MCS, 228, 275.
XG629	Sea Venom FAW.22	ex Culdrose, ADS, 831, 893.
XJ393	Whirlwind HAR.3	A2538, XD363/XD763 ntu. Ex Lee-on-Solent, Arbroath, Pershore, CS(A).
XN299	Whirlwind HAS.7	ex Culdrose, Wroughton, JWE Old Sarum, 847, 848. *Iron Chicken.*
	Varsity T.1	cockpit section.
425/17"	Fokker Dr I rep	BAPC.133. ex Brixham.
100545	Fa 330A-1	ex Farnborough. On loan.

MANADON

(HMS *Thunderer*, Plymouth) Within the Systems Building of the Royal Naval Engineering College, a small fleet of airframes are used for instruction. By 7/87 the fleet received its first new inmate since 1985 with the arrival of a Wessex. The rear end of Tempest 'KB418' left here on 10/4/87 for Cardington and then on to a well known warbird restorer.

XF321	Hunter T.7	ex RAE, 56, 130.
XL879	Whirlwind HAS.7	ex Lee-on-Solent, ex 824. Crashed 10/3/61. Cockpit section only.
XP984	Hawker P.1127	A2658, ex RAE Bedford.
XS122	Wessex HAS.3	A2707, ex Wroughton, 737. '655/PO'.
XS153+	Wessex HAS.3	ex Lee-on-Solent, 737 '662/PO'. Arrived by 7/87.
XV625	Wasp HAS.1	ex 815. '471'.
XZ249	Lynx HAS.1	ex *Avenger* Flt. *Purdy.* Wreck.

MORETONHAMPSTEAD

(On the A382 north west of Newton Abbot) Brian Hillman continues the good work with his Auster.

G-AIPW	J/1 Autocrat	ex Bristol. CoA expired 12/8/76. Under restoration.

PLYMOUTH AIRPORT

(Or Roborough) Rallye G-AYKF was rebuilt using bits from G-BAOF and it reflew by 8/86. Since then there have been no sightings of the remains of G-BAOF.

Dorset

BINDON

(North of the A352 west of Wareham) There has been no news of former Foulness Canberra B(I).8 WT333 nose section being out on the ranges here.

BLANDFORD FORUM

The NC.854S is still to be found in the area, under restoration.

G-BIUP	SNCAN NC.854S	ex Henstridge, G-AMPE ntu, G-BIUP, F-BFSC. CoA expired 24/4/84.

BOURNEMOUTH

The Whirlwind at Linwood Special School moved to Stoke 16/3/86. Bill Hamblen is thought still to be rebuilding his Harvard II. The 'spares ship' for this is believed only to be small pieces.

FX442	Harvard II	ex Sandhurst.

BOURNEMOUTH AIRPORT

(Or Hurn) Hunter One Collection Mike Carlton, the founder and dynamic of the world's first dedicated airworthy jet fighter collection, was killed in a Republic Seabee near Kariba, Zimbabwe, on 31/8/86. His tragic loss was also to lead to the break-up of the collection and on October 1, 1987, Christie's supervised the auction of the bulk of the fleet. (There were other aircraft in the sale, the remaining Thorpe Park replicas - see under Chertsey - and other candidates - see the Appendix. As a memorial to Mike Carlton, Brencham Ltd maintain the immaculate red 'gate guardian' outside their premises at Biggin Hill - which see. Sea Hawk G-SEAH was reported to have moved to Southampton by 10/86, but was certainly back here by 6/87 and was entered into the auction. Jet Provost T.4 fuselage XR654 was not the 'film star' as speculated in W&R10 (for that aircraft see under Finchampstead Ridges) and instead joined Lovaux at Macclesfield. Sea Hawk 'WM983' was returned to Chilton Cantelo by 3/87. It is given inverted commas because it consumed a lot of G-JETH in its rebuild to static display condition.The nose of Hunter T.7 ET-272 is currently unaccounted for. Sea Vixen FAW.2TT G-VIXN/XS587 was part owned by Mike Carlton and another party and was not involved in the auction - this is in external store on the airfield and can be found under 'Others'. The auction produced the following results. Please remember that monies quoted reflect 'high bids' only and not necessarily a sale at that price.

G-BOOM	Hunter T.7	£100,000, sold to LGH Aviation, base unknown.
G-HUNT	Hunter F.51	£150,000, sold in the USA. Cancelled 12/87.
G-JETH	Sea Hawk FGA.6	£ 1,500, sold and moved by road to Charlwood10/10/87.
G-JETM	Meteor T.7	£ 1,300, sold and moved by road to North Weald.
G-JETP	Jet Provost T.52	£ 55,000, sold, will be based at Elstree, via overhaul at Cranfield.
G-LOSM	Meteor TT.20	£ 22,000, sold to LGH Aviation, base unknown.
G-PROV	Jet Provost T.52	£ 60,000, sold, will be based at Elstree, via overhaul at Cranfield.
G-SEAH	Sea Hawk FB.5	£ 5,500, sold to Sark International Airways Ltd (!), base unknown.

Sykes Aviation Some of the Wessex stored here made a bid for stardom by acquiring period US Marine Corps camouflage and markings to take part in the film *Full Metal Jacket*, doubling as Sikorsky H-34s. Airworthy G-AYNC was used 'in anger', while others dressed up for static work only. G-AYNC joined the store after filming, along with G-AWXX which had been at Thruxton. All are now up for sale.
G-AVNE left by road on 24/11/87 for the BRM at Weston-super-Mare.

G-17-2	Wessex 60	ex Weston-super-Mare, Bristows G-AWOX, 5N-AJO, G-AWOX, 9Y-TFB, G-AWOX, VH-BHE, G-AWOX, VR-BCV, G-AWOX, G-17-1. USMC colours.
G-17-4	Wessex 60	ex Weston-super-Mare, Bristows, G-ATBZ.
G-17-5	Wessex 60	ex Weston-super-Mare, Bristows, G-AZBY, 5N-ALR, G-AZBY. USMC colours as 'EM-18', see notes above.
G-17-6+	Wessex 60	ex Thruxton, Bournemouth, Weston-super-Mare, Bristows G-AWXX, VH-BHX, G-AWXX. See notes above.
G-17-7	Wessex 60	ex Weston-super-Mare, Bristows, G-AZBZ, 5N-AJI, G-AZBZ. USMC colours as 'EM-11', see notes above.
150225+"	Wessex 60	G-AYNC, ex G-17-1, Thruxton, Bournemouth, Weston-super-Mare, Bristows, VH-SJD, G-AYNC. CoA expired 17/8/87. See notes above.

Lovaux Ltd Main base of operations for Lovaux is here, with the facility at Macclesfield having been wound down somewhat. Two static airframes from the latter have moved down here and the company also purchased a Hunter T.7 from the RAE, which flew in on 30/1/87.

G-BNCX+	Hunter T.7	ex XL621, RAE Bedford, 238 OCU, RAE. Flew in 30/1/87.

XJ690+" Hunter FGA.9 XG195, ex Macclesfield, Bitteswell, G-9-453, 208, 19, 1. Composite aircraft, nose of XG195, other parts largely from XJ690.
E-402+ Hunter F.51 ex Macclesfield, Dunsfold, G-9-433, Aalborg, Danish AF ESK.724.

Others Much tidying up to do here following on from the listing in W&R10. Flight Refuelling still store their two Sea Vixens and the Bf 109 restoration makes a 'return' having been totally ignored by W&R10! Sea Vixen G-VIXN has been transferred to this section as it is not strictly with the Hunter One Collection - which see. Bournemouth has been the venue for the storage of several BN-2 Islanders, the situation is very fluid, and most do not stay long enough to merit entry into W&R. Bell 47G-3B1 G-BBZK was flying again by 1987 and the hulk of Aztec F-BSUP moved on Bredhurst. Of the aircraft listed in W&R10, the following have not been noted for some time and are presumed to have moved on or passed on :- Twin Comanche G-ASJM; Cessna A.188B wreck G-BFOY; Cessna 414A wreck G-OFRL; Aztec 250D EI-BDN; former Cypriot Bell 47Gs 5B-CEQ, 5B-CER, 5B-CFA and 5B-CFB. One other departure has been CASA 352L G-BFHD acquired from Wessex Aviation & Transport by Aces High during 1987 and for crating to the National Air and Space Museum, Washington, USA. Westland-Bell 47G-4A G-AXKW is thought not to have turned up here and should be quietly deleted from W&R10. Current here are :-

G-ASLH+ Cessna 182F ex Ipswich, N3505U. Crashed 14/6/81, for rebuild. Arrived 31/8/87.
G-ASLL Cessna 336 ex Doncaster, N1774Z. CoA expired 6/1/74. Stored.
G-ATAH Cessna 336 ex N1707Z. CoA expired 5/12/76. Stored.
G-ATLC+ Aztec 250C ex Alderney Air Carter, N5903Y. CoA expired 30/9/78. Stored.
G-AVDR+ Queen Air B80 ex Shobdon, Exeter, A40-CR, G-AVDR. CoA expired 30/6/86. Stored.
G-AVDS Queen Air B80 ex Exeter, A40-CS, G-AVDS. CoA expired 26/8/77. Stored.
G-BEZB+ Herald 209 ex Channel Express *Blossom*, 4X-AHS, G-8-2. For spares by 11/87.
G-BNNG Cessna T.337D ex G-COLD, PH-NOS, N86147. CoA expired 15/7/85. Under rebuild.
G-VIXN Sea Vixen FAW.2TT XS587/8828M, ex FRL, RAE Farnborough, FRL, ADS, 899. See notes above.
EL-AJC Boeing 707-430 ex 3C-ABI, N90498, 9G-ACK. With fire service.
N1721Z Cessna 336 ex Isle of Mull. Wreck, in store.
WK570 Chipmunk T.10 PAX 8211M, ex Hamble, 663, HUL UAS, 663, RAFC. Still with 2 AEF.
XP924 Sea Vixen FAW.2 ex RAE Llanbedr, Farnborough, Llanbedr, Sydenham, 899. Stored.
XS577 Sea Vixen FAW.2 ex RAE Farnborough, 899. Stored.
XT415+ Wasp HAS.1 ex Wroughton. Fuselage arrived by 6/87 for spares recovery for RNZ Navy.
1190 Bf 109E ex Buckfastleigh, Canada, II/JG.26. Force-landed Sussex 9/9/40. Under restoration in hut on the airfield. See notes above.

BOVINGTON

(Off the A352 near Wool, west of Wareham) The Royal Tank Museum and the Junior Leaders Regiment, across the road, 'share' the Skeeter AOP.12 displayed here.

XM564 Skeeter AOP.12 ex 652, CFS, 12 Flt, 652. Gate guardian.

CHRISTCHURCH

Apparently guarding a *Queensway* mega-store, Sea Vixen XJ580 is in fact the property of the Sea Vixen Society and is a reminder that here (on the A35 Southampton road) once was Christchurch airfield.

XJ580 Sea Vixen FAW.2 ex Bournemouth Airport, FRL, RAE Farnborough, Llanbedr, 899.

COMPTON ABBAS

Not mentioned in W&R for some time, this lovely airfield is now home for the former RFC/RNAS Provost.

XF877+ Provost T.1 G-AWVF, ex Bourn, Booker, Chertsey, CNCS, RAFC. CoA expired 12/4/85. Arrived 1986, open store.

DORCHESTER

Wessex Aviation & Transport Collection Brian Woodford's collecton of DH-orientated airworthy aircraft are based at a private strip here. Aircraft from the collection can often be seen at flying displays and fly-ins, but readers should note that visits to their base are not possible. The Wessex Lysander is currently to be found listed under Booker and the Swallow is under restoration at Hungerford. See also under Bournemouth Airport for a disposal. Current fleet is as follows, all are airworthy :-

G-ABEV+ DH.60G Moth ex N4203E, G-ABEV, HB-OKI, CH-217.
G-ACZE+ Dragon Rapide ex G-AJGS, G-ACZE, Z7266, 3 FP, 6 AONS, G-ACZE.
G-ADHA+ Fox Moth ex N83DH, ZK-ASP, NZ566, ZK-ADI.
G-AGAT+ J3F-50 Cub ex NC26126.
G-AIYS+ Leopard Moth ex YI-ABI, SU-ABM.
G-AZMH+ MS.500 Criquet ex Booker, EI-AUU ntu, F-BJQG, French military. *Luftwaffe* c/s.

G-BMNV+ SNCAN SV-4L ex Booker, F-BBNI.
N4712V+ PT-13D Kaydet ex 42-16931.
T5672+ Tiger Moth G-ALRI, ex ZK-BAB, G-ALRI, T5672, 7 FTS, 21 EFTS, 7 FTS, RAFC, 4 EFTS.
V9281+" Lysander IIIA G-BCWL, ex Booker, Hamble, Blackbushe, Booker, Canada, RCAF.

Tim Lane Tim's magnificent Harvard IV restoration, G-CTKL, made its first flight from Dunkeswell on 10/6/87. The former Sandhurst example listed under this heading in W&R10 was not a whole airframe by any means and should be deleted. Tim is now working on the restoration of an Auster.

TW429+ Auster 5 G-ANRP, ex Warnham, Bournemouth, TW439, 9 MU, TCDU, 47 GCF, CFS, 20 MU, 1 FP. Arrived by 7/87.

NEW MILTON

The store here has been cleared : Hornet Moth G-ADKM to Kingsclere by 6/86 and Auster G-AJPZ to Wimborne by 3/86.

PORTLAND

Other than the addition of two Wasps for the firemen, things have changed little at this base.

XM326 Wessex HAS.1 ex Culdrose, 772 '615/PO'. Dump, poor state.
XS537 Wasp HAS.1 A2672, ex 703 '582'. Weapons loading trainer.
XT786+ Wasp HAS.1 A2726, ex Wroughton, 829.
XV623+ Wasp HAS.1 A2724, ex Wroughton, 829 '601'. On dump by 1/87, minus boom.

SHERBORNE

(On the A30 east of Yeovil) At the Westland Customer Training School three airframes have joined the Wessex. The 'gyrocopter' is thought to be a Bensen and was built here. Lynx XX469 moved to Lancaster but then was acquired by Jim Wilkie, moving to Heysham in a swop that involved the ground test airframe at Coventry Airport.

G-BIWY+ WG.30-100 ex Yeovil, BAH. CoA expired 30/3/86. Arrived 6/86.
+ 'Gyrocopter' first noted 9/87 - see notes above.
XR526 Wessex HC.2 8147M, ex RAE Farnborough, Odiham, 72. Damaged 27/5/70.
PA-12+ SA.330L Puma ZE449, ex Weston-super-Mare, Fleetlands, Portsmouth, Port Stanley, Argentine PNA. Arrived 17/9/87.

THORNICOMBE

(On the A354 south west of Blandford Forum) During 1987 one of the Hillers from the former store here returned to the fold, having previously been in 'Wales'.

G-ASTP+ Hiller UH-12C ex 'Wales', Thornicombe, Redhill, N9750C. CoA exp 3/7/82.

WEST MOORS

(On the B3072 north of Bournemouth) It is thought that the RAOC Fuel Depot here still has its Wasp.

XS535 Wasp HAS.1 ex Wroughton, 703 '500'. Fire training.

WIMBORNE

Wessex Aviation Society As W&R went to press good news from WAS with the announcement that they had gained permission for a full-blown museum on the site. New on site is a gale-damaged Auster. Construction of the Wight Quadruplane continues apace and the long-term project of a flyable Gloucestershire Gannet moves towards the construction phase. The identity of the Sioux is more accurately as given below and not as listed in previous editions. WAS's Rotabuggy is still on loan to the Museum of Army Flying at Middle Wallop - which see. Until the museum is open on a regular basis visitors are allowed on a strictly prior permission only basis on Sunday mornings. Contact : Wessex Aviation Museum, Wimborne Botanic Gardens, Stapehill Road, Wimborne, Dorset, BH21 7ND. Tel 0202 873931.

G-ADWO Tiger Moth composite, using parts from G-AOAC and G-AOJJ. Under restoration as BB807.
G-AJPZ+ J/1 Autocrat ex New Milton, Thruxton, F-BFPE. Damaged 2/3/84. Arrived 6/2/86.
WA984 Meteor F.8 ex Tarrant Rushton, 211 AFS, 19. Composite, parts from VZ530. 245 c/s.
WM571 Sea Venom FAW.22 ex Staverton, ADS, 831B, Handling Squadron. '742/VL'.
XT242 Sioux AH.1 ex Middle Wallop. Composite, with parts of XW179. Blue Eagles c/s.
BAPC164 Wight Quadruplane static replica, under construction.

Essex

ANDREWSFIELD

(Or Great Saling) The Rebel Air Museum had to close its doors here during late 1986, but will open up again at Earls Colne during 1988. Moving across will be PT-26 N9606H, the anonymous Meteor nose, Mystere IVA 319 and Flea BAPC.115. Flea G-ADXS moved to Southend during 1986. On the airfield the situation is as follows :-

G-ALNA+	Tiger Moth	ex 'N9191', T6774, 6 FTS, 3 EFTS, 25 RFS, 28 EFTS, 2 EFTS. Crashed 26/1/86. Remains, first noted early 1987. Stored.
G-AXTK	Cherokee 140B	Crashed 6/9/81. Wreck.
G-AXWF+	Cessna F.172H	Damaged 27/11/83. Wreck, first noted 6/87.

AUDLEY END

During 2/88 the Russavia Dragon Rapide arrived here from Duxford for storage pending rebuild.

NF875+	Dragon Rapide	G-AGTM, ex Duxford, Biggin Hill, Duxford, JY-ACL, OD-ADP, G-AGTM, NF875. Damaged 21/6/87. '603/CH'.

BASILDON

2243 Squadron ATC still have their Airtourer, complete with camouflage and roundels!

G-AWVH	Airtourer T.2	ex Southchurch, Goodwood. Crashed 15/3/81.

CHELMSFORD

In honour of Meteor WH132, Waterhouse Lane has been renamed Meteor Lane! This is the home of 276 Squadron ATC. In the town, a Tiger Moth has arrived for restoration.

G-ANPK+	Tiger Moth	ex Ardley, Netheravon, L6936, Pembroke Dock SF, St Eval SF, 21 EFTS, Manorbier SF, 2 EFTS, 15 EFTS, 17 EFTS, 12 ERFTS. Under rebuild.
WH132	Meteor T.7	7906M, ex Kemble, CAW, CFS, CAW, 8 FTS, 207 AFS. 276 Sqn ATC.

CHIGWELL

SAN DR.1051 G-BIOI moved during 1987 to Boston.

DOWNHAM

(North east of Billericay) In this general area Ricky Cole keeps the fuselage of Blackburn B-2 G-ACBH.

G-ACBH	Blackburn B-2	2895M, ex Ramsden Heath, Brentwood, G-ACBH. Composite with G-ADFO.

EARLS COLNE

Rebel Air Museum Previously located at Andrewsfield, RAM are moving to this former World War Two airfield during 1988 and plan to open up again to visitors. Aircraft due to move here are given below, enquiries concerning new opening times etc should be made to ; Rebel Air Museum, 14 Amyruth Road, Brockley, London, SE4 1HQ.

BAPC115+	HM.14 Pou du Ciel	ex Andrewsfield, Balham, South Wales.
N9606H+	PT-26 Cornell II	ex Andrewsfield, Southend, FH768, 42-14361.
+	Meteor	ex Andrewsfield, single seater, nose section only.
319+	Mystere IVA	ex Andrewsfield, Sculthorpe, French AF. '8-ND'.

Elsewhere A former La Ferte Alais Yak 18 appeared here by 3/87 and is under restoration.

097+	Yak 18	ex La Ferte Alais, Egyptian Air Force.

EAST TILBURY

Thameside Aviation Museum have established themselves in Coalhouse Fort here. Along with an extensive collection of aviation archaeology items, they took on the former RAM Flea during 1987. Contact : Thameside Aviation Museum, 80 Elm Road, Grays, Essex, RM17 6LD.

G-ADXS+	HM.14 Pou du Ciel	ex Andrewsfield, Southend, Staverton, Southend.

FOULNESS ISLAND

Proof and Experimental Establishment As ever, news from the ranges here is hard to come by and the listing that follows has hardly changed from that given in W&R10. During June 1986 there was a dramatic fire in the 'White City' area which is reported to have destroyed a Victor (must be XA937) and a number of Scimitars. The rear fuselages of Canberras B.2/8 WE121 and B.2E WK164 moved out to Abingdon on 28/8/86, but it is not known what is the status of the remainder of them. Whirlwind HAR.10

XR453 moved to Odiham by 10/85. Rolls-Royce continue to keep their plenum chamber burning test-bed Harrier here. It is hoisted upon an enormous rig when 'flying'. Please note that several of the airframes listed below have not been physically noted since September 1984.

WE121	Canberra B.2/8	ex Farnborough, Bournemouth, ETPS, 231 OCU. See notes above.
WH673	Canberra B.2	ex Farnborough, 7, CAW, RAFC. Fuselage only.
WJ643	Canberra B.2/8	ex Farnborough, RAE. Noseless fuselage.
WJ679	Canberra B.2	ex RAE.
WJ872	Canberra T.4	8492M, ex Halton, 360, 13, Akrotiri SF, 231 OCU. Noseless fuselage.
WJ880	Canberra T.4	8491M, ex Halton, 7, 85, 100, 56 Laarbruch SF, RAE, 16, Laarbruch SF, Gutersloh, 104. Noseless fuselage. See North Weald.
WJ990	Canberra B.2	ex RAE, RRE, RAE, 40.
WK164	Canberra B.2E	ex 100. 'CY'. Fuselage. See notes above.
WT507	Canberra PR.7	8548M/8131M, ex Halton, 31, 17, 58, A&AEE, 58, 527, 58. Noseless fuselage.
WT534	Canberra PR.7	8549M, ex Halton, 17. Noseless fuselage.
WT859	Supermarine 544	A2499, ex Culdrose, Fleetlands, Culdrose, Lee-on-Solent, RAE Bedford. Fuselage only, poor shape.
XA937	Victor K.1	ex St Athan, 214, 57, A&AEE, 10. Fuselage. see notes above.
XD215	Scimitar F.1	A2573, ex Culdrose, 764B, 800, 803, A&AEE. Fuselage.
XD219	Scimitar F.1	ex Farnborough, West Freugh, Brawdy, FRU, 736, A&AEE.
XD235	Scimitar F.1	ex FRU, 803. Fuselage.
XD241	Scimitar F.1	ex FRU, 803, A&AEE, 736, A&AEE. Fuselage.
XD244	Scimitar F.1	ex Brawdy, 803, 736, 803, 807. Fuselage.
XD267	Scimitar F.1	ex Farnborough, FRU, 764B, 803, 736, 800,736, 803, 804, 807. Fuselage.
XD322	Scimitar F.1	ex FRU, 803, A&AEE, 800, 807. Fuselage.
XD333	Scimitar F.1	ex FRU, 803. Fuselage.
XD857	Valiant BK.1	ex 49. Nose section.
XK525	Buccaneer S.1	ex Holme-on-Spalding-Moor, Brough, West Freugh, RAE. Fuselage.
XN259	Whirlwind HAS.7	A2604, ex Lee-on-Solent, Arbroath, 771, 829, 847, 848.
XN726	Lightning F.2A	8545M, ex Farnborough, Gutersloh, 92, 19, CFE.
XN771	Lightning F.2A	ex Farnborough, Gutersloh, 19, CFE.
XN926	Buccaneer S.1	ex Chatham, Honington, Lossiemouth, 736. Fuselage. '644/LM'.
XN933	Buccaneer S.1	ex Lossiemouth, 736. '632'. Fuselage.
XN955	Buccaneer S.1	fuselage.
XN960	Buccaneer S.2	ex Farnborough, RAE. Fuselage.
XS421	Lightning T.5	ex RAE, 23, 111, 226 OCU. Fuselage.
XV280	Harrier GR.1	ex Boscombe Down, A&AAEE, HSA. Fuselage.
XV357	Buccaneer S.2A	ex St Athan, 237 OCU, 208.
XV417	Phantom FGR.2	ex 29, 17, 14, 17, 14, 2, 228 OCU. Crashed 23/3/76.
XV798	Harrier GR.1	ex Dunsfold. Composite airframe. PCB rig - see notes above.
XW837	Lynx prototype	ex Boscombe Down, Yeovil.
XX153	Lynx AH.1	ex Westlands.
XX510	Lynx HAS.2	ex Boscombe Down.
	Lynx rotor rig	ex Yeovil. Plate reads WA/E/32.

FYFIELD

(On the B184 west of Chelmsford) The battered American Cherokee can still be found in the grounds of Fyfield Hall.

N3850K	Cherokee 140	battered fuselage.

HALSTEAD

(North east of Braintree) Tiger Moth G-APBI is still underway here.

G-APBI	Tiger Moth	ex Audley End, EM903. Crashed 7/7/80. Rebuild.

HORNCHURCH

Canberra T.4 nose WJ872 did not come here for the ATC unit, it *did* go to Kilmarnock.

LITTLE BURSTEAD

The remains of Mooney M.20 G-AVWW and Chipmunk T.10 WP778 were too small to bother about by 3/87.

NAVESTOCK

(Between the A113 and A128 south of Chipping Ongar) The Moth Minor is still at Jenkins Farm.

G-AFOJ	Moth Minor	ex E-1, E-0236, G-AFOJ. CoA expired 27/8/69. Stored.

NORTH WEALD

Aces High This specialist film flying operator opened up its superb 30,000 sq ft hangar during 1986 and has continued to supply enthusiasts with an ever-changing vista of aircraft. Although Robs Lamplough has his own workshop and hangar on the airfield now, and the Harvard Formation Team are due to start on their own premises, aircraft from both of these concerns can be found within the Aces High hangar from time to time. The following 'Aces' aircraft were entered in the Wilkins & Wilkins auction held here on 9/4/88 ; Beech G-BKRG; Seneca N503DM, Boxcar N2700, Meteor VZ638, Mitchel N9089Z and Venom J-1758 - the latter reported as sold - see the Appendix. It is planned in due course to open up the hangar on a regular basis to the general public but, until such time, special arrangements can be made to view the aircraft between April and September by contacting 037 882 2949. Other enquiries to : Aces High, Building D2, Fairoaks Airport, Chobham, Surrey. Tel 09905 6384.

See under Bournemouth Airport for details of a CASA 352L that was acquired by Aces High, but did not come here. Of the aircraft listed under this heading in W&R10, almost all have gone. The following can be found below listed under Robs Lamplough, Fokker Dr.I G-ATJM, P-51D G-BIXL, Skyraiders G-BMFB & G-BMFC, Yak C-11 G-KYAK. Pilatus P.2-05 G-PTWO left 27/3/86 for a new owner; C-47A N88YA flew out to Stansted 19/5/86 on its way to Classic Air in Switzerland; C-47B N951CA flew out 9/9/86 and became C-GJDM in Canada flying with Polish made engines; Lodestar OH-SIR/G-BMEW became N283M and flew out to Oslo 15/9/86. T-33A G-TJET flew in from Duxford 7/12/85, but flew out to Cranfield by 9/86. MiG 15 01420/G-BMZF came in from Retford and Gamston by road 27/12/86, moving out to the FAA Museum at Yeovilton during 1987. After all that only G-DAKS remains from the listing in W&R10, but there are plenty of additions :-

G-AMPO+	Dakota 3	ex Air Luton, LN-RTO, G-AMPO, KN566, 44-76853. Flew in 28/10/87. For the 4/88 auction.
G-AWHB+	CASA 2-111	ex Royston, Southend, Spanish AF B2-157. Arrived by 4/88, via use in 'crash' scene for *Piece of Cake* at Charlton Manor.
G-BKRG+	Beech C-45G	ex Duxford, N75WB, *Octopussy*, N9072Z, 51-11665. Arr 2/86. 4/88 auction.
	JetRanger	ex Fairoaks, static composite for *Biggles*.
G-29-1+	Lincoln 2	G-APRJ, ex Bitteswell, Blackbushe, Southend, Cranfield G-36-3, Napiers G-29-1, G-APRJ, RF342. Arrived 10/9/86. Dismantled.
D-HGBX+	Enstrom F-280C	hulk for film purposes. First noted 7/87.
N503DM+	Seneca 200	ex G-BNGB ntu, Biggin Hill, F-BTQT, F-BTMT. Arrived by 3/87, under restoration. 4/88 auction entrant.
N1042B+	B-25 Mitchell	ex Tallmantz. Flew in 9/4/88 - camera-ship. USAAF scheme.
N2700+	C-119G-FA Boxcar	ex Manston, G-BLSW, 3C-ABA, Belgian AF CP-9, 57-2700. Flew in 12/2/87. 4/88 auction entrant.
EN398"+	Spitfire IX rep	BAPC.184, ex Duxford. Arrived by 8/87. 'JE-J'.
HD368+	TB-25J-NC	N9089Z, ex Duxford, G-BKXW ntu, Southend, Biggin Hill, N9089Z, 44-30861. Arrived by road 11/87, entered in the 4/88 auction. *Bedsheet Bomber*.
KG374"	Dakota 3	G-DAKS, ex Duxford, *Airline* 'G-AGHY', TS423, RAE, Ferranti, Airwork, Gatow SF, 436, 1 HGSU, 42-100884.
VZ638+	Meteor T.7	G-JETM, ex Bournemouth Airport, Southampton, Southend, Kemble, CAW, RAFC, 237 OCU, 501, Biggin Hill SF, FCCS, 85, 54, 25, 500. Arrived 1/88. Repainted in black/dayglo Hal Far FRU scheme.
D2+600+	CASA 352L	G-BFHG, ex Duxford, Fairoaks, Blackbushe, Spanish Air Force T2B-262. Flew in 7/12/85.
J-1758+	Venom FB.54	N203DM, ex Cranfield, G-BLSD, Dubendorf, Swiss Air Force. Flew in 12/4/86. For sale in the 4/88 auction.

Harvard Formation Team During 1988 HFT have plans to start their own premises at North Weald and on that basis, the team's aircraft should be listed more formally. The Harvards can normally be found here, although Gary Numan's example is more properly based at Fairoaks. Robs Lamplough's G-BGPB is a regular performer with the team and is listed under his own heading. During 1986 HFT took on the remains of two former Dutch AT-16s for spares use. Of these, B-163 moved on to Gordon King at Windsor.

G-AZSC+	Harvard IIB	ex PH-SKK, Dutch AF B-19, FT323, 43-13064. Gary Numan, Japanese colours.
EX280+	Harvard IIA	G-TEAC, ex Portuguese AF 1523, SAAF 7333, EX280, 41-33253. Euan English.
FE992+	Harvard IIB	G-BDAM, ex LN-MAA, Fv16047, FE992, 42-12479. Euan English & Norman Lees.
FT239+	Harvard IV	G-BIWX, ex MM53846, USAF. Anthony Hutton.

HB275+" Beech D.18S N5063N, ex G-BKGM, CF-SUQ, RCAF 2324. SEAC colours.
B-168 Harvard IIB ex Amsterdam, Dutch Air Force, FE984, 42-12471. See notes.

Robs Lamplough Robs' collection took a major step forward with the completion of a hangar and workshop here. Robs also has a Spitfire under restoration in the Bristol area - which see. New with his collection are three of the Thorpe Park replicas, the former Watton P-51D project (via Fowlmere) and the long-promised single-seat *Spad* from Chad. Skyraider G-BMFC, Spitfire MV370 and Harvard 20385 (see also above) were entered in the 4/88 auction - see the Appendix. Current are :-

G-BMFB AD-4W Skyraider ex Bromma, SE-EBK, G-31-12, WV181, USN 126867. Stored.
G-BMFC AD-4W Skyraider ex Bromma, SE-EBM, G-31-2, WT951, USN 127949. Stored.
G-BMJY+ Yak C-18M ex La Ferte Alais, Egyptian AF 627. Arrived 6/7/87. Restoration.
G-KYAK Yak C-11 ex Duxford, Booker, Israel, Egyptian AF 590, Czech AF.
BAPC136+ Deperdussin rep ex Chertsey. Arrived by 2/88.
BAPC141+ Macchi M.39 ex Chertsey. Arrived by 2/88.
S1595"+ Supermarine S.6 BAPC.156, ex Chertsey. Arrived by 2/88.
MV370+ Spitfire XIV G-FXIV, ex Basingstoke, Whitehall, St Leonards-on-Sea, Henfield, Nagpur, Indian AF instructional T44, MV370. Arrived 15/4/86.
20385+" Harvard IV G-BGPB, ex Portuguese AF 1747, WGAF BF+050, AA+050, 53-4619. Part of Harvard Formation Team - see notes above.
152/17" Fokker Dr I rep G-ATJM, ex Duxford, Orlando, N78001, EI-APY, G-ATJM. Airworthy.
28+ P-51D-20-NA ex Fowlmere, Watton, Duxford, Israeli AF/DF. Arr during 1987.
72216 P-51D-20-NA G-BIXL, ex Duxford, Ein-Gedi, Israeli AF/DF 43, Fv 26116, 44-72216. First flight post restoration 5/5/87.
\+ AD-1N Skyraider ex Chad, French AF. Arrived 4/88.

North Weald Aircraft Restoration Flight Restoration work continues, centred around the Meteor, which now has one side painted in the colours of 39 Squadron. Proctor V G-AKIU was taken back by its owner and has been sold to another party in Leicestershire. The Canberra nose here is with 2263 Squadron ATC and is 'parented' by Stanmore. NWARF is open to the public April to October on Saturdays 1000 to 1730 and Sundays by prior appointment only. Contact : North Weald Aircraft Restoration Flight, North Weald Airfield, Epping, Essex. Tel 01 521 7683.

BAPC117 RAF BE.2 replica ex BBC *Wings*.
BAPC179 Sopwith Pup rep ex BBC *Wings*.
V7767" Hurricane replica BAPC.72, ex Coventry, *Battle of Britain*.
WJ880 Canberra T.4 8491M, ex Halton, 7, 85, 100, 56, Laarbruch SF, RAE, 16, Laarbruch SF, Gutersloh SF, 104. Nose, rest at Foulness. See notes above.
WM311" Meteor TT.20 WM224/8177M, ex East Dereham, CSDE Swanton Morley, 5 CAACU, 3 CAACU, 228 OCU. 39 Squadron colours on port side.
XK625 Vampire T.11 ex Southend, Woodford, St Athan, 8 FTS, 7 FTS.
C19/18" Albatros replica BAPC.118, ex BBC *Wings*.
483009" AT-6D-1-NT Texan ex Ashford, 42-44450. Dismantled.
Hunter nose section, posssibly WN957.

ORSETT

By 1987 P.68B G-BEXM at the strip here had been reduced to just a tail section.

PAGLESHAM

(North east of Rochford) A strip here holds a Beaver in open store and two agricultural wrecks.

G-BFEX+ Pawnee 235D wreck, for rebuild. Crashed 16/2/87.
G-BFDI+ W-Bell 47G-3B1 ex XT811. Crashed here 31/7/86.
N5595K+ Beaver ex Ipswich, Kenya AF 104. Arrived 27/1/86. Open store.

RAYLEIGH

1476 Squadron ATC still keep their Lightning F.1 nose at their headquarters in the town.

XG325 Lightning F.1 ex Southend, Wattisham, Foulness, A&AEE. Nose section.

SOUTHEND

Work continues on the Scion frame G-AEZF by the Southend Historic Aircraft Society and it can be seen at occasional events in and around Southend. Former Historic Aircraft Museum inmate Flea G-ADXS came here during 1986 from Andrewsfield before moving on to East Tilbury during late 1987.

G-AEZF Scion II ex Southend Airport. CoA expired 5/5/54. Under restoration.

SOUTHEND AIRPORT

With only a few depatures on the W&R scene to record and plenty of additions, the Southend entry is somewhat swollen. Of greatest interest is the very welcome arrival of Rod and Rex Cadman's B-26 Invader, which is under restoration to fly. Roy Jacobsen purchased a second Vulcan (his first is art Wellesbourne Mountford) and it flew in here 18/12/86. The Airport can boast some of the most tenacious civilian wrecks, the hulk of Rallye G-AWOC, for instance, celebrating ten years of decay in 1988! Avro XIX G-AGPG finally made it into the hands of a caring concern, going to Brenzett in 4/86, although it was in a terrible state by then. Widgeon 'MD497'/G-ANLW left by road by 3/86 for Tattershall Thorpe. Dragonfly HR.3 WG725/N9987Q left for the Cornwall Aero Park at Helston 21/9/86. 'Spares ship' for the A-26 Invader restoration, the nose of A-26K Counter Invader 64-17657 arrived here 21/7/86 but moved out to Canterbury by 3/86. Current here are as follows :-

G-AIJZ	J/1 Autocrat	ex Shobdon. Rebuild, crashed 25/10/70.
G-ALFM+	Devon C.2/2	ex VP961, Northolt, Air Attache Bangkok, 207, 60, MoA, 38 GCF, Queens Flight, HCCS, 31 NEAF CF, FCCS, Air Attache Bangkok, G-ALFM. Arrived 5/86 for storage. CoA expired 20/11/87.
G-AOHL	Viscount 802	BAF Cabin trainer. Withdrawn from use 6/2/81.
G-AOHT+	Viscount 802	ex BAF. In store by 12/86, wingless by 12/87.
G-APBW	Auster 5	ex Audley End. Rebuild, crashed 25/7/82.
G-APEX	Viscount 806	ex BAF, BA, BEA. wfu 26/ 3/84. Poor state.
G-APEY+	Viscount 806	ex BAF, BA, BEA. In store by 12/86.
G-APWA	Herald 100	ex PP-SDM, PP-ASV, G-APWA. Fuselage only.
G-APXT+	Tri-Pacer 150	ex N4545A. Crashed 26/12/85. Wreck, first noted 4/87.
G-ARAB+	Cessna 150	ex Elstree, N6485T. Damaged 25/1/86, first noted 12/86.
G-ASYN	Terrier 2	ex Sibson, VF519. Spares for flyable G-ASAK.
G-ATMN	Cessna F.150F	crashed 11/5/84. Wreck for spares.
G-AVCT+	Cessna F.150G	CoA expired 3/7/73. Arrived 12/85 for rebuild.
G-AVWZ	Fournier RF-4D	crashed 11/1/81. Fuselage, stored.
G-AVZB+	Z-37 Cmelak	ex OK-WKQ. CoA expired 5/4/84. Stored.
G-AVZO	Pup 100	ex Benedon. CoA expired 12/7/75. Fuselage.
G-AWCK	Cessna F.150H	crashed 30/9/75. Wreck.
G-AWLJ+	Cessna F.150H	crashed 20/11/84. Wreck, first noted 12/86.
G-AWOC	MS.892A Rallye	crashed 13/6/74. Wreck.
G-AYOX+	Viscount 814	ex Tees-Side, BMA, 4X-AVA, G-AYOX, D-ANAC. Fuselage arrived 4/9/86.
G-AYRK	Cessna 150J	ex 5N-AII, N61170. CoA expired 25/4/76. Stored.
G-AYYE	Cessna F.150L	crashed 26/4/78. Wrecks, spares use.
G-AZDZ	Cessna 172K	ex 5N-AIH, N1647C, N84508. Crashed 19/9/81. Wreck.
G-AZRW+	Cessna T.337C	ex 9XR-DB, N2614S. CoA expired 7/6/82. Stored.
G-AZZG	Cessna 188-230	ex OY-AHT, N8029V. CoA expired 1/5/81. For spares.
G-BCAB	MS.894A Rallye	crashed 25/2/77. Wreck.
G-BCTH	Cherokee 140	ex PH-VRN, N6661J. Crashed 14/11/76. Wreck.
G-BDOZ	Fournier RF-5	ex Chinnor, 5Y-AOZ. CoA expired 5/9/83. Stored.
G-BEPE	Belfast	ex G-52-14, XR362, 53 Squadron, G-ASKE. Spares use.
G-BKME+	Skyvan 3-100	ex Stansted, A40-SN, G-AYJN, G-14-57. Arrived 20/9/85. Stored.
G-MAST	Cherokee 180	crashed 14/7/81. Wreck.
N4806E+	B-26C Invader	ex Rockford, Illinois, 44-34172, Davis Monthan, 3 BW, 17 BW, 7 ADW. Under restoration. Arrived 16/7/86.
XB261	Beverley C.1	ex HAM, A&AEE. Kept outside *Roller City*.
XL426+	Vulcan B.2A	G-VJET, ex Waddington, 50, 617, 27, Scampton Wing, 83. Arr 11/12/86.
XR363	Belfast C.1	G-OHCA, ex Kemble, 53 Squadron. Open store.

STANSTED

As the earth-movers go in and London's Third Airport arises from the ground here, so the interest from the W&R point of view takes a nose-dive. Of the aircraft listed in W&R10, the three 'long termers', the Proctor, Dove and ATEL (now known as Qualitair) 707 still serve on, but the others have all gone, to be replaced with a Trident and a DC-8. Moving on have been Skyvan G-BKMD which is now flying; Skyvan G-BKME which left by road on 20/9/85 for Southend; Skyvan G-BKMF left by road at about the same time, bound for Mozambique; Boeing 707 N884PA was scrapped by 3/86; CL-44 9Q-CQU became N103BB of Bluebell and flew out 25/12/85. Current situation is as follows :-

G-ANPP	Proctor III	ex Duxford, HM354. CoA expired 5/5/69. Under restoration.
G-ANUW	Dove 6	ex CAA CAFU. Last flight 31/3/81. Open store.

G-APFG Boeing 707-436 ex BAAT, BOAC, Qualitair training airframe,
G-AWZU+ Trident 3B-101 ex Heathrow, BA, BEA, Flew in 5/3/86 for CAA fire crews,
5N-AVR+ DC-8-55 ex Intercontinental, N8065U, Spares recovery by 5/87,

STAPLEFORD TAWNEY
All of the aircraft listed in W&R10 have moved on, Apache G-ARMI, Aztec G-BBFW and Cessna F,152 G-BBHJ all moving in a clear-out during mid 1987, Auster J/5P G-AOBV had gone by 11/86 - destination unknown, New here are the following :-
G-AXGD+ MS,880B Rallye CoA expired 22/1/86, Stored,
G-BFOP+ Wassmer D,120 ex F-BHTX, CoA expired 2/7/80, Stored here since,
EI-BIE+ Cessna FA,152 ex Winsford, For rebuild as G-STAP, Arrived 4/87,

STONDON
(Off the A128 south east of Chipping Ongar) At Thurston Engineering *all* of the Tawney Owl is stored within the rafters,
G-APWU Tawney Owl Crashed on its first and only flight at Stapleford 22/4/60,

WETHERSFIELD
Courtesy of a 67 ARRS HH-53C F-100D Super Sabre 54-2265 was airlifted from its place on the gate 20/1/88 and is reported to be being shipped back to the USAF to go on charge with the USAF Museum at Wright Patterson, Seems a particularly expensive repatriation,

Gloucestershire

COLEFORD
(On the A4136 east of Monmouth) No firm news on the Flea here - could it be heading for *LOST!*?
BAPC,46 HM,14 Pou du Ciel ex Newent, Whitchurch,

FAIRFORD
Last time Fairford got a mention was to record the demise of Hastings T,5 TG553 and Argosy E,1 XP413 on the dump during early 1980, On 9/12/86, Fairford joined the Phantom BDR 'set',
37699 F-4C-21-MC ex Oregon ANG, Flew in 9/12/86, for BDR,

GLOUCESTER
2342 Squadron ATC gave up their Lightning F,1 nose XG331 to Innsworth 10/86,

GLOUCESTER/CHELTENHAM AIRPORT
(Or Staverton) Classic Aeroplane, under the command of John Eagles, continues to generate most of the W&R interest at this lovely airfield, The Cotswold Aircraft Restoration Group's Messenger G-AJOE arrived here from Innsworth on 16/8/87 for flight-testing, also under John's wing, Mentioned in W&R10 under the heading of Filton were the IS-28 motor-gliders that came here for fitting out, They should have been cleared up under this heading in that volume, but have slipped until now, The aircraft were

c/ns 50, 57, 58 and 59, which became and first flew as follows ; G-BMOM 20/6/86, G-BMMV 5/4/86, G-BMMX 28/4/86 and G-TODD 28/4/86. Auster 6A G-ASIP arrived by road from Nympsfield 25/9/86 before moving on to CARG at Innsworth during 1987. Of the Tiger Moths listed in W&R10, 'G-BNDW' became a legitimate registration on 10/12/86 but had left the airfield, along with G-ANOM, by that time for rebuild off-site, see below. Several of the Atlantic and Caribbean Sea Princes were entered for the Luton auction of October 1987 - see Appendix. Arriving during April 1985, Pembroke N46EA should be added to the ACA 'fleet' here. Cierva C.30A frame G-ACWM left to join the BRM at Weston-super-Mare in late 1986. Meta-Sokol G-ARSP first flew on 2/4/87 following restoration at the hands of John Eagles, and was placed in the Philips auction at Old Warden 13/5/87 - see the Appendix. Airtourer 115 G-AZTM left by road during late 1985 - destination unknown. Archer II G-BFXZ left during 1986, appearing at Sturgate. Finally, Harvard IV MM53432 left during 1986, reportedly for 'South Wales'. Current here are :-

G-AJOE+ Messenger 2A ex Innsworth, 'RH378'. Arrived 16/8/87 for flight testing.
G-AMBB Tiger Moth composite restoration by Classic Aeroplane. Reported to be ex T6801, in which case, ex Scampton SF, 6 FTS, 18 EFTS.
G-DACA Sea Prince T.1 ex Kemble, WF118, 750, A&AEE, 727, A&AEE, RAE Farnborough. Stored.
G-GACA Sea Prince T.1 ex Kemble, WP308, 750 - all its flying life. Stored.
G-RACA Sea Prince T.1 ex Kemble, WM735, 750, Bombing Trials Unit, A&AEE. Stored.
G-TACA Sea Prince T.1 ex Kemble, WM739, 750, Lossiemouth SF, 750, Yeovilton SF. Stored.
N46EA+ Pembroke C.1 ex St Athan, XK885/8452M, 60, 21, WCS, Seletar SF, B&TTF, Seletar SF, S&TTF, 209, 267. Arrived 4/85. Stored -see notes above.
WL349 Meteor T.7 ex Kemble, 1 ANS, 2 ANS, CFE, 229 OCU. On display.

Locally Two Tiger Moths, previously at the airport, are known to be under restoration in the area.

G-ANOM Tiger Moth ex Airport, Maidens Green, N6837, Finningley SF, 1 GU, 2 GS, 11 RFS, 11 EFTS, 217. Crashed 17/12/61.
G-BNDW Tiger Moth ex Airport, composite.

INNSWORTH

(West of the B4063, near Parton, north east of Gloucester) Cotswold Aircraft Restoration Group Since W&R10 CARG have carried on the good work of supplying countless pieces, large and small, to other worthy restoration projects. Their own airframes have been swollen considerably, and the Messenger G-AJOE moved to Gloucester/Cheltenham 16/8/87 in readiness for flight testing. CARG are 'lodgers' on RAF Innsworth and casual visitors cannot be allowed. Interested parties should contact :- Steve Thompson, CARG, Kia-Ora, Risbury, Leominster, Herefordshire, HR6 0NQ.

G-ADRG" HM.14 Pou du Ciel BAPC.77, ex Ross-on-Wye, Staverton.
G-ASIP+ Auster 6A ex Gloucester/Cheltenham, Nympsfield, Heathrow, VF608, 12 Flt, 652, 1904 Flt, Hague Air Attache. Damaged 7/5/73. Arr 1987. For spares.
VW453 Meteor T.7 8703M, ex Salisbury Plain, Hullavington, Takali, 604, 226 OCU, 203 AFS. Under restoration, for eventual display on the gate.
XG331+ Lightning F.1 ex Gloucester, Dowty, Foulness, A&AEE, EE. Nose section. Arr 23/10/86.
XK421 Auster AOP.9 8365M, ex Bristol, Caldicote, St Athan, Detmold, Middle Wallop. Spares.
XN412+ Auster AOP.9 ex Swindon, Dorchester, Middle Wallop, 20 Flt, 656, Seletar, Handling Squadron. Arrived 1/6/86.
XR267 Auster AOP.9 G-BJXR, ex Staverton, Congresbury, St Athan, 655, 652. On rebuild.
XW264+ Harrier T.2 ex Dowty, Boscombe Down, HSA. Damaged 11/7/70. Forward fuselage. Arrived 8/11/86.
Halifax substantial cockpit section, acquired locally.
\+ Tiger Moth anonymous frame, acquired 1987.

Gate Guardian The Javelin still guards the gate to RAF Innsworth :-

XH903 Javelin FAW.9 7938M, ex Shawbury, 5, 33, 29, 33, 23.

KEMBLE

At the base only the Meteor on the gate remains of W&R interest at present. Sea Devon C.20 XJ324 flew out 25/9/86 to join 771 Squadron. Harvard IV G-BJST (ex MM53795) became a film star (static?) in *Empire of the Sun* and was entered into the Luton auction 3/10/87. Its spares ship, MM53796, is unaccounted for.

WH364 Meteor F.8 8169M, ex 601, Safi SF, Takali SF, Idris SF, Takali SF, Safi SF, 85. Gate guardian in 601 Squadron colours.

MORETON-IN-THE-MARSH

(On the A44 north east of Cheltenham) There having been no concrete news concerning the glider projects with Eric Rolfe and Paul Williams the following are entered with a warning that they may well be no longer here.

BGA.964	Kranich II	ex Warwick, SE-STF, Fv 8226.
	Hutter H.17a	ex Chivenor. Under restoration.
BAPC.25	Nyborg TGN.III	ex Stratford. Under restoration.

NYMPSFIELD

Auster 6A G-ASIP moved to Gloucester/Staverton Airport 25/9/86. Kestrel BGA.1914/CYN was flying again by 1987, leaving no W&R 'fodder' here.

QUEDGELEY

(On the A430 south of Gloucester) At RAF Quedgeley, No 1 Site, can be found a Meteor T.7.

WF784	Meteor T.7	7895M, ex Kemble, 5 CAACU, CAW, FTU, 130, 26. Gate guardian.

STONEHOUSE

(On the B4008 west of Stroud) The Vampire T.11 continues to rot in the grounds of Standish Hospital.

XE979	Vampire T.11	ex Woodford, Chester, St Athan, 1 FTS, 8 FTS, RAFC. '54'. Poor state.

STROUD

1329 Squadron ATC in Browbridge Lane, near *The British Oak*, still keep their Chipmunk T.10 PAX Trainer. It is kept on the first floor of their building!

WP845	Chipmunk T.10	ex Nor UAS, AOTS, PFS, AOTS, ITS, 7 AEF, 2 FTS, HCCS, Lon UAS, RAFC, 14 RFS. PAX Trainer. NB, no 'M' number.

Hampshire

ALDERSHOT

Airborne Forces Museum at Browning Barracks, east of the A325 immediately south of Farnborough airfield. Easily identifiable by its Dakota 'guardian', the AFM is a fascinating display of artifacts and items depicting the history of airborne forces from 1940 to the Falklands. Open every day except Christmas Day, Monday to Friday 0900 to 1230 and 1400 to 1630; Saturday 0930 to 1230 and 1400 to 1630; Sunday 1000 to 1230 and 1400 to 1630. Contact : The Airborne Forces Museum, Browning Barracks, Aldershot, Hampshire, GU11 2DS. Tel : 0252 24431 ext 4619.

KP208	Dakota IV	ex Kemble, AFNE, Air Advisor New Delhi, AFNE, HCCF, 24, MEAF, USAAF 44-77087. 'YS'. Displayed outside.
	Hotspur II	full nose section and part of troop bay.
	Horsa II	full nose section.

ANDOVER

The Durney Collection Without any reports on the status of this group, it is difficult to be precise about their Dragon Rapide project. The aircraft has consumed parts from G-AFRK, G-AHGC, G-AHJS and G-ASRJ along the way. Contact address : 276 Weyhill Road, Andover, Hampshire.

G-ALAX	Dragon Rapide	ex Old Warden, Luton, RL948, ERS, 27 GCF. See notes above.

Museum of Army Flying The Museum uses Andover airfield as a rotational store for some of its airframes. The store is not open to the public and aircraft within are just staging through. Accordingly, all are listed under Middle Wallop.

BASINGSTOKE

Spitfire XIV MV370/G-FXIV moved to North Weald 15/4/86.

BLACKBUSHE

W&R10 chronicled the migration of the Warbirds of Great Britain fleet to Bitteswell and this edition chronicles its further move to Biggin Hill and elsewhere. Several airframes were listed under this heading in the last edition as unconfirmed in their move to Bitteswell. All should be regarded as moving to that new heading, where a 'clear-up' can be found!

CALMORE

As predicted in W&R10, Vampire T.11 XD596 did indeed move to Southampton.

CHILBOLTON

Where Swifts and other things Supermarine once flew, Agricopters have made a veritable hive of Hillers, with a smattering of Bell 47s. Of the two listed in W&R10, G-APMP moved to Tattershall Thorpe by 9/86. All of the choppers listed below are stored, some acting as spares. The reader is warned that helicopters very easily become so small as not to merit a mention in this tome, but leave tempting relics - such as rotor booms with the 'reggie' on - that may lead people astray into believing that there is more of the device than meets the eye.

G-ASAZ	Hiller UH-12E-4	ex Southend, N5372V. CoA expired 15/7/76.
G-AVKY+	Hiller UH-12E	ex CN-MAP. Crashed 26/6/84. Wreck, first noted 4/87.
G-AZSV+	Hiller UH-12E	ex Thruxton, EP-HAH, 5N-AGJ, ZS-HAV. Crashed 28/7/80. Cabin area only, first noted 7/86.
G-BBLD+	Hiller UH-12E	ex N31703, N31705 ntu, CAF 112279, RCAF 10279. Crashed 19/4/79. Wreck, first noted 4/87.
G-BDFO+	Hiller UH-12E	ex XS703 705. CoA exp 1/4/84. Cabin area only, first noted 4/87.
G-BEDK+	Hiller UH-12E	ex XS706 705. CoA exp 14/6/85. Cabin area only, first noted 7/86.
G-BGFS+	W-Bell 47G-3B1	ex XW192. CoA exp 21/3/85. Stored, first noted 4/87.
G-BGOZ+	W-Bell 47G-3B1	ex Bridge Hewick, XT545. Crashed 18/6/81. Wreck, first noted 4/87.
AP-ATV+	Hiller UH-12E-4	ex Bangladesh Army, c/n 2315. Cabin area only, first noted 7/86.
AP-AWQ+	Hiller UH-12E-4	ex Bangladesh Army, c/n 2219. Cabin area only, first noted 7/86.

FAREHAM

Nothing new on the Gnat nose (XM692 ex Farnborough?) section that was here, or for that matter on the Jet Provost cockpit section reported with 1350 Squadron ATC at Farm Road. Tiger Moth G-AOBO moved to Redhill in 1986.

FARNBOROUGH

Royal Aerospace Establishment As with W&R10, mostly subtractions to be recorded here and the situation may be further worsened through several airframes not having been physically encountered here for some time (airframes falling into the latter category are marked #). As with previous editions, the airframes that come and go through the Aircraft Accident Investigation Unit are not within the terms of reference of W&R. The following airframes have moved on for one reason or another since W&R10 :- DH.88 Comet G-ACSS moved to Hatfield for final assembly and flight test; Trident 1 G-ARPC forward fuselage consumed on the dump; Lockspeiser LDA-01 G-AVOR moved to Old Sarum to become G-UTIL, but perished in the disastrous fire there; Canberra T.4 WH844 left by road for the Pendine Ranges 1/88; Meteor T.7 WL405 assumed scrapped; Scimitar F.1 XD234 fuselage also assumed scrapped; Gannet AEW.3 XL471 put up for tender during 1986, still present 4/87, the bulk of it going to a yard in Lichfield, with the wings going to the Dumfries & Galloway group at Tinwald Downs; Whirlwind HAS.7 XL874 scrapped 2/84; Gnat T.1 XM692 nose thought gone to Fareham and status now uncertain; Buccaneer S.1 XN965 left by road 17/1/86 for the Pendine Ranges; Scout AH.1 XP167 assumed scrapped; Kestrel FGA.1 XS691 fuselage believed scrapped. That leaves the following, with a few additions :

G-ANNG	Tiger Moth	ex DE524. CoA exp 29/11/67. Stored, dismantled. #
G-AZGJ+	MS.880B Rallye	RAE Apprentices for rebuild. Cancelled 29/9/86. Arrived 10/4/86.
BGA.562	Olympia 1	ex G-ALJZ. Crashed 20/7/58. Stored in 'Q' Shed. #
	Broburn Wanderlust	Stored in 'Q' Shed. #
WE146	Canberra PR.3	ex RAE. Nose section only. #
WH774	Canberra PR.7	ex RAE. Stored.
WJ728	Canberra B.2	ex RAE Apprentices, 100, 231 OCU, 50, 61, 18, 9. Stored.

WJ865	Canberra T.4	ex ETPS. RAE Apprentices. #
WT308+	Canberra B(I).6	ex A&AEE. Stored. Omitted from W&R10.
XD860	Valiant BK.1.	ex 214, 138, 214. Nose section. #
XE531	Hunter T.12	ex RAE, A&AEE, RAE, Rolls-Royce. Crashed 17/3/82. Wreck. #
XF274	Meteor T.7	ex RAE, A&AEE, Glosters. Remains preserved with AAIU. #
XF844	Provost T.1	ex RAE, 6 FTS. Apprentices. #
XG158	Hunter F.6A	8686M, ex 5 MU, 4 FTS, TWU, 229 OCU, 4 FTS, 229 OCU, 65, DFLS. Fuselage. #
XJ396	Whirlwind HAR.10	ex RAE Lasham, XD776 ntu. Derelict. #
XJ411	Whirlwind HAR.10	ex Wroughton, 103, 110, CFS, 225, 110, Westlands. Derelict.
XM926	Wessex HAS.1	ex RAE Bedford. Spares use.
XN453	Comet 2E	ex RAE, G-AMXD. Sectioned.
XN688	Sea Vixen FAW.2	8141M, ex Halton, 893, 899, 890. Dump, poor state.
XP166	Scout AH.1	ex RAE, G-APVL. Stored. #
XP356	Whirlwind HAR.10	ex BAe SAR Flt Warton, CFS, RAE, CFS. Derelict. #
XP393	Whirlwind HAR.10	ex Wroughton, RAE, 28, 103, 225. Derelict.
XP516	Gnat T.1	8580M, ex 4 FTS. Structures Laboratory. #
XP532	Gnat T.1	8577M/8615M, ex 4 FTS. Derelict. #
XR479	Whirlwind HAR.10	ex Wroughton, RAE, 103, 110, 103. Derelict.
XR544	Gnat T.1	ex 4 FTS. Wreck. #
XS482+	Wessex HU.5	ex A&AEE. RAE Apprentices. Arrived 20/2/86.
XS565	Wasp HAS.1	ex Wroughton, 829 '445'.
XT272+	Buccaneer S.2	ex RAE Bedford. Arrived 1/12/87. Dismantled.
XV147	Nimrod prototype	ex Woodford, A&AEE. Sectioned.
XV631	Wasp HAS.1	ex Wroughton, Endurance Flt.
XX907	Lynx AH.1	ex RAE. Stored.
XX910	Lynx HAS.2	ex RAE. Stored.
+	TSR-2	nose section. First noted 10/87.

Locally It is believed the Pup continues its rebuild in the area.

HB-NBA	Pup 150	ex Redhill, c/n 177.

FLEET

The ATC here rapidly tired of their Wessex XP159 and it moved to Odiham in 1986.

FLEETLANDS

Royal Navy Aircraft Yard Following major expansion of the non-flying airframes here in W&R10, the scene for this edition is one of net loss. The RNAY undertakes overhaul and modification work on helicopters from all three services, although the Hunter's place in all of this is quite perplexing! Composite Whirlwind HAS.7 XN311 left for the dump at Lee-on-Solent 7/86 and former Argentine CH-47C AE-520 left for Wroughton by road on 8/9/86. The only addition is another Wasp, giving the Apprentices sequential airframes.

XL600	Hunter T.7	ex Scampton, 12, 4 FTS, Wattisham SF, 65.
XM836	Wessex HAS.3	ex Wroughton, 737 '651/PO'.
XM923	Wessex HAS.3	ex Wroughton. Fire dump.
XP110	Wessex HAS.3	ex Wroughton, 737 '655/PO'.
XS568	Wasp HAS.1	ex 829 '441'. Boom of XS539.
XS569+	Wasp HAS.1	ex Wroughton. First noted 11/85.
XS868	Wessex HAS.1	A2691/A2706, ex Wroughton. Gate guardian.
XS872	Wessex HAS.1	A2666, ex Leatherhead, '572/CU'.
XS888	Wessex HAS.1	FAA travelling airframe. Based here.
XT780	Wasp HAS.1	ex Wroughton, 703 '636'.

HAMBLE

Antique Aeroplane Company Ron Souch is now well established in his new workshop near here. Many of the aircraft listed in W&R10 are now flying again ; DH.60 Moth G-AAHY flying by 1986; Dragon Rapide G-ACZE completed and flying 1986; Tiger Moth G-AMHF flying by 1987; Tiger Moth G-ANLD flying by 1985; Super Cub D-EMVY to G-AMPF and flying by 1986; DH.60 Moth HB-OBU to G-AANV and flying by 1984. Hornet Moth G-ADMT moved to Kingsclere in late 1986. The following is the current situation with two classics joining those previously listed.

G-ABDX DH.60G Moth ex HB-UAS, CH-405 ntu, G-ABDX. Stored.
G-ADGP+ Hawk Speed Six ex Florida. Arrived 12/86, under restoration.
G-AEDT+ DH.90 Dragonfly ex Boise, Idaho, N2034, G-AEDT, VH-AAD, G-AEDT. Under restoration for Wessex Aviation and Transport.
G-AFSW Chilton DW.2 ex Chilton Manor. Stored.
G-AISX J-3C-65 Cub ex 43-30372, using parts from OO-ALY/43-30409.
C-7 Avro Cadet G-ACFM, ex Abbeyshrule, Terenure, EI-AGO, EI-AFO, C-7. Stored.
British Aerospace At the airfield factory site, the Gnat continues to be displayed.
XM693 Gnat T.1 7891M, ex Abingdon, Bicester, A&AEE. Red Arrows colours.
College of Air Training To clear up the sale of the CoAT fleet as listed in W&R10, Chipmunk G-ARMD went to Holbeach St Johns and Cherokee G-AVBA was also acquired by Dodson Aviation of Ottawa, Kansas, for spares use.

HAVANT

Military Vehicle Conservation Group This group have taken on the former Lasham Auster as complementary to their vehicles and it is under restoration in the area. Contact : MVCG, 86 Priorsdean Crescent, Leigh Park, Havant, Hants, TO9 3AU.
G-AGYL+ J/1 Autocrat ex Lasham, White Waltham. Crashed 6/7/64. Fitted with wings of VF505 and VX110. Arrived during 1986.

HOOK

(North of the M3, near Junction 5) At the farm strip Cub G-BMKC moved on to complete its rebuild. An Auster has been in store here since at least 1982.
G-AJXC+ Auster 5 ex TJ343. CoA expired 2/8/82. Under rebuild.

KINGSCLERE

(Or Hannington) Cliff Lovell's Hampshire Light Plane Services moved to new premises at Salisbury during August 1987. Of the aircraft listed in W&R10 under this heading, most have flown or moved on, as follows ; Tiger Moth G-ADCG airworthy by late 1987; Hornet Moth G-ADKL flying by 1987; Taylorcraft Plus D G-AHWJ moved to Whitchurch during 1986; Caudron C.270 G-BDFM first flew 16/9/86; Super Cub frame 18-1500 became G-WGCS and was flying by 1985. Two aircraft are unaccounted for ; Jackaroo G-AOEX and Super Cub frame D-EMKE (ex R-44, 52-2450).

For completeness, the following should also get a mention under this heading ; Hornet Moth G-ADKM came in from New Milton in late 1986; Hornet Moth G-ADMT arrived from Hamble 11/86, leaving for Salisbury by 8/87; Tiger Moth G-AOJK fuselage arrived from Henstridge by 12/86, but was not noted 6/87; Globe Swift G-AHUN came in from Spain during 1986, moving to Salisbury by 8/87; Stampe SV-4 G-AZNF arrived from Shoreham and Booker before that during 1987 for rebuild; Provost T.51 G-BKOS/178 arrived from Woodvale by 10/86, but had moved on to Upavon, in airworthy condition, by 9/87. Of these G-ADKM, G-AOJK and G-AZNF are not confirmed as moving on as W&R went to press.

LASHAM

Dan-Air During 1986 Dan-Air made the very positive move to donate their Ambassador and York to the Duxford Aviation Society. On 23/5/86 the *Yorkies* completed the dismantling of G-ANTK and she moved by road to Duxford, on 16/10/86 the *Elizabethans* (ie much the same crowd!) moved G-ALZO out to Duxford. This leaves the Dakota as the Dan-Air 'mascot', lovingly maintained outside their engineering headquarters here. 1986 also saw the removal of the three Boeing 707s listed in W&R10, G-BFBS and G-BFBZ had an appointment with the axe, while G-BFZF became G-BNGH (correcting W&R10) and flew out on 19/2/86 - its first flight for 1,512 days according to Dave Allport, who clearly kept a very close eye on it!. The nose section of Comet 4C G-BDIF has not been seen since April 1985 and is also thought to have been scrapped.
G-AMSU" Dakota IV G-AMPP mostly, ex Dan-Air, trooping serial XF756, Scottish Airlines, KK136, 12 MU, Military Mission Belgium, 1 TAMU, 147, USAAF 43-49456.
Royal Aerospace Establishment On their side of the airfield, amid the aerials and gizmos can still be see the forlorn Comet fuselage.
G-ALYX Comet 1 ex Farnborough. Noseless fuselage.

Second World War Aircraft Preservation Society SWWAPS have continued to consolidate their site on the airfield and a restoration programme is underway. The Meteor two-seater is a complex composite and, thanks to Bob Coles, we can now put its Israeli ancestry into focus. Auster G-AGYL went to Havant during 1986 and Wessex HAS.3 XM833 was due to move to Monkton Farleigh by the time these words are read. Open every weekend, other than over the Christmas period, further details from : Second World War Aircraft Preservation Society, Lasham Airfield, Lasham, Alton, Hants.

G-APIT	Prentice 1	ex Biggin Hill, Southend, VR192, 1 ASS, 6 FTS, CFS, 2 FTS, Blackburns. CoA expired 7/9/67.
VH-FDT"	Drover II	ex Blackbushe, Southend, G-APXX, VH-EAS.
4X-FNA	Meteor NF.13	ex Israel, WM366, A&AEE, RRE. Centre section, wings and tail, cockpit/nose from TT.20 WM234 ex Arborfield, Kemble, 3 CAACU, 151, Odiham Wing.
WF137	Sea Prince C.1	ex Yeovilton, Culdrose SF, Shorts Ferry Unit, Arbroath SF, 781. '999/CU'.
WH291	Meteor F.8	ex Kemble, 229 OCU, 85, CAW, 257.
WV798	Sea Hawk FGA.6	A2557, ex Chertsey, Culdrose, FRU, 801, 803, 787.
XE856	Vampire T.11	ex Welwyn Garden City, Woodford, Chester, St Athan, 219, North Weald SF, 226 OCU.
XK418	Auster AOP.9	7976M, ex Basingstoke, Thruxton, Middle Wallop, 654.
XN309	Whirlwind HAR.9	A2663, ex Faygate, Culdrose, Wroughton, Manadon, Culdrose SF, Lee SAR Flt, Endurance Flt, Culdrose SF, Endurance Flt, Culdrose SF, 845, 846, 814.
XP360	Whirlwind HAR.10	ex Fawkham Green, CFS, 225.
E-423	Hunter F.51	ex Elstree, Dunsfold G-9-444, Danish AF, Aalborg store, ESK-724.

LEE-ON-SOLENT

There is always much activity on the W&R front at HMS *Daedalus* with the Air Engineering School (AES) disposing of a lot of early-series Wessex airframes and taking on a whole fleet of HU.5s. Associated with the AES are several units or sub-units, including a Metalcraft school (MTW) and a Battle Damage Repair Training (BDRT) wing. The fire dump is an active consumer of redundant helicopter instructional airframes, although such devices are renowned for not surviving long once properly 'torched'. As ever with Lee, some matters outstanding from W&R10 to clear up. If Wasp HAS.1 XS570/A2699 *Jasper* left by road on 29/7/85, it was back, looking for all the world as though it had never left, by 2/87. W&R10 carried out an obituary on Whirlwind HAS.7 XM667/A2629 on the dump by 7/85. It had not died, but moved dumps, going to Predannack 11/9/86. Finally, another chopper carrying out these odd now-you-see-me-now-you-don't tactics was Whirlwind HAS.7 XN302/A2654 which was reported as leaving the base by road on 15/10/86. It was to be found on the dump by 1/87 however.

Departures since W&R10 have been numerous : Whirlwind HAS.7 XN308/A2605 left by road 30/6/86 for Corsham; Wessex HAS.1 XM329/A2609 moved to Predannack 11/86; Wessex HAS.3 XT256/A2615 was put up for tender in July 1987 and by 8/87 was getting ready to travel to Sweden of all places; Wessex HAS.1 XP149/A2669 left by road for Predannack 2/5/86; Wessex HAS.1 XS128/A2670 left by road 7/10/86 for Yeovilton; Wessex HAS.1 XS886/A2685 left during 2/87 for that famous naval base Birmingham; Wessex HAS.1 XS873/A2686 left 9/12/86 for Predannack; Wessex HAS.1 XS882/A2696 left by 4/87 for Portsmouth; Wessex HU.5 XT757/A2722 left 15/10/86 for Predannack; Wessex HAS.3 XM331 left during 1986 for Predannack; Wessex HAS.1 XM838 had joined BDRT here from AES by 5/86, but left for Predannack by 11/86; Wessex HAS.3 XS119 joined the dump by 5/86 and left later in the year for Predannack; Wessex HAS.3 XS153 moved to Manadon by 7/87.

The former Cyprus Whirlwind HAR.10s (see RAF Overseas) were transitted through here during late 1986 before moving on to Shawbury where they were quickly put up for tender. As with the rest of W&R11, the previous format of listing major instructional fleets by their 'A' or 'M' numbers has been laid to rest and the AES aircraft etc at Lee appear herewith in serial order.

WV382	Hunter GA.11	ex Shawbury, FRADU, 67. AES.
WV903	Sea Hawk FGA.4	A2632, ex Culdrose, Halton 8153M, Sydenham. AES.
WV911	Sea Hawk FGA.6	A2526, 801 Squadron colours as '115/C', AES 'flag-ship'.
XE339	Sea Hawk FGA.6	A2635, ex Culdrose, Halton 8156M. 803 colours '149/E'. AES.
XE712	Hunter GA.11	ex Shawbury, FRADU, 738, 43, 222. BDRT.
XL880	Whirlwind HAR.9	A2714, ex Wroughton, *Endurance* Flt, *Protector* Flt, 847, 848, 815. BDRT.
XM843	Wessex HAS.1	A2693, ex Wroughton, 771 '527/CU'. AES.
XM868	Wessex HAS.1	ex Wroughton, 737 '517/PO'. AES. Omitted from W&R10.
XM870	Wessex HAS.3	ex Wroughton, 737 '652/PO'. AES.
XM917	Wessex HAS.1	A2692, ex AES, Wroughton, 771 '528/CU'. Dump by 1/87.
XN302	Whirlwind HAS.7	A2654, ex AES, Southampton, Culdrose, 771, Lossiemouth SF, 847, 848. Dump.

XN311+	Whirlwind HAR.9	A2643, ex Portsmouth, Lee-on-Solent, Fleetlands, composite, Wroughton, Lee SAR Flt, *Endurance* Flt, Brawdy SF, 847, 705. Arrived 1986, dump. Broken up by 5/87.
XN359	Whirlwind HAR.9	A2712, ex Wroughton, *Endurance* Flt, Fleetlands, Arbroath, *Protector* Flt, 847, 719. BDRT.
XP116	Wessex HAS.3	A2618, ex AES, 737 '520'. Minus tail. MTW.
XP137	Wessex HAS.3	ex Wroughton, 737 '665/PO'. AES.
XP150	Wessex HAS.3	ex Wroughton, 829 *Antrim* Flt '406/AN'. AES.
XP151	Wessex HAS.1	A2684, ex AES, Wroughton, *Ark Royal* Flt '047/R'. Dump by 1/87.
XP157	Wessex HAS.1	A2680, ex Wroughton. AES.
XS483+	Wessex HU.5	ex Wroughton, 845 'YT'. Arrived 18/11/86. AES.
XS511+	Wessex HU.5	ex 845 'YM'. Arrived by 2/87. AES.
XS513+	Wessex HU.5	ex 772 '419/PO'. Arrived by 3/87. AES.
XS514+	Wessex HU.5	ex 845 'YL'. Arrived by 2/87. AES.
XS515+	Wessex HU.5	ex 845 'YN'. Arrived by 2/87. AES.
XS516+	Wessex HU.5	ex 845 'YQ'. Arrived by 2/87. AES.
XS520+	Wessex HU.5	ex 845 'YF'. Arrived by 2/87. AES.
XS522+	Wessex HU.5	ex Wroughton, 848 'ZL'. Arrived 7/11/86. AES.
XS529+	Wasp HAS.1	ex 829 *Galatea* Flt '461'. Arrived by 2/87. AES.
XS538+	Wasp HAS.1	A2725, ex 829 *Lowestoft* Flt. Arrived by 7/87. BDRT.
XS539+	Wasp HAS.1	ex 829 *Endurance* Flt '435/E'. Arrived 19/6/86. AES.
XS545	Wasp HAS.1	A2702, ex Wroughton. *Willy-never-Fly*. AES.
XS567+	Wasp HAS.1	ex 829 *Endurance* Flt '434/E', arrived 5/6/86. AES.
XS570	Wasp HAS.1	A2699. *Jasper*. see notes above. AES.
XS862	Wessex HAS.3	ex gate, AES, Wroughton, 737 '650/PO'. AES.
XS865	Wessex HAS.1	A2694, ex AES, Wroughton, 771 '529/CU'. Dump by /87.
XS866	Wessex HAS.1	A2705, ex Wroughton, 771 '520/CU'. AES.
XS867	Wessex HAS.1	A2671, ex Culdrose. Dump, poor state.
XS870	Wessex HAS.1	A2697, ex Wroughton. AES.
XS876	Wessex HAS.1	A2695, ex Wroughton, 771 '523/CU'. AES.
XS878	Wessex HAS.1	A2683, ex Culdrose. AES.
XT449+	Wessex HU.5	ex Wroughton, 845 'YC'. Arrived 5/11/86. AES.
XT453+	Wessex HU.5	ex 845 'YA'. Arrived by 2/87. AES.
XT455+	Wessex HU.5	ex 845 'YU'. Arrived by 2/87. AES.
XT459	Wessex HU.5	ex 845. Crashed 7/11/83. Dump.
XT482+	Wessex HU.5	ex Wroughton, 848 'ZM'. Arrived 18/11/86. AES.
XT484+	Wessex HU.5	ex 845 'YH', arrived 24/6/86. AES.
XT487	Wessex HU.5	A2723, ex MTW, Wroughton. Dump by 5/86.
XT762+	Wessex HU.5	ex Wroughton, RAE. Arrived 25/11/86. AES.
XT765+	Wessex HU.5	ex 845 'YJ'. Arrived by 2/87. AES.
XT795+	Wasp HAS.1	ex 829 *Leander* Flt '476/LE'. Arrived by 2/87. By 7/87 parked by main gate - new candidate?
XV644	Sea King HAS.1	A2664, ex AES, Farnborough. MTW.
	Lynx TA	built by RNAW Almondbank. AES.
	Lynx TA	built by RNAW Almondbank. AES.

Gannet Store The nest of Gannets is undisturbed.

XG888	Gannet T.5	ex Culdrose, Lossiemouth, 849.
XL500	Gannet AEW.3	A2701, ex Culdrose, Dowty-Rotol, Culdrose, Lossiemouth, 849.
XT752	Gannet T.5	ex Culdrose, Lossiemouth, 849, Indonesian Navy AS-14, G-APYO, WN365.

Historic Aircraft The Swordfish has been with the Station a long time, the Harvard is under restoration on behalf of the FAAHAF at Yeovilton. Status of the newly-arrived Sea Fury is uncertain.

EZ407	Harvard III	ex Yeovilton, Portuguese AF 1656, SAAF, EZ407, 42-84931.
NF389	Swordfish III	'5B', Blackburn-built.
VR930+	Sea Fury FB.11	8382M, ex Wroughton, Yeovilton, Colerne, Dunsfold, FRU, Lossiemouth, Anthorn, 801, Anthorn, 802. Arrived 1/5/86.

LOWER UPHAM

(On the A333 near Bishop's Waltham - and cunningly split in W&R10 to include 'Upham' as well - now remedied!) Despite what W&R10 predicted, the Dalotel Viking remains in store here. The Fokker D.VII is thought to be the aircraft to be used by the Duxford-based Old Flying Machine Company during the 1988 season. Tiger Moth G-ANTS came here briefly during 1986, following purchase at the Duxford auction. It moved on to the caring hands of Ben Cooper at Hungerford. Another Tiger arrived during 1986, and is under restoration.

G-AHUF+	Tiger Moth	ex Yeovilton, A2123, Arbroath A750, NL750. Arrived 1986, under rebuild.
G-BILA	DM-165L Viking	ex F-PPZE. CoA expired 14/9/83. Stored.
G-BFPL	Fokker D.VII rep	ex 'Upham', Sandown, Lands End, Chertsey, D-EAWM. See notes above.

MIDDLE WALLOP

Museum of Army Flying Continued hard work and dedication by the small staff at 'Wallop have made the MoAF one of the best laid out and fascinating museums in the UK. Their lively acquisitions policy continues to ferret out relevant display material, large and small, and a major achievement has been in securing all of the Hamilcar, Horsa and Hotspur bits held by the RAF Museum at Henlow. These are currently stored, along with similar finds made by the MoAF in its own right, but long term could form the basis of a magnificent assault glider collection and set-piece. MoAF also lend aircraft out and have their machines currently on loan at Beverley and Southampton and two aircraft are under restoration at Whitchurch.

The Museum is open 1000 to 1630 including weekends and holidays. Contact : Museum of Army Flying, Middle Wallop, Stockbridge, Hampshire, SO20 8DY. Telephone 0264 62121 extension 428.

There have been a couple of moves since W&R10 ; Auster AOP.6 TW536 is more correctly located under Whitchurch; Terrier 2 VF516/G-ASMZ was offered for sale during 1987 and as we go to press was awaiting collection; Skeeter AOP.12 XL770 moved to Southampton (with XL738 due to return in the opposite direction); and Whirlwind HAS.7 XL853 moved to Southampton by 3/86. A temporary inmate was Bleriot XI BAPC.189, ex Tooting, during 1986 until it was auctioned at the Christie's London sale of 11/86 after which it 'disappeared'. Readers are reminded that MoAF maintains a store at Andover, but as this is not available for inspection and aircraft are stored there on a temporary basis, they are included in the listing here, with the proviso that not all aircraft will be on show to the public.

G-APWZ	Prospector EP.9	ex Goodwood. Damaged 1/84. For spares use.
G-APXW	Prospector EP.9	ex Shoreham, Lympne. Remains, for spares. Crashed 30/9/73.
G-ARDG	Prospector EP.9	ex Shoreham, Lympne. Under restoration.
G-AXKS	W-Bell 47G-4A	ex Bristows, ARWF, G-17-8.
B-415"	AFEE 10/42 replica	BAPC.163, ex Wimborne. Flying Jeep. On loan.
P-5	Rotachute III	8381M, ex Henlow. On loan.
BAPC.10	Hafner R-II	ex Locking, Weston-super-Mare, Old Warden, Yeovil. On loan.
5984"	DH.2 replica	BAPC.112, ex Chertsey.
N5195	Sopwith Pup	G-ABOX, ex Redhill. Damaged 2/7/86. CoA expired 18/9/86. On loan.
LH208	Horsa I	sections, acquired locally. Stored with other Horsa components.
TJ569	Auster 5	G-AKOW, ex PH-NAD, PH-NEG, TJ569. CoA expired 26/6/82.
TK777	Hamilcar I	ex South Yorkshire, substantial sections, also parts from TK718 and centre section from NX836, ex Henlow.
TL659	Horsa II	BAPC.80, fuselage, composite.
WJ358	Auster AOP.6	G-ARYD, ex Perth, WJ358.
WZ721	Auster AOP.9	ex 4 RTR, 656, 6 Flt. *Dragon*.
XG502	Sycamore HR.14	ex gate, Wroughton, Bristols, JEHU.
XK776	ML Utility Mk 1	ex Cardington. Fitted with *Clouy* wing. On loan.
XK988+	Whirlwind HAR.10	A2646, ex Ilkeston, Middle Wallop, Lee-on-Solent, 103, 110, 103, CFS, JEHU. Arrived during 1987, stored.
XL738+	Skeeter AOP.12	7860M, ex Southampton, Middle Wallop. Arrived late 1987. Composite airframe, boom from XM565/7861M.
XL813	Skeeter AOP.12	ex 4 Regt, 9 Flt, ARWF.
XP821	Beaver AL.1	ex Shawbury, Kemble. White colour scheme.
XP822+	Beaver AL.1	ex Shawbury. Arrived by 7/87. For Museum gate guardian.
XP847	Scout AH.1	ex AETW.
XT108	Sioux AH.1	ex Duxford, Yeovilton, Middle Wallop, D&T Flight, Middle Wallop.
XT150	Sioux AH.1	7883M/7884M, composite airframe. Stored.
XT190	Sioux AH.1	ex UNFICYP. Stored.

XT236 Sioux AH.1 ex Sek Kong. Stripped frame, stored.
XT548+ Sioux AH.1 ex Arborfield, Middle Wallop, Arborfield, 658 'D'. Arrived early 1987.
XT550 Sioux AH.1 ex Wroughton, 651 'D'. Stored.
XV272 Beaver AL.1 cockpit section only. *Operation Drake* markings. Stored.
Scout CIM ex AETW.
11989 L-19A Bird Dog ex Fort Rucker, Alabama, N33600.
243809" WACO CG-4A BAPC.185, ex Burtonwood, Shrewsbury. Fuselage.
A-528 FMA Pucara 8769M, ex Cosford, Abingdon, Stanley Airport, Argentine AF.
A-533 FMA Pucara ZD486, ex Boscombe Down, Abingdon, Finningley, Portsmouth, Stanley Airport, Argentine AF.
AE-406 UH-1H Iroquois ex Fleetlands, Stanley Racecourse, Argentine Army, 72-21491. Plaything.
AE-409 UH-1H Iroquois ex Duxford, Middle Wallop, 656, Stanley Racecourse, Argentine Army, 72-21506.

Army Air Corps Historic Aircraft Flight The fleet is unchanged and can be seen at several air displays during the season.

XL814 Skeeter AOP.12 ex 1 Wing, 2 Wing, 651.
XP242 Auster AOP.9 reserve aircraft.
XR244 Auster AOP.9 ex AFWF.
XT131 Sioux AH.1 ex D&T Flight 'B'.

Gate Guardian The main entrance to the base is still guarded by the Auster.

WZ724 Auster AOP.9 7432M, ex 'WZ670', 656, FEAF.

Air Engineering Training Wing In terms of W&R content, the other element of interest is the instructional fleet of the AETW, based upon Stockwell Hall and at other locations within the airfield. Following the fleet is somewhat difficult and indeed the list below is much as it was in W&R10! This may well be the case, but the reader is advised that some changes are inevitable. The instructional airframe fleet includes purpose-built non-flying airframes (TADs - Training And Demonstration; CIMs - Classroom Instruction Models) and these are included for completeness.

XP191+ Scout AH.1 ex Shrivenham, Wroughton. Omitted from W&R10.
XP848 Scout AH.1 ex Wroughton
XP853 Scout AH.1
XP854 Scout AH.1 7898M/TAD.043.
XP856 Scout AH.1
XP857 Scout AH.1 ex Yeovil.
XP884 Scout AH.1
XP888 Scout AH.1 ex Wroughton.
XP905 Scout AH.1
XP907 Scout AH.1 fitted with boom of XR630.
XR436 SARO P.531/2 ex MoAF, A&AEE.
XR597 Scout AH.1 ex travelling display airframe.
XT616 Scout AH.1 ex Wroughton.
XT640 Scout AH.1
XV629 Wasp HAS.1 ex Wroughton. BDRT.
XW835 Lynx 1-02 ex Yeovil, G-BEAD.
XW836 Westland 606 ex Yeovil, Sherborne, Yeovil. Civil Lynx mock-up.
XW838 Lynx 1-03 TAD.009.
XW865 Gazelle AH.1
XW888 Gazelle AH.1 ex ARWF 'C'.
XW889 Gazelle AH.1 ex ARWF 'D'.
XW900 Gazelle AH.1 TAD.900.
XW912 Gazelle AH.1 ex 3 CBAS.
XX411 Gazelle AH.1 ex Falklands, 3 CBAS. Shot down 21/5/82. BDRT.
TAD.01 Gazelle CIM
TAD.02 Gazelle CIM c/n WA.22
TAD.04 Gazelle CIM
TAD.08 Gazelle CIM
TAD.007 Lynx CIM also marked TO.42.
TAD.010 Lynx CIM
TAD.011 Lynx CIM
TAD.012 Lynx CIM

TAD,018 Lynx CIM
TAU,3 Gazelle CIM ex Arborfield, Middle Wallop.

Others The contents of the dump are unaltered, if more frazzled! Sioux AH,1 XT548 did not go to Detmold as planned, but joined MoAF instead.

XL847 Whirlwind HAS.7 A2626, ex BDRT, AETW, MoAF, Lee-on-Solent, Lossiemouth SF, 771, 829, 820.
XX452 Gazelle AH,1 pod only.

ODIHAM

RAF Odiham Considerable changes here to report. Sadly, aircraft still slip through the net as the former gate guardian Meteor here proved during the summer of 1987 when it was scrapped without so much as a whisper to interested parties who could at least have used it for spares. A Whirlwind is slotted to replace it on the gate. The following helicopters, all Whirlwind HAR.10s, have moved on since W&R10 : XD182 left by road on 28/1/86 for Catterick; XK969 moved to Manston by 3/86; and XP333 also moved to Manston by 2/86. Aregntine UH-1H AE-413 is now fully airworthy as G-HUEY and as such no longer comes under the aegis of W&R. Former Akrotiri Whirlwind HAR.10 XK986 arrived here during early May 1987 for BDR, but had gone by 6/87. Current situation here is :-

WK968 Meteor F.8 8053M, ex gate, Kemble, CAW, 46, 56, 64. Scrapped 7/87, to the dump.
XK970+ Whirlwind HAR.10 8789M, ex Akrotiri, 84, 230, CFS, Khormaksar SAR Flt, 228, JEHU. Arrived 5/87 for BDR.
XN387 Whirlwind HAR.9 8564M, ex Wroughton, Lee-on-Solent SAR Flt, Lossiemouth SF, 846, 719. BDR.
XP159+ Wessex HAS.1 8877M, ex Fleet, Leatherhead, *Ark Royal* Flt '047/R'. Arr 1986, for BDR.
XR453+ Whirlwind HAR.10 8873M, ex Foulness Island, 2 AFTS, CFS, 230, 1563 Flt, CFS. Arrived 10/85, for the gate.
XR681+ Jet Provost T.4 8588M, ex Abingdon, RAFEF, CATCS, 6 FTS, RAFC. Nose section, with 1349 Sqn ATC, kept on airfield. First noted early 1986.
XS871 Wessex HAS.1 8457M, ex Wroughton. 72 Sqn colours, instructional airframe.
Scout AH.1 gutted fuselage, for BDRT.
61-2414 Boeing CH-47A ex Boeing. Instructional airframe.

Locally Steve Markham continues to store his two SIPAs, with G-BDKM airworthy from his strip.

G-AMSG SIPA 903 ex OO-VBL, F-BGHB.
G-AWLG SIPA 903 ex F-BGHG. CoA expired 22/8/79.

POPHAM

As W&R11 went to press there were unconfirmed reports that Jim Espin's strip and much surrounding land had been acquired by Charles Church, but it will have to be W&R12 that records any changes that there may be. In the meantime the W&R stock here has been reduced to a solitary Cessna. Cavalier G-BDLY was flying again by 1987 and Tipsy Junior G-AMVP left on 7/6/86 becoming airworthy again.

G-AYXV Cessna FA.150L Crashed 5/9/79. Dismantled.

PORTSMOUTH

HMS *Phoenix* The Navy safety and fire school here acquired Whirlwind HAR.9 XN311 from Lee-on-Solent by 7/86, but were not happy with it as it returned to Lee-on-Solent by 3/87. It was replaced by a Wessex.

XS882+ Wessex HAS.1 A2696, ex Lee-on-Solent, Wroughton, 771 '524/CU'. Arr by 4/87.

John Pounds Yard The report in W&R10 that the forlorn Anson here left on a low loader can now be clarified as the poor thing *lives* on a Queen Mary in the yard!

VS562 Anson T.21 8012M, ex Llanbedr, A&AEE, AST Hamble, CS(A). Poor state.

ROMSEY

Auster J/5L G-APLG has moved on, destination unconfirmed.

SEAFIELD PARK

The Naval Air Medical School, just west of Lee-on-Solent, still uses its two airframes.

XS869 Wessex HAS.1 A2649, ex Lee-on-Solent, Manadon, 771 '508/PO'.
Buccaneer S.2 ex 809 '022/R'. Nose section only.

SOUTHAMPTON

Southampton Hall of Aviation There have been a few additions to the Museum's exhibits, as it expands its coverage of the history of aviation in Southampton and the Solent area. At Ocean Park, opposite the museum building, some of the larger aircraft are on show. The Seagull nose section on loan to the Museum from the Science Museum is too small for W&R's terms of reference, but should not be confused with the amazing Walrus/Seagull caravan that was donated to 424 Squadron ATC - see below. Skeeter AOP.12 XL738 returned to Middle Wallop having been replaced by another example.

The Museum receives much co-operation from the Science Museum, the Museum of Army Flying and from the local ATC unit. Please note that the Spitfire Society is no longer based at the Museum, and that neither the Society nor the Museum are currently involved in the building of a replica of the prototype Spitfire. The Museum is open daily except Mondays and over the Christmas period, 1000 to 1700 (Tuesday to Saturday) and 1400 to 1700 (Sundays). Contact : Southampton Hall of Aviation, Albert Road South, Southampton, SO1 1FR. Telephone 0703 35830.

G-ALZE	BN-1F	ex Cosford, Kemble, Bembridge Harbour. On loan.
BAPC.7	SUMPAC	ex Old Warden, Southampton.
+	Airwave Hang-glider prototype, on show late 1987.	
VH-BRC	Sandringham 4	ex Lee-on-Solent, N158C Antilles Air Boats, VP-LVE *Southern Cross*, VH-BRC Ansett *Beachcomber*, TEAL ZK-AMH *Auckland*, Sunderland III JM715 - no operational service.
N248	Supermarine S.6A	ex Cowes, Southampton, Henlow, Southampton Pier, 'S1596' in *First of the Few*, Calshot, RAFHSF.
PK683	Spitfire F.24	7150M, ex Kingsbridge Lane, Kemble, Colerne, Changi, Singapore Aux AF.
XJ481+	Sea Vixen FAW.1	ex Ilkeston, Yeovilton, Portland, Yeovilton, Boscombe Down, LWRE Woomera, Australia. Arrived by 10/86. On loan.
XK740+	Gnat F.1	8396M, ex Hamble, Cosford, Bicester, Church Fenton, MoS, Filton. Arr 4/87.
XL770+	Skeeter AOP.12	8046M, ex Middle Wallop, Shrivenham, Wroughton, 15/19 Hussars, 652, 654. Arrived 1987. On loan.
XL853+	Whirlwind HAS.7	A2630, ex Middle Wallop, Lee-on-Solent, Wroughton, Yeovilton SF, 824. Arrived by 3/86. On loan.

424 Squadron, ATC The unit works in close co-operation with the Southampton Hall of Aviation and is also headquartered in Albert Road South. There is now some confusion relating to the airframes it holds and anyone who can put the compiler out of his misery will be welcome. Vampire T.11 XD596 did indeed move out of Calmore during late 1986. The Walrus/Seagull caravan donated to the unit has not been seen for some time.

XD596+	Vampire T.11	7939M, ex Calmore, St Athan, CATCS, CNCS, 5 FTS, 4 FTS.
XD614	Vampire T.11	8124M, nose section. Identity open to dispute. '65'.
XJ476	Sea Vixen FAW.1	ex Boscombe Down, A&AEE. Nose section.
XM415	Jet Provost T.3	ex Kemble, 3 FTS, 2 FTS. Nose section.

Crofton Aeroplane Services Les Groves and Ian Hammond's workshop remains active. Auster J/1N G-AJYB was flying again by 1987 and moved to its new base just outside of Stamford. Tiger Moth G-ANRM moved here from Reading and was airworthy by 9/87. The other airframes are believed unchanged.

G-AHHU	J/1N Alpha	ex Sandown. Crashed 10/6/63. Stored.
G-AJGJ+	Auster 5	ex Shoreham, RT486. CoA expired 23/11/71.
G-APAA	J/5R Alpine	Crashed 9/8/75. Stored.
9M-ANN	Chipmunk 22	ex N70727 ntu, R Malaysian AF FM1026, WP909, 19 RFS, 8 RFS. Stored.
18-1528	Super Cub	F-MBCH, ex Kingsclere, ALAT. Stored.

Others Restoration of the Terrier is thought still to continue in the area. A former French Cub has been stored since at least 1983. The Bf 109 that was stored in the area moved to Tangmere on loan.

G-ARLH	Terrier 1	ex White Waltham, EI-AMB. Composite of TW528, VF635 and VX109.
G-BDMS+	J-3C-65 Cub	ex F-BEGZ, 44-80753. Stored.

SOUTHAMPTON AIRPORT

(Or Eastleigh) After an absence, the airport reappears as the site of an ambitious restoration project to put a Sea Vixen in the air in civilian hands. Two former Cosford airframes have arrived, one of which will fly. The dump has inherited a new breed that W&R will have to contend with all the more, the geriatric biz-jet. Sea Hawk FB.3 G-SEAH/WM994 is reported to have moved here from Bournemouth Airport during 11/86, but moved back whence it came early in 1987.

G-JSAX+ HS.125-3B/RA ex G-GGAE, VR-BGD, D-CAMB. CoA expired 14/8/85. Fire dump by 5/86. Noseless by 9/87.
XJ571+ Sea Vixen FAW.2 8140M, ex Cosford, Halton, Sydenham, 893, 892, 899. Arrived 17/9/87.
XJ607+ Sea Vixen FAW.2 8171M, ex Cosford, Cranwell, 890, 892, 766, 892. Arrived 15/10/87.

STOCKBRIDGE

In the car park of the White Hart Inn Hiller UH-12C G-ARTG was scrapped during the summer of 1986. The pub is still worth a visit, however!

THRUXTON

Two of the entries in W&R10 for here transpired to be far too small to bother with - another case of helicopter disease, people reporting booms and hoping there is more! With a Bell 47G hanging on and a gutted JetRanger joining it, the entry here is somewhat depleted this time. Brantly 305 G-ASXF moved in early 1986 to Binfield; Westland-Bell 47G G-AXKT and Hughes 269C G-BGYW are the two culprits mentioned above and should be deleted; C-47A N5595T moved out 16/2/87 bound for Benington. The famous Mil Mi-24 *Hind*, based upon Whirlwind HAS.7 XN382, did not perish for the promotional movie it was used in and was to be noted back at the airfield by 5/86. It left by road on 19/1/87 and is assumed to be the 'Mi-24' reported on the dump at West Freugh. That leaves :-

G-BCYY W-Bell 47G-3B1 ex XV318. Crashed 6/7/83. Wreck.
G-ICRU+ B.206A JetRanger ex Carlisle, C-GXVE ntu, N7845S. Crashed 24/5/84. First noted 5/86.

UPHAM

This entry in W&R10 should have been under the heading of 'Lower Upham' - which see.

WARSASH

(South of the A27 west of Fareham, or across the Hamble from Hamble!) The Naval College of Nautical Studies has a Wessex in its grounds, probably for instructional purposes.

XM327+ Wessex HAS.3 ex 829 *Kent* Flt. First noted 9/87.

WHITCHURCH

A workshop here is working on two aircraft for the Museum of Army Flying at Middle Wallop.

G-AHWJ+ T'craft Plus D ex Kingsclere, Wincanton, LB294. CoA expired 30/6/71. Under rebuild.
TW536+ Auster AOP.6 G-BNGE, ex Middle Wallop, 7704M, Innsworth, Bristol. Under rebuild to fly.

WINCHESTER

Charles Church (Spitfires) Ltd Under the engineering command of Dick Melton, Charles Church has established a beautifully equipped workshop in this area and its first product, two-seater conversion G-CTIX, made its first flight from the strip on 25/7/87. A trio of Spitfires have since moved in to the workshop to take their turn in the restoration process. P-51D NL12066/G-SUSY was flown in on 28/11/87 and is based. The remains of Hurricane 5481 arrived during June 1986 from Canada, but since moved on to the other Charles Church workshop at Sandown - which see. Additionally, see under Woodford for the operation's most ambitious acquisition, the unfortunate Lancaster.

G-CCIX Spitfire IX ex Nailsworth, G-BIXP ntu, Duxford, Israel, Israel DF/AF 2046, Czech AF, RAF TE517 313. Under restoration.
G-SUSY+ P-51D-20-NA ex NL12066, Nicaraguan AF GN120, USAAF 44-72773. Flew in 28/11/87.
MV262+ Spitfire XIV ex Bitteswell, Blackbushe, Calcutta, Indian AF, ACSEA, 9 MU. Arr 7/8/86.
PL344+ Spitfire IX ex Netherlands, Anthony Fokker School, 129, 130, 401, 442, 602. Under major rebuild.
PT462 Spitfire Tr IX G-CTIX, ex Nailsworth, Israel, Israel AF/DF 2067/0607, Italian AF MM4100, RAF PT462 73 (?), 253. First flew 25/7/87.
RR232+ Spitfire IX ex Australia - Nowra, Bankstown, Point Cook, South Africa - Cape Town, Ysterplaat, SAAF 5632, RAF RR232, 47 MU, ECFS. Tail from JF629, wings from RM873. Arr 13/1/87.

Hereford & Worcester

EWYAS HAROLD

(On the A465 south west of Hereford) Perhaps because nobody dares go near, there are no reports on the continued good health (or otherwise) of the Trident fuselage used by the men of the SAS for whatever they use such things for. Last confirmed sighting was 4/84 - who dares wins?

G-AVYB Trident 1E-140 ex British Airways, Heathrow. Fuselage only - see notes above.

FOWNHOPE

(On the B4224 south east of Hereford) Mark Biggs has two Tiger Moth frames stored in the area.

HEREFORD

RAF Hereford (Credenhill) After the removal of Spitfire XVI TE392 to the Doug Arnold collection in 1984, the RAF station suffered for two years without an aircraft. Then Sea Vixen FAW.2 XP921/8226M trundled in from Halton on 20/11/86. The arrester hook and folding wings clearly put them off, as it left again on 12/1/88, for North Luffenham. Meanwhile, the local ATC's Vampire arrived, for purposes unknown. On 2/2/88 a more potent Hunter FGA.9 arrived for gate duties.

XE982+	Vampire T.11	7564M, ex Hereford, St Athan, RAFC. Arrived by 3/87 - see notes above.
XG252+	Hunter FGA.9	8840M, ex Cosford, 1 TWU, 2 TWU, 1 TWU, TWU, 45, 8, Wittering SF, MoA, 54, 66. Arrived 2/2/88.

Others 124 Squadron ATC's Vampire T.11 XE982 moved to RAF Hereford by 3/87. Clive Hardiman brought Tiger Moth replica 'K2572' here from Lutterworth. Clive also has G-DHTM at Shobdon - which see.

K2572+" Tiger Moth rep ex Lutterworth, Holme-on-Spalding Moor. Arrived 9/86.

POWICK

(South of Worcester) Meteor NF.13 WM367 is reported to have left here, destination unknown in 1985.

SHOBDON

Things remain much the same W&R-wise at this delightful airfield. Going back to W&R10, Skeeter AOP.12 XN351/G-BKSC did not go to Jim Wilkie and is thought to have gone to Lossiemouth, although this is currently unconfirmed. Skeeter AOP.12 XL809 became G-BLIX and moved to Clapham. The identity of Tiger Moth 'G-ANOR' under rebuild here is open to debate. (See under Chislet.) Clive Hardiman's Tiger Moth Replica is here under construction, and his former Ulster Auster - Clive also has a non-flyer at Hereford, which see.

G-AHHK+	J/1 Autocrat	ex Newtownards. CoA expired 22/3/70. First noted 8/86. Rebuild.
G-AJIT	Auster Kingsland	CoA expired 29/7/66. Highly modified J/1 Autocrat. Under restoration. Left airfield 10/86, but had returned by mid 1987.
G-ANOR	Tiger Moth	ex Billingshurst and DE694. Under restoration using surviving parts from G-ACDA which burnt out 27/6/79. See notes above.
G-APSO	Dove 5	ex N1046T ntu. CoA expired 8/7/78. Stored, dismantled.
G-AYFA	Twin Pioneer 3	ex Flight One, Prestwick, G-31-5, XM285, SRCU, 225, Odiham SF, 230. CoA expired 24/5/82. Open store.
G-BEPN	Pawnee 235D	ex N54877. CoA expired 6/4/79. Fuselage frame only.
G-DHTM+	Tiger Moth replica under construction using original components.	

UPPER HILL

(Between the A4110 and the A49 south of Leominster) Lion Motors/Sheppards Crane Hire still has one of the tastiest of gate guardians looking after the stock.

WK275 Swift F.4 ex Hatfield, Filton, C(A).

WORCESTER

The Javelin with 187 Squadron ATC was put up for tender 1/87 and acquired by the Avon Aviation Museum. It moved to Monkton Farleigh during 7/87.

Hertfordshire

BENINGTON

(South of the B1037 east of Stevenage) EMK Aeroplane have their workshop here and continue to work on a varied range of restoration projects. The former Duxford SPAD XIII arrived here during 1986 for restoration to flying condition and the Dakota that for a long time had dominated ther skyline at Thruxton arrived here for storage during 1987. Of the aircraft listed in W&R10, two have reflown and should be deleted ; Emeraude G-ARDD was flying again during 1987 and Taylor Monoplane G-AVPX was flying by 8/86. The two Miles Hawk Trainers, G-AIUA and G-ANWO both moved during 1987, destination unconfirmed. Current here are the following :-

G-AIXN	M.1C Sokol	ex Booker, OK-BHA. CoA expired 13/4/77. Under restoration.
G-AKHW	Gemini 1A	ex Sherburn. CoA expired 10/10/79. Under restoration.
G-AOBG	Somers-Kendal SK.1	ex 'Sussex', Eaton Bray, Cranfield. Stored.
BAPC132	Bleriot XI	ex Duxford and Colerne. 'G-BLXI'.
N5595T+	C-47A-85-DL	ex Thruxton, Blackbushe, G-BGCG, Spanish AF T3-27, N49V, N50322, 43-15536. Arr here by road 2/87. Stored dismantled.
S4523+	SPAD XIII	N2727V, ex Duxford, Orlando. Arr by 5/86. For restoration.

BERKHAMSTED

(Last located in 'Berkshire', now remedied!) Stuart McKay's store remains the same as it ever was.

G-AVPD	Jodel D.9 Bebe	ex Langley. CoA expired 6/6/75. Stored.
G-AWDW	Bensen CB-8M	CoA expired 7/10/71. Stored.
G-AZZZ	Tiger Moth	ex Langley, Maidenhead, F-BGJE, NL864. Wings from G-BABA. Stored.
G-BBGP	Berg Cricket	Wfu 7/1/74. Stored.

BISHOP'S STORTFORD

Russavia Collection With the tragic accident to the Dragon Rapide at Duxford during June 1987 and the subsequent closing down of pleasure flying operations, this heading (previously shunted under 'Hemel Hempstead' following disturbed random neuron meanderings of the compiler, now corrected) now forms the central reference for this pioneering collection of light aircraft and gliders. The future of the collection is under assessment and enquiries can be made to the following address, although readers should note that the aircraft held are not currently available for inspection ; Russavia Ltd, Woodend Green, Henham, Bishop's Stortford, Herts, CM22 6AY.

Russavia aircraft can also be found under the following locations;- Audley End, Bedford, Duxford and Eaton Bray. Hawkridge Dagling BGA.493 can now be found at Eaton Bray. Currently held here are the following :-

G-EBQP	DH.53 Humming Bird	composite, with wings of G-AEYY. Stored.
G-AKKH+	Gemini 1A	ex Duxford. CoA expired 1/10/84. Stored locally.
G-MNDV+	Sirocco 377GB	airworthy. Acquired 1987.
BGA 162	Willow Wren	*Yellow Wren*. Stored.
BGA 651	Slingsby Petrel	ex EI-101, IGA.101, G-ALPP. Under overhaul.
BGA1147	Kranich II	'D-11-3224'. Stored.
BGA2500	Fauvel AV-36CR	ex D-6200. Stored.
BGA3166+	Lippisch Falke rep	airworthy. Acquired 1987.

BUSHEY

Vintage Aircraft Team W&R10 gave the view that the former store for Lincoln Field Vintage and Historic Aircraft Collection / Vintage Aircraft Team had been cleared. Not so, it hangs tenaciously on to a slot in this edition. The pod of Vampire T.11 XH330 was acquired by Derek Leek and moved to Bridgnorth. The pod of fellow XK632 did not go to Croxley Green as W&R10 would have you believe, but it certainly has gone - any clues appreciated. Vampire FB.5 VZ304 did not go to Cranfield, and is still here, although its removal to Bedfordshire cannot be too far off. Also here is the Mystery Jet fuselage mock-up and the nose of the Venom FB.4. These have been acquired by Alan Allen of Ruislip and will move soon.

VZ304	Vampire FB.5	7630M, ex Carlisle, 3 CAACU, 249. See notes above.
	Venom FB.4	ex Tinwald Downs. Identity not confirmed. Pod only. See notes above.
	Mystery Jet MJ-1	ex Southend. Fuselage mock-up. See notes above.

Breakers An original name for the car breakers yard here that proudly displays the bent fuselage of a Sundowner among its other wares. The yard is west of the M1, just south of the A41 crossing.

G-BARI Sundowner Crashed 23/4/75. Battered fuselage only.

CLOTHALL COMMON

(On the A507 south east of Baldock) At the airstrip the Tri-Traveler is certainly still in store, although when last seen it was in danger of being swallowed by a mountain of grain (good planning, Maggie). The Auster has not been seen since 5/85 - is it now under EEC control?

G-AIJS	J/4 Arrow	ex Compton. Stored, dismantled. CoA exp 14/12/71. See notes above.
G-APYU	Tri-Traveler	ex Moreton-in-the-Marsh. Crashed 23/4/72. Stored.

CROXLEY GREEN

(On the A412 south west of Watford) Peter Gardner gave up both of his Vampire T.11 pods that were held here. XK632 did not come here, please see Bushey. The two that came here from Bushey were WZ415 which moved on to Leavesden and XH328 which moved on to Hemel Hempstead.

ELSTREE

Airfield By 11/87 both of the airframes listed as being wrecked here had gone, being Varga Kachina G-JLTB and Pawnee frame G-BEHS (c/n 25-5207) - the latter flying again. The Kachina had already been replaced by another of the breed, which is currently the only long term hulk at Elstree.

G-CHTT+ Varga Kachina Crashed 27/4/86. Hulk, first noted 4/87.

Locally SIPA 903 G-BBDV is thought to have left the area, for restoration in deepest Bedfordshire.

FOWLMERE

(North of the A505, near Royston) Robs Lamplough is thought to have moved his P-51D fuselage through to North Weald but the Hurricane is thought still to be here.

	Hurricane	ex Israel. Bare frame and other components.

GOFF'S OAK

A farm here houses the long-lost Brandis Corner Hiller which is thought to have come here in 1984.

G-ATKG+	Hiller UH-12B	ex Brandis Corner, Thornicombe, Redhill, Thai AF 103. CoA exp 28/11/69. Thought arrived 1984. First noted 12/87.

HATFIELD

Polytechnic The anonymous Jetstream test-shell is still to be found within the campus grounds. Upon inspection it would seem to be a lot more than a pressure test shell - any thoughts?

Locally Gerry Atwell and Frank Telling continue the restoration of their Auster.

G-AKXP	Auster 5	ex Claygate, NJ633. Crashed 9/4/70. Under restoration.

HATFIELD AIRFIELD

British Aerospace are actively trying to establish a Heritage Centre here and have acquired a Trident 3B to kick it off. Plans include the Comet 4 at Heathrow, but have yet to materialise. Two of the Mosquito Aircraft Museum airframes were held here in temporary storage for a while, but returned to London Colney during early 1988 - which see. British Aerospace use Hatfield as the base for most of the airframes in their travelling sales roadshow and these are now listed here accordingly. Biggest news from Hatfield was the first flight following restoration of the DH.88 G-ACSS *Grosvenor House* on 17/5/87. The aircraft had been restored by BAe here and by the RAE Apprentices at Farnborough on behalf of the Shuttleworth Trust. Sadly, this unique aircraft was ground looped at Hatfield on 4/7/87 and repairs are currently underway.

G-ACSS+	DH.88 Comet	ex Farnborough, Old Warden, Leavesden, K5084, G-ACSS. See notes above.
G-APLU+	Tiger Moth	ex Hemel Hempstead, Luton area, VR-AAY, F-OBKK, T6825, 22 EFTS. On rebuild. Arrived during 1987.
G-ARYB	HS.125 Srs 1	ex Astwick Manor, Hatfield. wfu 5/6/68.
G-AWZO+	Trident 3B-101	ex Heathrow, BA, BEA. Flew in 18/4/86.
+	ATP mock-up	ex Woodford, Kemble, St Athan, Kemble, 84, Handling Squadron. Based upon Andover C.1 XS647. Arrived early 1987.
+	HS.125-800	ex Chester Airport, IAAC 236, G-AYBH. Crashed 27/11/79. Based upon an HS.125-600A fuselage.
+	Jetstream 31	ex East Midlands, N14234. Based upon Jetstream 1 fuselage.

HEMEL HEMPSTEAD

For reasons best known to himself the compiler has placed the Russavia Collection here in the last couple of editions. This is now corrected and can be found under 'Bishop's Stortford'. 1187 Squadron ATC received the pod of Vampire T.11 XH328 from Croxley Green during 1987, but it quickly moved on to Cranfield. Tiger Moth G-APLU moved to Hatfield Airfield during 1987.

HITCHIN

The rebuild of the Super Cub is thought to continue in the area.

G-BKEZ	PA-19-95	ex Kingsclere, OO-SPL, 51-15628. Under restoration.

HODDESDON

(On the A41 south of Ware) 1239 Squadron ATC keep their Vampire T.11 in Old Highway, opposite the John Warner School.

XD616	Vampire T.11	ex Old Warden, Woodford, Chester, St Athan, 8 FTS, 1 FTS, 8 FTS, 65. '56'.

KINGS LANGLEY

(On the A41 north of Watford) In the Holme Park Industrial Estate, near the canal, the Sea Vixen continues to be displayed.

XJ494	Sea Vixen FAW.2	ex Farnborough, FRL, A&AEE, HSA Hatfield, Sydenham, 899, Sydenham, 892.

LEAVESDEN

Three former Red Arrows Gnats arrived here by road during late 1987, two for jet collector Arnold Glass and one for onward shipment to the USA for Mark Birtz. Which is which has yet to be fathomed, so all three are presented here. On the edge of the airfield 2 Squadron ATC keep their Vampire T.11 pod, lovingly upside down - a nice touch that. The aircraft came here via Croxley Green and not direct from Bushey as stated in W&R10.

G-AJPR	Dove 1B	ex Biggin Hill. wfu 30/10/69. Forward fuselage, derelict.
WZ415	Vampire T.11	ex Croxley Green, Bushey, Keevil, Exeter, 3/4 CAACU, 226 OCU, CS(A). See notes above.
XP535+	Gnat T.1	A2679, ex Culdrose, SAH, Red Arrows, 4 FTS, CFS. Arr 3/11/87.
XR572+	Gnat T.1	A2676, ex Culdrose, SAH, Red Arrows, CFS, 4 FTS. Arr 28/10/87.
XR991+	Gnat T.1	A2709, ex Culdrose, SAH, Cranwell 8637M, Red Arrows, Yellowjacks, 4 FTS. Arrived 11/11/87.

LEVERSTOCK GREEN

(On the road between Abbotts Langley and Hemel Hempstead) At the *The Swan at Pimlico* falling-down-water emporium, a Provost was installed as a plaything during 4/87.

WW442+	Provost T.1	7618M, ex Cranfield, Booker, St Merryn, Houghton-on-the-Hill, Kidlington, Halton, CNCS, 3 FTS. Arrived 4/87.

LONDON COLNEY

(Off the A6 between London Colney and South Mimms) Mosquito Aircraft Museum With a Queen Bee project and the addition of the remains of the Radlett-built *Toucan* MPA, it would seem that the hard-working lads at MAM have been taking it easy since W&R10. Not so! Consolidation at this superb museum continues and their restoration will bear fruit with the rolling out of the complete Hornet Moth G-ADOT - to a very high standard. Other projects are well underway and work on outbuildings, displays etc is extensive. Venom NF.3 WX853 and Vampire T.11 XE985 were both temporarily away stored at Hatfield, but had returned by early 1988. The fuselage section of the Horsa acquired from Banbury went to Robertsbridge. The frame of Tiger Moth G-ANFC left for Hadfield on 13/4/86 in exchange for the Queen Bee. See under Wyton for a sad tale relating to a Comet salvage.

MAM is open from Easter to the end of October on Sundays and from July to the end of September on Thursday afternoons and is also open Bank Holidays. Groups are welcome at other times by prior arrangement. Opening times are Sunday 1030 to 1730 and Thursdays 1400 to 1730. Contact : Mosquito Aircraft Museum, PO Box 107, Salisbury Hall, London Colney, near St Albans, Herts, AL2 1BU. Telephone 0727 22051 during Museum opening hours as outlined above.

G-ABLM	Cierva C.24	ex Hatfield. On loan from the Science Museum.
G-ADOT	Hornet Moth	ex Hatfield, Southampton, X9326, 5 GCF, 23 OTU, 24GCF, Halton SF, 2 CPF, G-ADOT. See notes above.

-ANFP	Tiger Moth	ex Denham, Rush Green, N9503, 2 RFS, 7 RFS, 2 RFS, 4 RFS, 4 EFTS. Fuselage frame.
-ANRX	Tiger Moth	ex Belchamp Walter, N6550, SLAW, 25 EFTS, 18 EFTS, 241, 14 EFTS, 56 ERFTS. Under restoration.
-AOJT	Comet 1XB	ex Farnborough, Air France F-BGNX. Fuselage only.
-ARYC	HS.125 Srs 1	ex Hatfield, Filton, Rolls-Royce.
-AVFH	Trident 2	ex Heathrow, BA, BEA. Forward fuselage.
APC146+	Toucan MPA	ex Hitchin, Old Warden, Radlett. Centre body plus props. Arr 11/85.
APC186+	Queen Bee	ex Hadfield, Redhill. Arrived 13/4/86. See notes above.
-IFSB	Dove 6	ex Hatfield, BFS, D-CFSB, Panshanger, G-AMXR, N4280V.
1325	RAF BE.2e	ex Norway, Norwegian AF '37' and '133'. Under restoration.
4050	Mosquito I	ex Hatfield, Chester, Radlett, E-0234. Prototype.
A122	Mosquito FB.6	ex Soesterberg, 4, 2 GCS, 48, 4, 605, 417 ARF. Fuselage, being rebuilt with the wing of TR.33 TW233 ex Israel.
A634	Mosquito TT.35	ex Liverpool, G-AWJV, Aldergrove, 3 CAACU, APS Schleswigland, APS Ahlorn, APS Sylt, 4 CAACU. Under restoration.
J118	Mosquito TT.35	ex Elstree, Exeter, 3/4 CAACU. Nose section. See also under Oxford.
L615	Horsa II	ex Brize Norton. Under restoration.
P790	Chipmunk T.10	ex Rush Green, G-BBNC, WP790, BIR UAS, WAL UAS, PFTS, AOTS, 1 ITS, RAFC, MAN UAS, G&S UAS, STN UAS, 24 GCF, 5 RFS, 17 RFS.
X853	Venom NF.3	7443M, ex Debden, Shawbury, 23. See notes above.
E985	Vampire T.11	ex Woodford, Chester, St Athan, 5 FTS. Composite, with wings of WZ476. See notes above.
G730	Sea Venom FAW.22	ex Southwick, ADS, 893, 894, 891. '499/A'.
J565	Sea Vixen FAW.2	ex RAE Bedford, 899, 893, 766B.
-1008	Vampire FB.6	ex Hatfield, Swiss AF.

ANSHANGER

here seems every chance that this airfield will become a housing estate before too long so another harismatic airfield bites the dust. To clear up W&R10, Sioux XT248 became G-BKNF and then went to ustralia. The store of Autair choppers is thought to be very much as it always was, but for one major iece of editorial 'knifing'. With this edition two fixed wing types make an entry into the tome. The ajor change is that the former Danish AF S-55s (S-881, '882, '884-887) are thought to have been crapped a long time ago, but the dreaded booms live on - which, at least in terms of this tome, means he S-55s have gone over the hill for an earth sandwich, ceased to be, etc. The remains of Scout 5X-UW were acquired by Jim Wilkie and moved to Heysham.

-ASOL	Bell 47D-1	ex N146B. CoA expired 6/9/71. Stored.
-BARJ	Bell 212	ex BEAS, VR-BGI, G-BARJ, EI-AWM, G-BARJ, EI-AWN, G-BARJ. Crashed 24/12/83.
-BJYO+	Tomahawk 115	Crashed 31/5/84. Cockpit section with Flying Club. First noted 5/87.
-BMLA+	UH-1H Iroquois	ex Headcorn, FIGAS VP-FBD, Stanley Racecourse, Argentine Army AE-424, 77-22930. Damaged 14/1/87. Arrived 2/87 for repair. Cancelled 3/9/87.
N-OQS+	Bell 212	ex Cranfield, G-GLEN, Arrived early 1987. Stored.
5052P+	Comanche 180	ex G-ATFS, N5052P. Stored.
T148	Sioux AH.1	ex Wroughton. Stored.
T803	Sioux AH.1	ex High Melton, Wroughton. Stored.
-708	B.206 JetRanger	ex Ugandan AF. Wreck. Stored.

ATMORE

North west of Bishop's Stortford) It is assumed that the Cricket is still stored here.

-AYDJ	Cricket	CoA expired 13/4/72. Stored.

OTTERS BAR

erry Twyman keeps his Auster restoration in High Street. It is thought that the Wassmer D.120 is till under restoration in the area.

-AGYH	J/1N Alpha	CoA expired 10/10/72. Under restoration.
-BNZM	Wassmer D.120A	c/n 319. Under rebuild.

ABLEY HEATH

Off the A1M south of Stevenage) Near a plant nursery an Auster AOP.9 is kept in open store.

P241	Auster AOP.9	ex St Athan, 653, Aden.

ROYSTON

Mike Barnett and Ross Skingley have an Auster-orientated workshop here. CASA 2-111 G-AWHB was stored here after its removal from Southend. It was acquired at auction by Kermit Weeks, but remained in store here. It moved to North Weald 2/88.

G-ASBY Airedale CoA expired 22/3/80. Under rebuild.
G-BKXP Auster AOP.6 ex Oakington, Belgian AF A-14, VT987. Under restoration.
A-20 Auster AOP.6 ex Oakington, Belgian AF, VT994. Spares use.

ST ALBANS

College of Further Education The three Vampires continue to serve the College.

WZ584 Vampire T.11 ex Hatfield, CATCS, 1 FTS, 2 CAACU, 32.
XE956 Vampire T.11 ex Hatfield, CATCS, 1 FTS, 8 FTS, 3 CAACU, APS, 67.
XH313 Vampire T.11 ex Hatfield, CATCS, Wattisham SF, 111.

Others C J Musk's store of aircraft is thought reduced to just one. Tiger Moth G-ALTW is reported to have moved on to Essex. That leaves :-

G-APJZ J/1N Alpha ex Dorset, 5N-ACY, VR-NDR ntu, G-APJZ. Crashed 10/11/75. Stored.

WARE

936 Squadron ATC in Broadmeads, off Amwell Road, still have their Vampire. A Vampire T.11 pod moved into the area for storage in late 1987 from Cranfield. It is nothing to do with the ATC unit however.

XD459+ Vampire T.11 ex Cranfield, Bushey, Keevil, 3/4 CAACU, 229 OCU, 233 OCU, 151, 253, 56. Pod only. See notes above.
XE849 Vampire T.11 7928M, ex St Athan, CNCS, 5 FTS, 7 FTS, 1 FTS, 4 FTS. 'V-3'.

WATFORD

Restoration of Tri-Traveler G-APYT was completed during 1987 and it flew again.

WATTON-AT-STONE

With Skysport over at Hatch, there are a few entries to clear up from here. SNCAN SV-4C G-AYZI was flying again by 1987. Nieuport 28 N5246 left for 'Suffolk' in 1985. Fieseler Fi 156C-3 G-FIST is unaccounted for, not having been seen over at Hatch.

Humberside

BEVERLEY

Army Transport Museum The Beverley at Beverley is now intact and represents a phenomenal relocation and restoration project. It will be used as the venue for many exhibits on airborne forces. The Beaver is on loan from the Museum of Army Flying.

XB259 Beverley C.1 ex Paull, Luton, Court Line, RAE, Blackburns, G-AOAI.
XP772 Beaver AL.1 ex Middle Wallop, 6 Flt.

Locally A gyroplane operator has acquired the long lost Bensen G-ASME for spares for his operational G-ATOZ and up and coming G-AWPY.

G-ASME+ Bensen B.8M ex Shetland, Manchester, Liverpool. CoA expired 18/4/67. Spares.

BILTON

(On the B1238 north east of Hull) Neville Medforth continues his restoration of the Tiger here.

G-ANEJ Tiger Moth ex Paull, Leicester, DE638. Crashed 15/5/65. Under restoration.

BREIGHTON

There has been a marked reduction in the number of candidates at this interesting airfield. The hulk of Cessna F.172H G-AVDC was largely used in the rebuild of G-AVKG and this reflew during 1986. The hulk of G-AVKG stayed here for some time, causing great confusion, but it left for Sherburn eventually. AA-5B Tiger hulk G-BFPC moved to Mullaghmore for spares use. That leaves :-

G-ATKY Cessna 150F ex Sherburn. Crashed 15/12/79. Under rebuild.
G-BBWZ+ AA-1B Trainer wfu 5/8/81. Stored. First noted 9/86.
N2254X Nord 3202 G-BMBF, ex Sibson area, French AF No 65. under restoration.

BROUGH

PC-9s for the Saudis dominate the work here, although much Phantom work goes on via the flying base at Scampton. Buccaneer support work appears to be trailing off and to mark this the cockpit section of S.2B XK527 left in an unmarked lorry by road during 12/87 - where to? With this departure there is not enough left of this particular *Brick* to continue to list it under this heading. Other airframes are much the same :-

XN982	Buccaneer S.2C	ex Holme-on-Spalding Moor, RAE Farnborough. For testing to destruction.
XT858	Phantom FG.1	ex Holme-on-Spalding Moor, Leuchars, Aldergrove, Hucknall, A&AEE, RAE Bedford, Hucknall, 700P, RAE Bedford. Fatigue testing.
XV155	Buccaneer S.2B	8716M, ex St Athan, 12, 237 OCU, 12. Apprentice training.
E-427	Hunter F.51	ex Holme-on-Spalding Moor, Brough, Dunsfold, G-9-447, Danish AF, Esk.724. Customer training airframe.

CLEETHORPES

Bomber County Aviation Museum have had to vacate the site here at Cleethorpes. Thanks to a kind offer, the whole museum will be moving to re-establish itself at the former bomber airfield at Hemswell. As moving will take some time and is not scheduled to be completed for some time into the currency of this edition, all airframes will be listed under this heading for now. Whirlwind HAR.10 XP339 was exported to West Germany during 6/87. Please note that neither location is available for public inspection until further notice. Contact ; Bomber County Aviation Museum, Wayne Drurey, Curator, c/o 75 Sixhill Street, Grimsby, South Humberside, DN32 9HS.

G-EASQ"	Bristol Babe rep	BAPC.87, ex Selby. Incomplete.
G-AEJZ	HM.14 Pou du Ciel	BAPC.120, ex Brough.
G-AFFI"	HM.14 Pou du Ciel	BAPC.76, ex Nostell Priory, Rawdon.
BAPC161	Stewart Ornithopter *Coppelia*.	
WH796	Canberra PR.7	ex Macclesfield, St Athan, Wyton SF, 58, MoA, 13, 58, 100, 542, 82, 542. Nose section only.
WH946	Canberra B.6(M)	8185M, ex Macclesfield, Ewyas Harold, Coningsby SF, 76, 21, 542, 617. Fuselage only.
WJ975	Canberra T.19	ex Cambridge, 100, 7, 100, 85, West Raynham TFF, 228 OCU, 44, 35, 231 OCU.
XD445	Vampire T.11	ex Huddersfield, Woodford, Chester, St Athan, 4 FTS, 5 FTS, Buckeburg SF.
XG195	Hunter FGA.9	G-9-453, ex Macclesfield, Bitteswell, 208, 1, 19. Composite, nose of GA.11 WT741 and other parts from XG297/G-9-452.
XG506	Sycamore HR.14	7852M, ex Misson, Halton, HDU, MCS, 72, 118, 225, 118, 275.
	Wessex HAS.1	ex Holme-on-Spalding Moor, Farnborough. Forward fuselage.
101	Mystere IVA	ex Sculthorpe, French AF '8-MN'.

HOLME-ON-SPALDING MOOR

To clear up the entry in W&R10, Terrier G-ASCH was not flying again by 1985. Instead it moved to the Yorkshire Air Museum's care at Elvington.

STORWOOD

(South east of York and put under 'North Yorkshire' in W&R10!) Melbourne Autos, a scrap dealer here, has the former Cleethorpes Dragonfly. A report to hand has a Whirlwind coming here as well, most likely to be XP345 from Tattershall Thorpe - which see.

WP503	Dragonfly HR.3	ex Cleethorpes, Elsham Hall, Stansted, RAE Bedford, North Coates, Lee-on-Solent, Lossiemouth SF.

Isle of Man

ISLE OF MAN AIRPORT

(Or Ronaldsway) Ken Gomm's Percival Q.6 is making good progress and may well fly before the end of 1988. Lake Skimmer EI-ANR returned to Eire and is thought to be airworthy again. The other W&R candidates mentioned in W&R10 are thought to be unchanged. Leopard Moth G-ACLL has been in store here since late 1984.

G-ACLL+ Leopard Moth ex AW165, AFEE, 7 AACU, 6 AACU, Ringway SF, G-ACLL. CoA exp 7/9/84.
G-AFFD Percival Q.6 ex Sutton Coldfield, Duxford, Redhill, G-AIEY ntu, X9407, MCS, 510, Old Sarum SF, Halton SF, Heston SF, Northolt SF, 6 AACU, G-AFFD. CoA exp 31/8/56. Under rebuild.
G-BAEO Cessna F.172M ex Manchester, Barton. Crashed 7/5/78. Fuselage.

Isle of Wight

GENERAL

Two aircraft are known to be stored on the island and are best categorised under this vague banner!
G-AZJE JB.01 Minicab ex Sandown. CoA expired 7/7/82. Stored.
G-BCMF Levi Go-Plane One and only flight 16/11/74. Stored.

BEMBRIDGE

At the Pilatus Britten Norman plant the following BN-2 Islander airframes are known to be in long term store ;- c/ns 917, 920, 2033/G-BJOG, 2036, 2041, 2042, 2043.

SANDOWN

Biggest event here is the establishment of the second Charles Church workshop under the command of Dave French. The main base of operations is at Winchester, which see. The former Sheriff hangar is used as their premises. Steve Vizzard's Airframe Assembly organisation is also here and working on the former Holywood Spitfire for Nick Grace. Over at ARV Aviation, a test fuselage of the Super Two has appeared outside. Through the intervention of Ross Sharp, the unflown SA.1 Sheriff was saved and moved through to East Midlands 1/7/86. The parts of the second aircraft, G-BPOP, are too small for W&R to consider. Former Strathallan Battle 1 1899/R3950 arrived here 12/1/87 but moved out to Bournemouth for the Christie's auction 11/5/87, subsequently moving on to Duxford on loan. P-51D G-SUSY/NL12066 flew in here on 21/6/87, but moved on to its permanent base at Winchester 28/11/87. Current situation here is as follows ;-
G-AYTD Aztec 250C ex Southend, 5Y-ACA, N5727Y. CoA expired 24/2/83. Hulk with firemen.
G-HUNN+ HA-1112M-I-L ex Whitehall, Duxford, G-BJZZ, N48157, *Battle of Britain*, Spanish AF C4K-235. Arrived 8/85. Charles Church. First flew 15/8/87.
ARV-2 Super Two test airframe. See notes above.
TE184+ Spitfire XVI ex Holywood, Aldergrove, Finningley, Royton, Newcastle-upon-tyne, CGS, 607, 203 AFS. Arrived by 2/88.
5481+ Hurricane ex Winchester, Canada, RCAF. Arrived 2/12/86. Bare frame. CC.

Kent

ASHFORD

With nothing definite on Brian Knock's Jackaroo rebuild here, we list it with a degree of caution.
G-ANFY Jackaroo ex NL906. wfu 5/68. Under restoration.

BENENDEN

Autocar G-ARNB moved to Bredhurst during 1986.

BREDHURST

(South of Junction 4 of the M2, south of Gillingham) At the home of RE Aviation it is a case of all change regarding the W&R inmates here. Aztecs F-BFKL and F-BSUP (the latter ex Bournemouth Airport) were both reduced to produce by 1986. Auster J/5G Autocar G-ARNB arrived from Benenden during 1986, but left by road during 7/87 - destination unknown. The stored Zlin lives on and has been joined by a small fleet of 'tin'.

G-AWFF+	Cessna F.150H	ex Leavesden. Damaged 2/85. Fuselage only, first noted 7/87.
G-BAXV+	Cessna F.150L	ex Eversden, Sandtoft. Crashed 25/7/82. Wreck, first noted 7/87.
G-BEYT+	Cherokee 140	ex West Germany, D-EBWO, N6280W. First noted 1980!
G-BEZA	Zlin Z.226T	ex D-EMUD, OK-MUA. Stored.
G-BLAL+	Cessna F.150L	ex Banstead. Crashed 12/4/82. Wreck, sectioned, first noted 7/87.

BRENZETT

(On the A2070 north west of New Romney) Brenzett Aeronautical Museum The already impressive collection of material here has gained three airframes since W&R10. In addition to the predicted DC-3 nose section and the Godalming Canberra, BAM have also saved the pathetic Avro XIX G-AGPG which had been supposedly 'preserved' already! It moved on to the site during 1986, but the team here will face an incredible amout of work on it. The museum is open Sundays and Bank Holidays from Easter to October 1100 to 1700 and additionally Tuesdays, Wednesdays and Thursdays July to August from 1400 to 1700. Contact : Brenzett Aeronautical Museum, Ivychurch Road, Brenzett, Romney Marsh, Kent TN29 0EE.

G-AGPG+	Avro XIX Srs 2	ex Southend, Pye, Ekco, Avro. wfu 5/11/75. Arrived during 1986.
G-AMSM+	Dakota 4	ex Booker, Brenzett, Duxford, Brenzett, Lydd, Skyways, Eagle, Starways, KN274, TCDU, 77, St Eval SF, Azores SF, 43-49948. Damaged 17/8/78. Nose.
WH657+	Canberra B.2	ex Godalming, RAE, 231 OCU. Arrived by 5/87.

CANTERBURY

Rod and Rex Cadman moved the nose of a B-26K here duirng 1987 from Southend.

N99218+	B-26K Invader	ex Southend, Chino, USAF 64-17657. Nose section only.

CHALLOCK LEES

(On the A251 north of Ashford) The much-travelled (if not in the air!) Baldo 75 came back to open storage here in 1987.

G-BCRH+	Baldo 75	ex Little Snoring, Hardwick, Challock Lees, I-DONP, Italian AF MM53647.

CHATHAM

Royal Engineers Museum The Sioux is still not on public display here, although the construction of a large covered courtyard, to illustrate the post-War period should see it on show from 1989/90. There is much to see here however, with extensive galleries and exhibits. The museum is open Tuesday to Friday and Bank Holidays 1000 to 1700 and Sundays 1130 to 1700. Contact : Caroline M Reed, Curator, Royal Engineers Museum, Brompton Barracks, Chatham, Kent ME4 4UG. Telephone 0634 44555 ext 2312.

XT133	Sioux AH.1	7923M, ex Arborfield, Middle Wallop. Stored.

1404 Squadron ATC have a detached flight here, their headquarters being at Manston. Located in Boundary Road, they continue to keep a Chipmunk fuselage here.

WZ846	Chipmunk T.10	8439M, ex G-BCSC, Bicester, Manston, WAL UAS, AOTS, 202, 228, CFE, West Raynham SF, G&S UAS, BRI UAS, 1 AEF, St Athan hack, NOTT UAS, 63 GCF, EDN UAS, STN UAS.

Others The light aircraft store here remains unaltered.

G-AXDB	J-3C-65 Cub	ex Whitwell, Bembridge, F-BFQY, HB-OXV, F-BFNN ntu, F-OATN, 43-29258. Damaged 13/12/72.
G-AYVP	Woody Pusher	Unfinished homebuild project.
G-BCNC	GY-201 Minicab	ex F-BICF. Under rebuild.

CHATTENDON

(On the A228 north of Rochester) The impressive gate at the Defence Ordnance Disposal School at Lodge Hill Camp is still guarded by a Canberra and two *squibs*.

BAPC158	Fieseler Fi 103	gate guardian.
BAPC159	Yokosuka Ohka II	ex Cranwell. Gate guardian.
WT301	Canberra B.6(mod)	ex 51, 192. 'W'. Gate guardian.

CHISLET

(North of the A28 south of Herne Bay) Tiger Moth G-AOET took to the air for the first time following restoration on 25/10/87. A new Tiger has moved in here for restoration on behalf of Guy Black - but see under Shobdon.

G-ANOR+ Tiger Moth ex Shobdon, Billingshurst, DE694. see notes above.

HAWKINGE

(On the A260 north of Folkestone) Kent Battle of Britain Museum run by the Hawkinge Aeronautical Trust, the KBBM is based upon the Operations, Armoury, Flight Simulator buildings of the former Battle of Britain airfield and the newly-opened Dowding Memorial Hangar. Adding to the impressive use of former *Battle of Britain* film replicas and a whole host of memorabilia during 1987 was the former Old Warden V-1 and, care of a 67 ARRS HH-53C, a former Binbrook Lightning. The museum is open Sundays and all Bank Holidays Easter to the end of October 1100 to 1700 and from May to the end of September Monday to Saturday 1100 to 1700. Contact : Kent Battle of Britain Museum, c/o Little Milton, Pay Street, Hawkinge, Kent.

BAPC.36+	Fi 103 (V-1) rep	ex Old Warden, Duxford, Old Warden. Arrived during 1987.
BAPC.64	Hurricane replica	ex Chilham Castle, *Battle of Britain*.
BAPC.65	Spitfire replica	ex Chilham Castle, *Battle of Britain*. 'QV-K'.
XP701+	Lightning F.3	8924M, ex Binbrook, LFT, 5, 11, 56, 29, 111, 29, A&AEE. 'Flew' in 18/12/87. See notes above.
1480	'Bf 109' replica	BAPC.66, ex Chilham Castle, *Battle of Britain*.

HEADCORN

(Or Lashenden) Lashenden Air Warfare Museum Located on the airfield, Trevor Matthews and crew continue to work on their charges and to increase what has always been a compelling collection of artifacts from primarilly the east Kent area. LAWM is open Sundays and Bank Holidays 1030 to 1800 from Easter until the end of October. Parties are welcome at other times by prior arrangement. Contact : LAWM, Headcorn Airfield, Ashford, Kent TN27 9HX. Telephone 0622 890226.

BAPC.91	Fi 103R-IV	ex Rochester, Horsham, Farnborough, Rechlin. Genuine piloted version.
WZ589	Vampire T.11	ex Woodford, Chester, St Athan, 56. '19'.
XN380	Whirlwind HAS.7	ex Wroughton, 705, 771, 829, 824, 825.
84	Mystere IVA	ex Sculthorpe, French AF. On loan from Robertsbridge AS.
63938	F-100F-16-NA	ex Sculthorpe, French AF. '11-MU'.

Airfield Quite a few changes to record with the inmates here. The terrible snows of 1/87 caused a hangar collapse and several aircraft were damaged. Among these was Bell UH-1H Iroquois G-BMLA/AE-424 which had arrived from the Falklands by 9/86, it moved on to Panshanger for repair by 2/87. The Pawnee frame that inhabited the blister hangar had gone missing by this time. Of the local Auster population G-AJIO moved out to France 24/9/86 to complete its restoration there. Also arriving during 9/86 was Pucara G-BLRP, it is hoped to restore this to flying condition as a long term project.

G-AHAV	J/1 Autocrat	ex HB-EOM ntu. CoA expired 21/6/75. Stored.
G-AJRE	J/1 Autocrat	ex Bigin Hill area. CoA expired 15/10/70. Under restoration.
G-ANHZ	Auster 5	ex TW384, 1960 Flt, A&AEE. CoA expired 29/5/73. Under restoration.
G-BLRP+	FMA Pucara	ex Stanley, Argentine AF A-517. Arrived 9/86, see notes above.

LYMPNE

The British Air Reserve, the East Kent Memorial Flight and other such names fizzled out here by 1986 and the Sea Fury FB.11 WJ288/G-SALY moved through to Duxford by 5/86. Of the Fiat G.46 nothing is known and an up-date would be appreciated. The Avro XIX G-AGPG, claimed to be owned by this organisation(s) was left to rot into a scandalous condition at Southend and has since been taken under Brenzett's wing.

BAPC.79 Fiat G.46-IV ex Southend, Shoreham, Italian AF. See notes above.

MAIDSTONE

Chris Webb and Graham Smith continue with their Auster rebuild in the area, as does Colin Wood with his Falke restoration.

G-ARRL	J/1N Alpha	ex VP-KFK, VP-KPF, VP-KFK, VP-UAK. CoA expired 7/6/68. Rebuild.
G-AYYL	T.61A Falke	ex Sittingbourne, Manston. Damaged 11/82. Under rebuild.

MANSTON

Memorial Building and Gate Guardians Under the aegis of the Medway Branch of the Royal Aeronautical Society/Medway Aircraft Preservation Society (see under Rochester) the display building has been extended and by the time these words are read, Hurricane LF751 will have been housed in it following total restoration at Rochester. The Canberra and Javelin continue to flank the building.

LF751+	Hurricane II	5466M, ex Rochester, Bentley Priory, Waterbeach, 27 OTU, 1681 BDTF. Composite aircraft, using parts from Z3687 and PG593. See notes above.
TB752	Spitfire XVI	7256M/7279M/8086M, ex Rochester, Manston, Lyneham, 5 CAACU, 103 FRS, 102 FRS, 403, 66. 'KH-Z'.
WE168	Canberra PR.3	8049M, ex 231 OCU, 39, 69, 540.
XH764	Javelin FAW.9	7972M, ex 'XA639', 29, 64.

Central Training Establishment of the Air Force Department Fire Service The fire school here remains active and continues to consume airframes, although several of the inmates are now quite long term. Devon C.2/2, listed in W&R11O as being a whole airframe here was not as such, its wings going to VP953 and rear end going on to VP963. Two airframes have moved into the care of 1404 Squadron ATC and appear under 'Others', thse are Hunter FGA.9 XJ695 and Jet Provost T.3 XN602. Shackleton AEW.2 WL741 had perished by late 1987; Vampire T.11 XD527 was reduced to just a pod by 3/86 and to ashes by 11/87; Victor K.1A XH650 passed on by 8/86; Jet Provost T.4 XP583 had gone the same way by late 1985.

G-BDRC	Viscount 724	ex Exeter, Alidair, Air Inter F-BMCG, TCA CF-TGO. Upside down by 10/87.
VP953	Devon C.2/2	ex Kemble, 26, SCS, MCS, 12 Sector. Wings of VP960. Poor state by 7/87.
VP963	Devon C.2/2	ex Kemble, 207, 21, 26, TCCS, NCS, 13 Sector, FCCF, 13 Sector, MCS, AAAFCE, FCCS, HCCS, 31, FCCS, BCCS, Paris Attache, 240 OCU, Handling Squadron. Rear end of VP960.
VP965	Devon C.2/2	8823M, ex Northolt, 207, WCS, MCS, Upavon CF, MCS, 31.
XG327	Lightning F.1	8188M, ex St Athan, RAE Bedford, Warton, A&AEE.
XH590	Victor K.1A	ex 55, 57, 55, 15. Poor state.
XH616	Victor K.1A	ex 57, TTF, 232 OCU, 90, 15, 57. Poor state.
XJ430	Whirlwind HAR.10	ex Wroughton, 1310 Flt, 228, 275, 22, Westlands, 22.
XK968	Whirlwind HAR.10	8445M, ex Wroughton, 28, 103, 110, 22, JEHU.
XK969+	Whirlwind HAR.10	8646M, ex Odiham, Abingdon, Wroughton, SAR Wing, 202, 230, 202, 228, CFS, 225, JEHU. Arrived by 3/86 and in poor state by 8/86.
XL386	Vulcan B.2A	8760M, ex 101, Wadd Wing, 230 OCU, 27, 230 OCU, 27, 230 OCU, Scamp Wing, 9.
XL511+	Victor K.2	ex Marham, 57, 55, Victor Tr Flt, Witt Wing, 139. Flew in 2/7/86.
XM657	Vulcan B.2A	8734M, ex 44, Wadd Wing, Cott Wing. On its nose 10/87.
XN855	Argosy E.1	8556M, ex 115, 242 OCU, AOCU, 114.
XP333+	Whirlwind HAR.10	8650M, ex Odiham, 2 AFTS, CFS. Arrived by 2/86, minus boom.
XP357	Whirlwind HAR.10	8499M, ex Wroughton, 22, 230, 110, 225. Damaged 13/6/76.
XP394	Whirlwind HAR.10	ex Wroughton, CFS.
XP400	Whirlwind HAR.10	8444M, ex Halton, Wroughton, 103, 110, 230. Poor state by 8/86.
XP741+	Lightning F.3	8939M, ex 5, LTF, 11, 5, 111, Wattisham TFF, 111, Wattisham TFF, 111. Flew in 29/9/87. 'AR'.

Others The Devon fuselage is reported to still be in the Leadership Training Building. 1404 Squadron ATC have taken on two former CTE airframes and now look after them on the parade ground. 1404 also have a detached flight at Chatham.

VP956	Devon C.2/2	ex Kemble, 207, 21, WCS, MCS, AAFCE, MCS, FCCS, Wyton SF, Booker SF, MECS, Iraq CF. See notes above.
XJ695	Hunter FGA.9	8677M/8738M, ex CTE, Kemble, 1 TWU, TWU, 229 OCU, 58, 45, 20, 14, 20. Fitted with tail of XF519. See notes above.
XN602	Jet Provost T.3	8088M, ex CTE, Brize Norton, Halton, Brampton, Shawbury, 6 FTS. See above.

Civil Side Attempts to preserve the Britannia went in the right direction when Roger Hargreaves was successful in finding at a temporary home at Brooklands, it moved there 5/4/88. C-119G N2700 finally got up and flew away on 12/2/87 off to North Weald.

ROCHESTER

Disaster struck Edward Hulton's fabulous Sunderland when gales wrecked the flying boat on 16/10/87 - the 50th anniversary of the first flight of the prototype Sunderland. Its future is now uncertain, it seems extremely doubtful if it will ever fly again. Several possibilites are being persued at present and it is hoped that W&R12 will have happier news.

G-BJHS	Sunderland V	ex Calshot Spit, Antilles Air Boats, N158J, Ansett VH-BRF, RNZAF NZ4108, ML814. CoA expired 29/12/84. See notes above.

ROCHESTER AIRPORT

Medway Branch of the Royal Aeronautical Society / Medway Aircraft Preservation Society The craftsme here completed Hurricane II LF751 and in 3/88 it moved to Manston ready for installation in the newl expanded memorial building. Taking its place in the workshop has come Spitfire PR.XI PL965 fro Overloon, this will be the group's first restoration to flying condition. Following this is T-6 MM54099 which will be restored for the Old Flying Machine Company - see under Duxford. The F-84F ha been restored in the colours of the USAF Thunderbirds team and the group's Meteor F.8 restoration no guards the airfield's entrance. The workshop facilities are open to the public on Sunday mornings an Monday evenings, but Airport rules must be observed. Contact : R T Twine, c/o GEC Avionics, Airpor Works, Rochester, Kent. Telephone 0634 44400.

LF738	Hurricane II	5405M, ex Biggin Hill, Wellesbourne Mountford, 22 OTU, 1682 BDTF. Under restoration.
PL965+	Spitfire PR.XI	ex Overloon, Bruggen, Overloon, Deelen, Twenthe, 16, 1 PP. Arr 4/87, see notes above.
WK714"	Meteor F.8	WK914, ex Manston, 85, CAW, 5 CAACU, 19. 500 Sqn colours 'K'.
6771"	F-84F-51-RE	FU-6, ex Southend, Belgian AF FU-6, USAF 52-7133. Thunderbirds colours.

Airfield In W&R10 the compiler asked for details of the report that Tiger Moth G-ANFC was flying fro here when the frame was at London Colney. He asked for an explanation, and has had several. *Forge* the reference to G-ANFC here! *Snapdragon*, the Beech 18 is still in open store.

N96240	Beech D.18S (3TM)	ex Spain, Wellesbourne Mountford, Blackbushe, G-AYAH, N6123, RCAF 1559.

SEVENOAKS

Biggin Hill Air Museum and Friends of Biggin Hill The Museum/Friends have launched an appeal t preserve the only E-type blast pens left in Kent, but plans are still long term relating to a th establishing of a museum at *The Hill*. Aircraft are in dispersed storage and visiting is by prio arrangement only, contact : Peter Smith, Curator, 34, Derry Downs, St Mary Cray, Kent BR5 4DU Whirlwind HAS.7 XM665 is still on loan to the Booker Aircraft Museum at Booker - which see.

G-AAXK	Klemm L-25.1A	Damaged 3/62. Fuselage, on loan from Russell Vick.
G-BAYV+	Noralpha	ex Booker, Hawkinge, Maidstone, Ford, F-BLTN, French AF. Crashed 23/2/74. Arrived during 1987. Painted as a 'Bf 109'.
K5054+"	Spitfire replica	BAPC.190, built by Peter Smith. Static replica.
WP250	Vampire NF.10	ex Booker, Sandhurst, A&AEE. Fuselage pod only.
XD535	Vampire T.11	ex Preston, Croston, Woodford, Chester, St Athan, 4 FTS, 5 FTS, 1 ANS, 93.
+	Typhoon IA	cockpit section under restoration.
	Chipmunk T.10	ex Henley-on-Thames. Cockpit, on loan from 1924 Sqn ATC.

Locally During 1987 an Airedale moved into the area to act as spares for G-ATCC.

G-AWGA+	Airedale	ex Biggin Hill, Bicester, EI-ATA, G-AWGA, D-ENRU. See notes above.

SHORNCLIFFE

(Near Lydd) At the Sir John Moore Barracks, a Wessex, possibly an HC.2, was in use as an embarkatio training aid. It was offered for tender 4/87.

SMEETH

(On the A20 between Ashford and Sellinge) The Aztec 250 is still to be found in the garden.

G-ASER	Aztec 250B	ex Biggin Hill. Crashed 14/9/72. Hulk.

TUNBRIDGE WELLS

David and Mollie Wood's Tiger Moth collection is though unchanged since W&R10.

G-ADGT	Tiger Moth	ex Bromley, Ludham, BB697. CoA expired 8/5/67.
G-ANOD	Tiger Moth	ex New Milton, T6121, 19 RFS, 10 RFS, ULAS, 24 EFTS, Northolt SF, 60 OTU.
G-APJO	Tiger Moth	ex Bournemouth, NM126. Largely G-APJR, ex T7391, 1 GU, 2 GS, 14 RFS, 6 RFS, 6 EFTS. Crashed 28/5/61.
G-ISIS	Tiger Moth	ex G-AODR, Biggin Hill, NL779. Crashed 18/9/61.

WEST MALLING

Another lovely airfield threatened by the property developers. Stored here since 1987 has bee a Auster that was mangled in the hangar collapse at Rochester 14/1/87.

G-AGYK+	J/1 Autocrat	ex Rochester. Damaged 14/1/87. Stored.

Lancashire

BACUP

Pennine Aviation Museum Work continues on PAM's Moorlands Park site and on the aircraft held, with the Ablemarle project gaining momentum. This will be a forward fuselage restoration - the largest segment of this aircraft type anywhere in the world (unless the Soviets will cough up!) - and parts, help, contact with former Albemarle workers are eagerly sought. The size of this project is such that it can be entered in the line-by-line listings below. PAM have stores off-site and their latest acquisition is held in one of these. An exchange was arranged with Moston College, PAM ferrying Cherokee G-ATOO to Moston in return for the College's fire-damaged Piper Caribbean. The latter was in worse state than originally thought and was reduced to components and traded around the country. The fuselage frame still exists in store. Until opened up fully to the public, access to PAM is still by prior permission only, contact : David Stansfield, School House, Sharneyford, Bacup, Lancashire OL13 9UQ. Telephone 0706 875967.

G-ARHT+	Caribbean 150	ex Moston, Bournemouth Airport, N3712Z. CoA expired 14/9/85. Fuselage frame - see notes above.
BAPC157	CG-4A Hadrian	ex Ormskirk. Complete fuselage frame.
VV901	Anson T.21	ex Burtonwood, Cosford, Irton Holme, Leconfield, CFCCU, DUR UAS, 1 RFS.
WF911	Canberra B.2	ex Preston, Samlesbury G-27-161, 231 OCU. Nose section only.
WN149	Balliol T.2	ex Salford, Failsworth, RAFC. Nose section only.
WN534	Balliol T.2	ex Salford, Failsworth, 22 MU, RAFC. Nose section only.
XG297	Hunter FGA.9	ex Macclesfield, Bitteswell, HSA, 20, 28, 20, 4. Nose section only.
XK627	Vampire T.11	ex Hazel Grove, Woodford, Chester, St Athan, 8 FTS, CFS.
	Albemarle	ex Carlisle, Westnewton. Major restoration, composite - see above.

BARROW-IN-FURNESS AIRPORT

(Or Walney Island) A consortium of Air Furness employees acquired Dragon Rapide G-AEML from Babbacombe during 1986 and are hard at work on its restoration. During late 1987 it was acquired by Victor Gauntlett, but will be restored to flying condition on his behalf here.

G-AEML+	Dragon Rapide	ex Babbacombe, Land's End, Coventry, Liverpool, X9450, Armstrong Whitworth, AFEE, 6 AACU, G-AEML. CoA expired 2/4/71. See notes above.

BLACKBURN

The ATC unit here is 1262 Squadron, located in Preston Old Road, Witton Park, and they still have their Chipmunk T.10 PAX Trainer. We still do not have an identity for it, however.

BLACKPOOL AIRPORT

(Or Squires Gate) Major expansion in terms of W&R airframes here has come from Jim Wilkie of the Helicopter Museum of Great Britain who has established an out-station and flying base here. As Jim's aircraft will swop about with the main museum site at Heysham, all HMoGB inmates will be listed under 'Heysham' and not here. There has been some expansion in other W&R airframes, although in general Squires Gate is a much 'tidier' airfield than it used to be - ah! progress. As can be seen from the listing below, both the long-term Gemini and Messenger are still to be found on the airfield, kept in the lock-ups. The hulk of Sundowner G-AXSX has not been seen since 10/85 and may well be no longer with us, or queueing up for fame in the *LOST!* column. The BAC Petrel G-BACA moved here from Warton for storage by early 1986 and was scrapped here during mid 1987.

G-AJWB	Mesenger 2A	ex Woodvale. CoA expired 13/11/69. Under rebuild.
G-AKEK	Gemini 3A	ex Doncaster, Willingale. wfu 11/74. Under rebuild.
G-ASXR+	Cessna 210	ex 5Y-KPW, VP-KPW, N6532X. CoA exp 7/6/86. Arr 1986 for rebuild.
G-ATRS	Cherokee 140	CoA expired 18/10/70. Stored dismantled.
G-AVPH+	Cessna F.150G	ex Woodvale. Wreck, arrived by 7/87.
G-AXSX	Sundowner	Crashed 18/8/83. Hulk -see notes above.
F-BHMU	Cessna 180	G-BHVZ, ex N4793B. Under restoration.
F-BMGR+	CEA DR.1051/M1	G-BHTC, ex Popham, Lydd. Arrived 4/87 for restoration.
XL391	Vulcan B.2A	ex 44, 101, 44, 9/35, BCDU, MoA. Manchester Vulcan Bomber Society.
XN511	Jet Provost T.3	ex Kemble, CFS, 1 FTS, CFS. Nose section only, with 177 Sqn ATC.

COCKERHAM

(Or Banks End, on the A588 between Lancaster and Fleetwood) Black Knight Parachute Centre still have their para-trainer here.

G-ARZE Cessna 172C ex Blackpool Airport. Crashed 12/9/76. Para-trainer.

HEYSHAM

Helicopter Museum of Great Britain Jim Wilkie's pioneering museum collection has made great strides with Whirlwind HAS.7 XK940/G-AYXT now airworthy and surely the last piston engined Westland-built Whirlwind still flying. Jim has a large out-station at Blackpool Airport where restorations to flying condition are maintained and other airframes stored as conditions dictate. Contrary to W&R10, Skeeter AOP.10 XK482/G-BJWC was not sold off and is still with the collection. See also under Lancaster for an interesting plot. As explained under the Blackpool Airport entry, the changing nature of what-is-where means that all are best held under this heading. Please note that the Blackpool facility is available for inspection on a strict prior permission only basis. The museum at Heysham is also under a state of flux, as Jim has acquired a parcel of land in Morecambe for a larger development. Accordingly for the time being would-be visitors should make prior arrangements to see the collection. Contact : Jim Wilkie, 'Wavecrest', 4 Rydal Road, Morecambe, LA3 1DT. Telephone 0524 413253.

G-AWRP+	Grasshopper III	ex Shoreham, Redhill. CoA exp 12/5/72. Arrived 4/9/87. Complete airframe.
G-AXFM+	Grasshopper III	ex Shoreham, Redhill. Arrived 4/9/87. Ground running rig.
G-AZAU+	Grasshopper III	ex Shoreham, Redhill. Arrived 4/9/87. Power and lift grouping only.
5X-UUW+	Scout	ex Panshanger, Uganda Police Wing. Wreckage, for spares.
XK482	Skeeter AOP.10	G-BJWC, ex Horsham, Ottershaw, 7840M, Middle Wallop, HTF, Handling Squadron, MoS. See notes above.
XK940	Whirlwind HAS.7	G-AYXT, ex Carnforth, Panshanger, Elstree, Luton, Fleetlands, 771, Culdrose SF, 705, 825, 824, 845. Airworthy.
XN386+	Whirlwind HAR.9	A2713, ex Wroughton, Yeovilton, Fleetlands, *Endurance* Flt, 846, 814. Arrived by 3/87.
XX469+	Lynx 1-07	G-BNCL/A2657, ex Lancaster, Sherborne, Westlands. Arr by 10/86.
130191	Whirlwind HAR.21	G-BJWY/WV198, ex Carnforth, Gosport, A2576 Lee-on-Solent, Arbroath, 781, 848, USN 130191. USMC colours.

LANCASTER

Jim Wilkie effected an exchange with the Headquarters, Lancashire Fire Brigade for their Lynx naval prototype XX469. Jim acquired this example, it moving to Heysham by 10/86. In its place came static rig RG-05 from Coventry on 25/6/86. It is thought that the Brigade still hold this airframe, although a precise location has yet to be determined for it.

RG-05+ Lynx static rig ex Coventry Airport, Yeovil. Arrived 25/6/86.

MUCH HOOLE

The thick plottens here with the Sabre 4 'G-ATBF'. A visit to Dandy's Farm in 1987 brought the intriguing quote from the owner, "it moved two years ago to Scampton". Now Scampton is, of course, the venue (at least for the present) of Lancaster NX611 which was also one of Lord Lilford's properties. Does this mean that the man at Much Hoole was a little confused about four Merlins *versus* Orendas and swept wings, or has it moved to a Lincolnshire-sited Lilford estate?

PRESTON

Spitfire PR.XIX PS915 was completed by the BAe Apprentices at Strand Road and moved through to Samlesbury where it made its first flight on 16/12/86 moving on to BBMF at Coningsby by 3/87. At the W R Tuson Technical College all of Vampire T.11 XD535 made the journey through to Sevenoaks by mid-1986.

RAMSGREAVE

(Between the A59 and the A6119 north of Blackburn) The Dragonfly is still to be found in the grounds of a house here.

WG751 Dragonfly HR.3 ex Ancoats, Wisbech.

SAMLESBURY

Summer 1988 witnesses the closure of Samlesbury and BAe are busy disposing of the Canberras to interested preservation parties for a token sum. Samlesbury will remain a BAe plant and the newly-placed gate guardian Canberra will be staying. At this stage, only the Solway people have managed to remove their example, T.4 WE188 going to Carlisle Airport 4/88. Other known allocations are given below. During Spring 1987 the former Kuwaiti Strikemasters came down by road from Prestwick for storage and possible resale - with Malawi being the front-runner at present. As they may well not be 'long termers' they will receive only a 'watching' mention here, see under Prestwick for details.

WE192	Canberra T.4	ex St Athan, 231 OCU, 360, 231 OCU, 39, 231 OCU, 3, 231 OCU.
WH665	Canberra T.17	8763M, ex Cosford, 360, RNZAF, 45, 10.
WH846	Canberra T.4	ex St Athan, Laarbruch SF, 231 OCU.
WH850	Canberra T.4	ex St Athan, Laarbruch SF, Wildenrath SF, 14, 88, Marham SF. For South Yorkshire APS, Firbeck.
WH914	Canberra B.2	G-27-373, ex frustrated Argentine AF B.62, 231 OCU, 35, 76, 50, 61, 100. Dismantled.
WJ639	Canberra TT.18	ex 7, 57. For North East Aircraft Museum, Sunderland.
WJ721	Canberra TT.18	ex 7, 50, 40.
WK122	Canberra TT.18	ex 7, 15, 61.
WT483	Canberra T.4	ex 231 OCU, 39, 231 OCU, 16, Laarbruch SF, 68, Laarbruch SF, 69.
WT488	Canberra T.4	ex CSF, 360, 98, 360, 231 OCU, 360, 98, 231 OCU, 360, 231 OCU, Wyton SF, 360, 98, 245, 527, CSE.
WT537	Canberra PR.7	ex 13, 31, 17. Gate guardian.
XH583	Canberra T.4	G-27-374, ex frustrated Argentine AF T.64, St Athan, 231 OCU.
497	Canberra T.4	G-27-116, ex frustrated Indian AF B.52, Bracebridge Heath, Samlesbury, Kemble, WH847, 231 OCU, 45, 231 OCU.

WARTON

A considerably expanded listing here by way of a lot of new intake and the former Saudi Lightnings coming 'of age'. These have remained in open store and their chances of resale must now be very small indeed - yet they are rotated through the hangars for 'check-ups' regularly! Rumblings continue regarding the possibility of a Lightning drone programme and these airframes must be the only likely candidates as the operational Binbrook examples will have very few cycles left when they are finally retired from front line usage. Lightning F.2A G-27-239 was acquired by Aces High and registered as G-BNCA 12/86 but was subsequently sold to Peter Hoar/Militair and moved by road to Cranfield 28/10/87 for use as spares for the ex-Newton two-seater. The Oliver MPA BAPC.145 has not been seen for a considerable period of time and is thought to have been dismantled or scrapped. The BAC Petrel G-BACA was stored here until moving to Blackpool Airport during 1986. The Strikemaster Mk 80s held unflown in store here are reported to have been sold to Botswana, but have yet to make a move. Current situation here is as follows :-

G-16-32	Strikemaster Mk 80	ex Bournemouth, Warton. Stored.)
G-16-33	Strikemaster Mk 80	ex Bournemouth, Warton. Stored.) see notes
G-16-34	Strikemaster Mk 80	ex Bournemouth, Warton. Stored.) above
G-16-35	Strikemaster Mk 80	ex Bournemouth, Warton. Stored.)
XN973	Buccaneer S.1	ex EASAMS, nose on dump by 4/87.
XX736	Jaguar GR.1	G-27-327, ex Indian AF JI013, XX736. Stored.
XX740	Jaguar GR.1	G-27-331, ex Indian AF JI017, XX740. Stored.
ZA403+	Tornado GR.1	with Saudi Support Unit by 5/85.
ZF577+	Lightning F.53	ex RSAF 53-668, G-27-38. Flew in 1/86. Open store.
ZF578+	Lightning F.53	ex RSAF 53-670, G-27-40. Flew in 1/86. Open store.
ZF579+	Lightning F.53	ex RSAF 53-671, G-27-40. Flew in 1/86. Open store.
ZF580+	Lightning F.53	ex RSAF 53-672, G-27-42. Flew in 1/86. Open store.
ZF581+	Lightning F.53	ex RSAF 53-675, G-27-45. Flew in 1/86. Open store.
ZF582+	Lightning F.53	ex RSAF 53-676, G-27-46. Flew in 1/86. Open store.
ZF583+	Lightning F.53	ex RSAF 53-681, G-27-51. Flew in 1/86. Open store.
ZF584+	Lightning F.53	ex RSAF 53-682, G-27-52. Flew in 1/86. Open store.
ZF585+	Lightning F.53	ex RSAF 53-683, G-27-53. Flew in 1/86. Open store.
ZF586+	Lightning F.53	ex RSAF 53-688, G-27-58. Flew in 1/86. Open store.
ZF587+	Lightning F.53	ex RSAF 53-691, G-27-61. Flew in 1/86. Open store.
ZF588+	Lightning F.53	ex RSAF 53-693, G-27-63. Flew in 1/86. Open store.

ZF589+	Lightning F.53	ex RSAF 53-700, G-27-223. Flew in 1/86. Open store.
ZF590+	Lightning F.53	ex RSAF 53-679, G-27-49. Flew in 1/86. Open store.
ZF591+	Lightning F.53	ex RSAF 53-685, G-27-55. Flew in 1/86. Open store.
ZF592+	Lightning F.53	ex RSAF 53-686, G-AWON, G-27-56. Flew in 1/86. Open store.
ZF593+	Lightning F.53	ex RSAF 53-692, G-27-62. Flew in 1/86. Open store.
ZF594+	Lightning F.53	ex RSAF 53-696, G-27-66. Flew in 1/86. Open store.
ZF595+	Lightning T.55	ex RSAF 55-714, G-27-73. Flew in 1/86. Open store.
ZF596+	Lightning T.55	ex RSAF 55-715, G-27-71. Flew in 1/86. Open store.
ZF597+	Lightning T.55	ex RSAF 55-711, G-27-70. Flew in 1/86. Open store.
ZF598+	Lightning T.55	ex RSAF 55-713, G-27-72. Flew in 1/86. Open store.
+	Canberra	nose section on dump, first noted 4/87. Possibly WJ857.
+	Tornado ADV	in fatigue rig, prod no AV.023, built in between ZE154 and ZE155.
+	Strikemaster	composite airframe with Saudi Support Unit, first noted 4/87. Nose spare from BAC.167 production line, centre section mock-up, rear end from JP T.3 XN634, one wing from a JP T.5 one from a JP T.3!

Leicestershire

BITTESWELL

(Sorry, Asda *Magnapark*) No sooner having got the slimmed down Warbirds of Great Britain collectio installed in this location than the airfield was sold to MFI/Asda to turn it into a mega-hyper-storag and distribution centre. (Some of the buildings going up look like they could house a Brabazon o two.) WoGB started to move down to Biggin Hill - in a still more slimmed down form. (Bournemouth i also quoted as being a store for WoGB, and it may be that some of the crated items have gravitate there.) The whereabouts of several airframes in this collection have yet to be confirmed. It i believed that about a third of a hangar full of "sizeable" crates still remained here by 4/88 Accordingly some aircraft cannot have forwarding 'addresses' yet. Known relocations have been a follows :- Boeing A75N-1 G-AWLO was flown out 5/86 and now lives at Shoreham; B-17G G-FORT flew ou 9/5/87 to Luton and then Southend, ending up at Duxford before being ferried to the USA; Spitfire IX G MKIX/NH238 flew out 28/11/87 to Biggin Hill; P-51D G-PSID flew out 3/3/87 to Duxford; Spitfire XIV G WWII left by road for Duxford 9/86; Lincoln 2 G-29-1 moved by road to North Weald 10/9/86; Lancaster KB889/G-LANC moved out to Duxford 14/5/86; Spitfire XIV MV262 to Winchester 7/8/86; Spitfire XIV NH79 left by road for Duxford 9/86; Spitfire XIV RM694 did not apparently come to the UK from the USA an should be deleted; Spitfire XVI TE356 came in from the Leeming gate by 4/86, became G-SXVI and the moved to East Midlands Airport; P-47D 13064 (correcting W&R10) left for Cardington during 1986 finally three Gnats in fair condition were noted leaving during 12/87 by road; these are thought t have come from Halton - which see - and may have been on their way to the USA.

The following are unaccounted for ; Spitfire XVIII G-BRAF/SM969 which is known to have been crate during its stay at Bitteswell; Spitfire XVI RW386/G-BXVI; Spitfire XVI TE392; Bf 109K T2-124; Bf 109G 10 ex Yugoslavia; P-47D 13021. Additionally, the Spitfire from South Africa auctioned by Christie's i London (see the Appendix) 31/10/86 is also believed to have been acquired by the collection, but ha not been seen since.

BRUNTINGTHORPE

Phoenix Aviation Museum rationalised their aircraft holdings down to the Vampire T.11 WZ553 which wer into the care of an ATC unit at South Wigston. Avro XIX G-AGWE was acquired by a private individua and moved to Lutterworth. Buccaneer S.1 XN964 was privately owned and was acquired by the Newark Ai Museum, it moved to Winthorpe 3/88. The two former French Air Force aircraft (technically on loan fro the USAF Museum, Wright Patterson) remain as 'gate guardians' with the airfield's owners, C Walton Lt Hunter F.51 E-407 was 'homeless' in W&R10, it 'surfaced' at Lutterworth.

85	Mystere IVA	ex East Midlands Airport, Sculthorpe, French Air Force.
42239	F-100D-15-NA	ex East Midlands Airport, Sculthorpe, French Air Force.

COTTESMORE

There have been two further additions to the W&R airframes here. On the dump the Sea Vixen and Vulcan nose are used for burning and cutting, but so far the Lightning is untouched, save for the loss of its underbelly tank. A Hunter T.7 arrived for BDR work during 11/86 and is kept near the visiting aircraft ramp. The Canberra continues to guard the gate.

WH791	Canberra PR.7	8165M/8176M/8187M, ex St Athan, 81, 58, 82, 542. Gate guardian.
XJ582	Sea Vixen FAW.2	8139M, ex Halton, Sydenham, 766. Fire dump, poor state.
XL618+	Hunter T.7	8892M, ex Shawbury, Kemble, 1 TWU, 229 OCU, Jever SF, Gutersloh SF. Arr 19/11/86 for BDR.
XM656	Vulcan B.2A	8757M, ex 9, 35, Wadd Wing, 35. Nose only, fire dump.
XR716+	Lightning F.3	8940M, ex Binbrook, 5, LTF, 5, 11, 5, LTF, 56, 29, 226 OCU, 111, Wattisham TFF, 111. Flew in 6/10/87. For the fire dump.

EARL SHILTON

(On the A47 north east of Hinckley) The Auster is still stored here.

G-AMUI	J/5F Aiglet Tr	ex Leicester Airport, Shoreham, Crowland. CoA exp 15/2/66.

EAST MIDLANDS AIRPORT

East Midlands Aeropark Visitors Centre Sadly, a change in airport policy has brought about a drastic change in the operations of the Aeropark and items such as the regular flying days and a heavy concentration on local aeronautical history and education appear to have gone by the board. The centre is still open daily from 1000. Closing times vary with the time of year. Contact : East Midlands Airport Aeropark, Castle Donington, Derby DE7 2SA. Telephone 0332 810621. Three airframes have joined the collection :-

G-BEOZ+	Argosy 101	ex ABC/Elan, N895U, N6502R, G-1-7. CoA exp 28/5/86. Arr 6/87.
G-FRJB+	SA.1 Sheriff	ex Sandown. Arrived 1/7/86.
VR-BEP+	Whirlwind Srs 3	ex Cuckfield, G-BAMH, Bristows, Redhill, XG588. Arr 5/86.
WL626	Varsity T.1	G-BHDD, ex Coventry, 6 FTS, 1 ANS, 2 ANS, 201 AFS.
XM575	Vulcan B.2A	G-BLMC ntu, ex 44, Wadd Wing, Scampton Wing, 617.

Airfield Site The airport itself is a hive of interesting airline activity and thanks to the presence of Trent Aero and Rolls-Royce (who base G-ALGT/RM689) also enjoys the sound of the Merlin. Trent Aero received Spitfire XVI TE356/G-SXVI from Bitteswell during 1986 for restoration on behalf of Warbirds of Great Britain. It made its first flight, in the hands of Mike Searle, on 16/12/87, but so far has shown no willingness to go to Biggin Hill. The nose section of Britannia 312 G-AOVN left during late 1986 for a local, and private, fire school - any further details? Merchantman G-APEJ was restored and flew again following storage 22/1/87. DC-8 EC-DEM became C-FDWW and flew away 8/12/86. Finally, during 5/86 the Catalina C-FHNH flew out to Exeter for long term storage. ABC/Elan had Argosy 101 G-BEOZ parked out following withdrawal during 1986 until donating it to the Aeropark during 6/87. Jetstream 1 N14234 fuselage (ex Pacific Coast Airlines) arrived via Liverpool Docks 11/86 and was prepared by Fields for use as a travelling Jetstream 31 demonstrator, it moved to Hatfield 5/87.

G-APEG	Merchantman	ex Airfast, ABC, BEA. CoA expired 18/5/83. Open store.
G-AZLR	Viscount 813	ex BMA, ZS-SBU ntu, SAA ZS-CDU. wfu 10/82. BMA cabin trainer.
G-BFMW	Viscount 735	ex Alidair, YI-ACK. CoA expired 15/6/82. Fire service.
G-BKTJ+	Cessna 404 Titan	ex Farnborough, Birmingham, LN-VIN, SE-GYL, N88721. Crashed 27/11/85. Wreck, stored.
G-SXVI+	Spitfire XVI	TE356/7001M, ex Bitteswell, Leeming, Cranwell, Little Rissington, North Weald, *Battle of Britain*, Bicester, 2 CAACU, 34, 695. Arr 1986. First flew 16/12/87.
MJ730+	Spitfire IX	G-BLAS, ex St Leonards-on-Sea, Duxford, Kabri, Israel AF/DF, 0606, 2066, Italian AF MM4094, RAF 249. Arr 1987, under rebuild for Fred Smith, USA.

HUSBANDS BOSWORTH

To clear up the reference to Firefly AS.6 WD833 in W&R10, it left by sea for the USA 4/86. Minicab G-BBFL was flying again by 7/86, being based at nearby Sywell. By 6/87 a Mosquito gyroplane was stored.

G-AWIF+	Mosquito	ex Shipdham, Tatershall Thorpe, Clitheroe. Cancelled 30/5/84.

LEICESTER

Leicester Museum of Technology The two Austers at the Abbey Pumping Station, Corporation Road, remain away from the public view, under slow restoration. The airframes and the massive amount of archive material held on Austers can be seen, but strictly on a prior notice basis. At Leicester Airport the Museum maintains the engine installation prototype Auster J/1 G-AGOH in airworthy condition and Plus C G-AFTN under restoration. Contact ; Peter Stoddart, Leicestershire Museums, 96 New Walk, Leicester LE1 6TD. Telephone 0533 765532. The Museum itself is open Monday to Saturday 1000 to 1730 and Sundays 1400 to 1730.

G-AJRH	J/1N Alpha	ex Harrogate, Wigan. CoA expired 5/6/69.
XP280	Auster AOP.9	ex St Athan, 2 Wing, Queen's Dragoon Guards, 2 RTR, 651.

Others Auster G-AMPW moved to Leicester Airport during late 1986.

LEICESTER AIRPORT

(Or Leicester East) As described above, Leicestershire Museums keep two more of their 'Austers' here. Also here is Ron Neal's RN Aviation, which attracts Austers from far and wide for rebuild, or line maintenance. Of the aircraft held at the airfield, there have been few changes from W&R10, although it should be noted that a couple of aircraft are listed here, but are located just off-site. Auster J/5F G-ARLY was sold in Switzerland and left 11/87 to complete its restoration there. Auster J/5B G-AMPW arrived from Leicester 12/86 for conversion into a ground trainer for Bangladesh and it left these shores 4/87.

G-AEXZ	J/2 Cub	CoA expired 2/11/78. Under restoration, off-site.
G-AFTN	T'craft Plus C2	ex Heavitree, HL535, G-AFTN. Under restoration.
G-AGOH	J/1 Autocrat	Leicestershire Museums. Airworthy.
G-AGVG+	J/1 Autocrat	ex Paull. Wrecked 2/1/76. Stored, off-site.
G-ANWX	J/5L Aiglet Tr	Damaged 1981. Under rebuild.
G-APMH	J/1U Workmaster	ex F-OBOA, G-APMH. Crashed 22/12/70. Under restoration.
G-ARNN	GC-1 Swift	ex VP-YMJ, VP-RDA, ZS-BMX, NC3279K. Crashed 1/9/73. Rebuild, off-site.
G-ATFU	Leopard Moth	ex HB-OTA, CH-366. Damaged 7/84. Under rebuild, off-site.
NJ695+	Auster IV	G-AJXV, ex Nottingham, F-BEEJ, G-AJXV, NJ695. CoA exp 13/5/82. Arr 12/86.
XK417	Auster AOP.9	G-AVXY, ex Tattershall Thorpe, Wisbech, Henstridge, St Athan, 652, 9 Flt, 18 Flt, Middle Wallop. Under restoration.

LOUGHBOROUGH

The University's Department of Transport Technology gave up its Hunter F.4 XE677 and anonymous Payne Knight Twister fuselage frame to the Lincolnshire Aviation Society and they moved, initially to Tattershall, in 6/87. This leaves only the Jet Provost, which is on loan from Shuttleworth.

G-AOBU	Jet Provost 1	ex Luton, XM129, G-42-1.

LUTTERWORTH

A private owner here stores two former Bruntingthorpe aircraft, the Hunter having previously been thought exported. Following up from W&R10, the static Tiger Moth replica 'K2572' moved to Hereford

G-AGWE+	Avro XIX Srs 2	ex Bruntingthorpe, East Midlands, Strathallan, Thruxton, Kemps Aerial Surveys, TX201. CoA expired 5/3/73. Arr during 1986. Poor state.
E-407+	Hunter F.51	ex Bruntingthorpe, East Midlands, Dunsfold G-9-435, Aalborg, Danish AF Esk.724. Arrived during 1985.

MARKET HARBOROUGH

Kibworth Aviation Group W&R10 was a bit premature in moving KAG's Vampire pod here in 1985, the exact arrival date is as shown below.

WZ608	Vampire T.11	ex Lutterworth, Bitteswell, Woodford, St Athan, 3 CAACU, 5 FTS, 266, Fassberg SF, 11 Vampire Flt, 5, Wunsdorf SF, 266. Arrived 21/8/86.

NORTH LUFFENHAM

Has seen a recent expansion in the number of airframes held on the base, with two more Sea Vixens, a Hunter and a Whirlwind arriving. The Meteor gate guardian can be seen at the Edith Weston end of the base at the main gate, but the 'Vixens and the Hunter can now been seen from the A6121 Ketton to Morcott road.

WS776 Meteor NF.14 7716M, ex Lyneham, 228 OCU, 85, 25. Gate guardian. 'K'.
XG194+ Hunter FGA.9 8839M, ex Cosford, 1 TWU, TWU, 229 OCU, 1, 92, 111, 43. Arr by 3/88.
XJ608 Sea Vixen FAW.2 8802M, ex Bournemouth, FRL, Hatfield, RAE Llanbedr, 899. BDR.
XN699+ Sea Vixen FAW.2 8224M, ex Halton, Sydenham, 890. NBC training. Arrived early 1987.
XP344+ Whirlwind HAR.10 8764M, ex Cranwell, Finningley, Chivenor, 22, SAR Wing, CFS. Arr by 4/88.
XP921+ Sea Vixen FAW.2 8226M, ex Hereford, Halton, 890. Arrived by 4/88.

SOUTH WIGSTON

Phoenix Aviation Museum / 1461 Squadron ATC In a unique co-operative move where cadets work on the restoration of the aircraft, guided by museum volunteers, PAM's Vampire T.11 WZ553 moved from Bruntingthorpe to here during 1985. Visitors can see the aircraft on a prior arrangement basis, contact : Ian Rose, Phoenix Aviation Museum, 14 Ashford Road, Hinckley, Leicestershire LE10 0JL.

WZ553 Vampire T.11 ex Bruntingthorpe, Loughborough, East Midlands, Liverpool, Woodford, Chester, St Athan, 4 FTS, 7 FTS, 202 AFS.

STANFORD

(Off the B5414 north east of Rugby) Percy Pilcher Museum Within Stanford Hall is a small museum display dedicated to Sir Percy Pilcher. Centrepiece is a Hawk glider replica.

BAPC.45 Pilcher Hawk rep ex Coventry.

Lincolnshire

BINBROOK

Lightning Engineering Servicing Flight/Store That lovely lass from Lancashire, living in Lincolnshire, t'Lightning, is finally coming to the end of its operational career. Recent scenes at Binbrook of mass carnage as the scrapman earned his living were last seen in the mid-1970s at Wattisham when F.3s and some F.1As were butchered. While MoD has yet to make its mind up exactly when the Lightning will bow out with 11 Squadron and if there will be a residual unit operating in a target facilities role for Tornado F.3 development work it is clear that few of the lovely beasties will see their way to preservation groups, unless they can beat the scrapman in the tendering game and have access to an airfield. Lightnings do not travel (groundwise) at all well. The cost of moving by road and reassembling a Lightning will be beyond most groups. Even if it could be achieved, the inevitable cutting of the wings outboard of the undercarriage bay will give a permanent droop to those rakish lines. MoD is currently looking into the feasibility of a Lightning Display Flight, but the policy of ekeing out the airframe and cycle hours on each aircraft may well mean that such a venture is short lived. Binbrook itself will continue as a relief landing ground and may well keep her gate guardians.

The scrapping of Lightnings has so far taken place during September 1987 and January 1988 and has wiped out the listing as given in W&R10. Those scrapped by September are known to have been handled by Swefling Engineering, an East Anglian based concern. Of the aircraft listed in W&R10, scrapping took place during 9/87 as follows ; F.1As XM181 and XM183; F.3 XP695; T.5s XS418, XS423, XS449, XS450, XS454. During 2/88 the long-serving (suffering?) T.4 on the dump, XM969/8592M, was scrapped. Two F.3s flew out on the same day, 30/9/87 for tenuous new lives ; XP741 to Manston and XR716 to Cottesmore. The following aircraft entered long term store with LESF after W&R10 and were scrapped, mostly after a brief life out on the decoy line ; F.3 XP749/8926M (ex LTF 'DA') 1/88; XP750/8927M (ex LTF) 1/88; XP751/8928M (ex LTF 'DA') 1/88; XP764/8929M (ex LTF 'DC') 1/88 and XR720/8930M 1/88; and F.6 XR752 (ex 11 'BL') 9/87. Two others in this category left by other means, F.3 XP701/8924M with the help of a Woodbridge HH-53C flew out 15/12/87 on a long, multi-stage flight to Hawkinge via Sculthorpe, Woodbridge and Manston; F.3 XP706/8925M left by road on 20/12/87 for Strubby. The current W&R Lightning situation is given below, although readers should bear in mind that it will change rapidly.

XP694+ Lightning F.3 ex Binbrook pool, LTF, Binbrook pool, LTF, 5, 56, 29, 11, 29, Wattisham TFF, 29, A&AEE, BAC. Joined decoy line by 12/87.
XP702 Lightning F.3 ex 5, 56, 29, 56, 74. Ex store, decoy line by 1/88.
XS420 Lightning T.5 ex LTF, 226 OCU. Decoy line by 1/88, for tender 3/88.
XS457 Lightning T.5 ex 5, LTF, 11, 226 OCU. Decoy line by 10/87, for tender 3/88.

XS895+ Lightning F.6 ex 11, 5, 11, LTF, Binbrook pool, 23, 111, 23, 5, 74. Withdrawn by late 1986. Stored.
XS927+ Lightning F.6 ex 11, Binbrook pool, 23, 11, 74. Withdrawn by late 1986, stored.

Gate Guardians/Preserved Airframes Regarding preserved airframes here, the prototype P.1A WG760 moved to Cosford 1/86 to join the Lightning development line-up there. With much praise to the base, the Starfighter Preservation Group have been allowed to lodge their F-104G here, until such time as a suitable home can be found for it.

PK664 Spitfire F.22 7759M, ex Waterbeach, 615, 'V6-B'. Gate guardian.
XP748 Lightning F.3 8446M, ex 11, 111, 56. Gate guardian. 5 and 11 Squadron marks.
22+57 + F-104G Starfighter ex Manching, JBG34, 'DD+239', 'KE+438'. Arrived 23/7/87 - see above.

BOSTON

Dick Yates continues to produce fine rebuilds from his workshop in this area. One airframe that has so far slipped the W&R net here is that of former Italian Army Super Cub MM542619 'EI-276' which was in long term store, until registered as G-BNXM in November 1987 and flown by 12/87. Two airframes listed in W&R10 were flying by 1986, CEA DR.1051 G-BGRI and Wassmer D.120A G-BJYK. Omitted from W&R10 was Stinson HW.75 G-AFYO, this flew after restoration during 1987. K&S Cavalier G-BBUW came here from Crowland by 9/86, but did not stay long, moving to East Kirkby by 11/87. Current situation here is as follows :-

G-AWUB Gardan GY-201 ex F-PERX. CoA exp 23/10/80. Fuselage, stored.
G-BDBV Aero Jodel D.11A ex D-EGIB. Crashed 2/1/77. Stored.
G-BFDM Wassmer D.120 ex F-BHYB. CoA expired 26/7/84.
G-BGEW SNCAN NC.854S ex F-BFSJ. Under rebuild.
G-BIOI+ SAN DR.1051M ex Chigwell, F-BLJQ. Arrived during 1986.
F-BBGH Brochet MB.100 ex F-WBGH. Stored.
F-PFUG Adam RA-14 spares use.

BOSTON AIRFIELD

(Or Wyberton) The two Pawnee frames remain stored here, but the other two inmates recorded in W&R10 have moved on ; Auster G-AJEI moved to Bristol via a brief sojourn at Fiskerton and Cessna 150F G-ATKE was scrapped during 1986.

G-ASFZ Pawnee 235 ex N6672Z. CoA expired 8/2/80. Frame only, stored. Original frame, rest of the original G-ASFZ rebuilt using spare frame 25-6309 and re-registered as G-BSFZ.
G-BGPO Pawnee 235D ex N9181T ntu. Crashed 4/6/83. Frame only, stored.

CABOURNE

(On the A46 south west of Grimsby) The Auster continues its storage, in a barn loft.

G-AIPV J/1 Autocrat CoA expired 1/6/68. Stored.

CASTLE BYTHAM

(East of the A1, north of Stamford) The former French Cub is still held here for spares use.

F-BBBN J-3C-65 Cub ex Boston, 43-1092. See above.

CONINGSBY

Battle of Britain Memorial Flight The visitor centre here continues to make great strides, thanks to the Flight, the Lincolnshire County Council and volunteers from Lincolnshire's Lancaster Association. Now open Monday to Friday (except Bank Holidays) 1000 to 1700 - the last guided tour taking place at 15.30. Booking is not required, but is advisable. Please note that the aircraft of the Flight may not all be present as they may well be positioning back from or to a display. Contact ; BBMF Visits, RAF Coningsby, Lincoln LN4 4SY. Tel ; 0526 44041. For further details of the work of Lincolnshire's Lancaster Committee contact ; D C Richardson, 113 Gordon Fields, Market Rasen, Lincs LN8 3AE.

There have been several changes with the fleet, biggest of which was the arrival, by air, of the newly-refurbished Spitfire PR.XIX PS915 from BAe at Preston during March 1987. The restoration of PR.XIX PS853 has taken longer than anticipated and it is felt this will occur during 1988 now. The Lancaster received a major overhaul and repaint by West Country Aircraft Services at Exeter and now boasts 103 Squadron markings. Hurricane IIC PZ865 was overhauled during the winter of 1987/1988 by CIT at Cranfield and now sports 303 Squadron colours.

P7350 Spitfire IIA ex *Battle of Britain*, G-AWIJ, Colerne, John Dale Ltd, Colerne, 57 OTU, CGS, 64, 616, 603, 266. 41 Squadron colours as 'EB-Z' *Observer Corps*.
AB910 Spitfire VB ex *Battle of Britain*, Allen Wheeler G-AISU, 29 MU, RWE, 527, 53 OTU, 402, 242, 133, 130, 222. 457 Sqn colours as 'BP-O' *In Memory of R J Mitchell*.
LF363 Hurricane IIC ex Biggin Hill SF, 41, 41 GCF, Waterbeach SF, Odiham SF, Thorney Island SF, FCCS, Middle Wallop SF, 61 OTU, 41 OTU, 62 OTU, 26, 63, 309, 63. 85 Sqn colours as 'VY-X'.
PA474 Lancaster I ex 44, Wroughton, Cranfield College, RAE, Flight Refuelling, 82. 103 Sqn colours as 'PM-M²', ex 101 Sqn colours as 'SR-D' - see notes above.
PM631 Spitfire PR.XIX ex THUM Flt, Buckeburg SF, 206 OCU, 203 AFS. 91 Sqn colours as 'DL-E'.
PS853 Spitfire PR.XIX ex West Raynham, CFE, North Weald SF, Biggin Hill SF, THUM Flt, 16, 268, 16. PRU Colours. Under conversion to Griffon 58 and 24 volt system.
PS915+ Spitfire PR.XIX 7548M/7711M, ex Samlesbury, Preston, Brawdy, St Athan, Coningsby, Brawdy, Leuchars, West Malling, Biggin Hill, THUM Flt, 2, PRDU, 541. Flew in 3/87. PRU colours.
PZ865 Hurricane IIC ex Hawker Siddeley G-AMAU. 303 Sqn colours as 'RF-U', ex 'JU-Q'.
VP981 Devon C.2/2 ex Northolt, 207, 21, WCS, Wildenrath CF, AAFCE, MinTech, AAFCE, Paris Air Attache, Hendon SF, AFWE. Flight 'mother ship'.
WK518 Chipmunk T.10 ex Man UAS, Lon UAS, Liv UAS, Lee UAS, Hul UAS, Cam UAS, 1 AEF, Coltishall SF, FWS, 63 GCF, RAFC. Flight 'hack'.

Others Elsewhere on this now totally Tornado base, the W&R airframes have hardly changed, save for the arrival of the former Tattershall Vampire T.11, which was on loan to the Lincolnshire Aviation Museum.
WJ815 Canberra PR.7 8729M, ex 13, 58, 82, 540. Fuselage on dump.
WZ549+ Vampire T.11 8118M, ex Tattershall, Coningsby, CATCS, 1 FTS, 8 FTS, FTU, C(A). Arrived by 1/86, kept inside.
XM987 Lightning T.4 ex 226 OCU, LCS. BDRT airframe.
XN774 Lightning F.2A 8551M, ex 92, 19. Surface decoy.
XW528 Buccaneer S.2B 8861M, ex St Athan, 15. BDR airframe.

CRANWELL

RAF College Engineering Wing Split into the Airframe Technology Flight and the Servicing Instruction Flight, the Wing has acquired another Hunter, a Jet Provost PAX trainer and its first, long-promised, Jaguar. Three airframes have moved on ; Gnat F.1 XK724 left by road early in 1986 for Cosford; Lightning F.1 XG329 was ferried by Chinook to Swinderby 23/9/86 and Whirlwind HAR.10 XP344/8764M had moved to North Luffenham by 4/88. The fire dump was cleared during 5/87, with the tired, mortal remains of Canberra B(I).8 WT339/8198M being shovelled away.
XF375 Hunter F.6 8736M, ex ETPS, Warton, Armstrong Whitworth, C(A).
XF516 Hunter F.6A 8685M, ex 1 TWU, 229 OCU, 92, 56.
XG209+ Hunter F.6 8709M, ex Halton, Kemble, 12, DFLS, 111, 14. Arrived 4/1/88.
XJ634 Hunter F.6A 8684M, ex 1 TWU, TWU, 229 OCU, 92.
XJ639 Hunter F.6A 8687M, ex 1 TWU, TWU, 229 OCU, 4.
XK149 Hunter F.6A 8714M, ex 1 TWU, TWU, 229 OCU, 54, 1, AFDS.
XL577 Hunter T.7 8676M, ex 2 TWU, 237 OCU, 1 TWU, TWU, 229 OCU.
XN643+ Jet Provost T.3 8704M, ex Abingdon, RAFEF, 1 FTS, 3 FTS. Crashed 30/7/81. Nose section only, arrived by 9/87.
XX821+ Jaguar GR.1 8896M, ex Coltishall. Arrived 30/7/86.

Campus Grounds A Hunter joined the on display aircraft within the campus during 1986. All of these are painted in bogus markings :-
WH699" Canberra B.2 WJ637/8755M, ex Wyton, 231 OCU, 35. Outside Trenchard Hall.
XD429" Vampire T.11 XD542/7604M, ex Colerne, Melksham, FWS, CGS. On plinth.
XF979+" Hunter F.51 E-408/8565M, ex Brawdy, Dunsfold, G-9-436, Danish AF, Aalborg store, ESK-724. Arrived by 6/86. Displayed outside Trenchard Hall.

CROWLAND

The SA.102 Cavalier G-BBUW moved to Boston by 9/86.

DIGBY

The RAF base is still guarded by its long-term inmate, the Meteor.
WH166 Meteor T.7 8052M, ex CFS, 5 CAACU, CAW, 4 FTS, 205 AFS, 210 AFS, 208 AFS.

EAST KIRKBY

Lincolnshire Aviation Heritage Centre Phase One of the LAHC, operated in conjunction with the Lincolnshire Aviation Museum/Society was opened on 19/7/87 on a limited basis while much work continues to prepare the site. As W&R was closing for press, the Lancaster from the gate at RAF Scampton was in the process of being dismantled and moved by the RAFEF here, where a hangar will go up in readiness for it. As 1988 will represent a year of some considerable change at the site, viewing details can be obtained from ; LAM, Lancaster Farm, Tumby Woodside, Mareham-le-Fen, Boston, Lincs PE22 7SP.

Two aircraft were transferred here by W&R10 following the move from Tattershall, but they did not, in fact, make it ; Emeraude G-BLHL returned to Wigan and Vampire T.11 WZ549 to Coningsby. Dove G-AHRI and Vampire T.11 XD447 both left by road 2/88 for Long Marston. The following aircraft are on site, although many are dismantled. The Lancaster will be listed under Scampton for this edition, there have been three other additions :-

G-ADFV	Blackburn B-2	2893M, ex Tattershall, Wigan, Caterham, 4 EFTS Hanworth. Forward fuselage.
G-AJOZ	Argus II	ex Tattershall, Wigan, Market Drayton, Wigan, Southend, Sywell, FK338, Kemble, ATA 2 FP, 42-32142. Crashed 16/8/62. Under restoration.
G-AXEI	Ward Gnome	ex Tattershall. Local homebuild.
G-BBUW+	SA.102 Cavalier	ex Boston, Crowland. Fuselage only, arrived by 11/87.
G-BEEX	Comet 4C	ex Tattershall, Woodford, Lasham, Dan-Air, SU-ALM. Nose section.
BGA.794	T.8 Tutor	ex Tattershall. Stored off site.
BAPC 43	HM.14 Pou du Ciel	ex Tattershall, Wellingore.
BAPC 61	Stewart Ornithopter	ex Tattershall, Wigan. *Bellbird II.*
BAPC101	HM.14 Pou du Ciel	ex Tattershall, Sleaford. Fuselage only.
BAPC154	D.31 Turbulent	ex Tattershall, Nottingham. Unfinished project, PFA.1654.
+	Knight Twister	ex Loughborough, Biggin Hill. Fuselage frame, arrived 6/87.
NP294	Proctor IV	ex Tattershall, Friskney, Poynton, Andover Down, Cosford, 4 RS, 2 RS.
VV119	Supermarine 535	7285M, ex Tattershall. Cockpit section. Identity questionable.
WD954	Canberra B.2	ex Tattershall, Bicester, 76, Upwood, Hemswell.
WW421	Provost T.1	7688M, ex Tattershall, Lytham St Annes, St Athan, 3 FTS.
XA909	Vulcan B.1	ex Tattershall, Waddington, Wadd Wing, 50, 101. Nose section.
XE677+	Hunter F.4	ex Loughborough, Dunsfold, 229 OCU, 111, 93, 4. Arrived 6/87.
XH670	Victor B.2/BS	ex Tattershall, Woodford, Radlett, Wittering Wing, 543, MoA. Nose section.
XM561	Skeeter AOP.12	7980M, ex Tattershall, Moston, Middle Wallop, Arborfield, Wroughton, HQ 1 Wing, HQ 2 Wing, 651.
E-424	Hunter F.51	ex Tattershall, Cosford, Dunsfold G-9-445, Danish AF, Aalborg, ESK-724.
100502	Fa 330A-1	ex Tattershall, Wigan. On loan from TAC.

FENLAND

(Or Holbeach St Johns) The three Cessnas listed in W&R10 remain current, although the hulk of G-LOOK is due to be scrapped. Cessna 172C G-ARWH arrived here in dismantled form 9/86 only to leave a little later to gain fame at Golders Green.

G-ASTV	Cessna 150D	ex Panshanger, Luton, N6005T. CoA expired 18/10/75. Under rebuild to 'taildragger', using G-AWAX below for spares.
G-AWAX	Cessna 150D	ex OY-TRJ, N4153U. Crashed 3/2/80. See above.
G-LOOK	Cessna F.172M	ex PH-MIG. Crashed 11/8/85. For spares recovery.

HEMSWELL

This former bomber airfield is in the process of becoming the new home for the Bomber County Aviation Museum. As this issue has caught them in mid-move, their entry can still be found under Cleethorpes.

HOLBEACH

In Chapel Street, K&L Aero Services have established themselves and by 4/86 were working on a former Hamble Chipmunk.

G-ARMD+	Chipmunk 22A	ex Hamble, WD297, 666, 1 BFTS. CoA expired 5/6/76. Arrived by 4/86.

LINCOLN

The parts of Chipmunk T.10 WG362 held at City Scrap and Salvage in Firth Road are now too small to consider as an entry in W&R.

MARKET RASEN

By 10/86 an ATC unit here was noted to have the cockpit section of a Vulcan. More details appreciated.

ROPSLEY

(South of the A52 between Grantham and Boston) The Pawnee frame is still stored at the strip here.

G-BFBN	Pawnee 235D	Crashed 22/3/79. Fuselage frame only. Stored.

SCAMPTON

That well known landmark, the Lancaster on the gate here, was due to move to East Kirkby during April/May 1988, care of the Abingdon-based RAFEF. It will be listed under this heading for this edition. Reports have it that two airframes will replace it on the gate. Vulcan B.2MRR XH563 was put up for tender during 8/86 and was scrapped on site during 11/86. The nose went to Rotherham, the remainder going to a yard in the Sheffield area. The tail-less Vulcan still serves the firemen.

NX611	Lancaster VII	ex Blackpool Airport, Hullavington, Lavenham, Biggin Hill, G-ASXX, *Aeronavale* WU-15, St Athan, Llandow. Gate guardian - see notes above.
	Vulcan B.2A	on fire dump. Identity given as XL384 or XH500.

Central Flying School Tragedy struck the Vintage Pair while displaying at Mildenhall on 25/5/86 when Meteor T.7 WA669 and Vampire T.11 XH304 collided in mid air, killing the two on the Meteor. In September 1987 Meteor T.7 WF791 performed a single act, and this is due to continue in 1988. Vampire T.11 XE920 arrived at CFS from Henlow during 1987 and may well become the new Vampire component for a reborn Vintage Pair. The Red Arrows still have the Gnat on show outside their headquarters.

WF791	Meteor T.7	ex Leeming, Little Rissington, CFS, 3 FTS, RAFC, CFS, 5 CAACU, CFS, RAFFC, 8 FTS, 4 FTS, 205 AFS, 26, Wunstorf SF, 26. Airworthy - see above.
XE920+	Vampire T.11	8196M, ex Henlow, Shawbury, CATCS, 8 FTS, 5 FTS, 1 FTS. Arrived during 1987 - see notes above.
XR571	Gnat T.1	8493M, ex Cosford, Kemble, Brampton, Kemble, 4 FTS.

Trade Management Training School The expansion of airframes for TMTS as given in W&R10 was mostly illusory as four of the 'M' number allocations actually materialised at Cosford! The following should therefore be deleted from the listing :- Hunter T.7s XL569, XL572, XL576 and XL617. Other airframes are unchanged :-

XE653	Hunter F.6A	8829M, ex Kemble, 1 TWU, 229 OCU, 111, 43. 'D'.
XF515	Hunter F.6A	8830M, ex Kemble, 1 TWU, 229 OCU, 43, 247. 'C'.
XG160	Hunter F.6A	8831M, ex 1 TWU, 229 OCU, 111, 43. 'B'.
XG172	Hunter F.6A	8832M, ex 1 TWU, 229 OCU, 263, 19. 'A'.
XL587	Hunter T.7	8807M, ex 208, 237 OCU, 1 TWU, 229 OCU.
XL592	Hunter T.7	8836M, ex 1 TWU, TWU, 229 OCU.

SKEGNESS

(Or Ingoldmells) This airfield makes a come-back with this edition with a withdrawn Auster.

G-AHAL+	J/1N Alpha	CoA expired 18/7/86. Spares for G-AJEI.

SLEAFORD

Spitfire XIV MV293/G-SPIT, which was stored here, moved to Duxford 11/86.

STRUBBY

This airfield last got a mention when the dump was cleared (of Varsity WL622) in 1974. On 20/12/87 a new resident arrived by road in the form of Stuart Scott and John Jackson's Lightning which will be restored here and possibly opened up to public inspection from time to time.

XP706+	Lightning F.3	8925M, ex Binbrook, LTF, 11, 5, LTF, 23, 111, 74. Arr 2o/12/87.

STURGATE

At the airfield an unidentified para-trainer Cessna was joined by an Archer wreck in 8/87.

G-BFXZ+	Archer II	ex Staverton, N7548F. Crashed 11/7/84. Wreck, first noted 8/87.
+	Cessna	para-trainer. More details?

SUTTON BRIDGE

(On the A17 west of King's Lynn) At Lindsey Walton's airstrip, the two Nord 1002s are still stored.

G-ASTG	Nord 1002	ex F-BGKI, French AF. CoA expired 26/10/73. Stored.
G-ASUA	Nord 1002	ex Elstree, F-BFDY. Crashed 30/7/64. Stored.

SWINDERBY

The Station's backdrop for passing out parades inside the hangar, Mosquito TT.35 TJ138 left by road in 11/86 for St Athan. Its replacement came slung underneath a Chinook on 23/9/86 from Cranwell in the form of a pre-production Lightning. On the dump, Devon C.2/2 WB530/8825M was consumed by 10/87.

WG362	Chipmunk T.10 PAX	8630M/8630M, ex Filton, BIR UAS, WAL UAS, OXF UAS, Swanton Morley, Carlisle, Mildenhall, 100, EDN UAS, 3 BFTS, 16 RFS, 3 BFTS, 7 RFS.
WT520	Canberra PR.7	8184M/8184M, ex CAW, 31, 17, 31, 17, 31, 80. 80 Sqn c/s.
XD506	Vampire T.11	7983M, ex Finningley, CATCS, CNCS, 5 FTS, 206 AFS. Gate guardian.
XG329+	Lightning F.1	8080M, ex Cranwell, A&AEE, Warton. Ferried in 23/9/86.

TATTERSHALL

To clear up the move to East Kirkby, as covered in W&R10, Emeraude G-BLHL and Vampire WZ549 did not make the move, going respectively to Wigan and Coningsby.

TATTERSHALL THORPE

The airfield here holds a host of aircraft hulks, as one of its specialities lies with insurance write-offs. The other penchant here is for rare helicopters and their rebuild - the passion of Roger Windley. Some of the hulks do not have long term existences and it is always difficult catching up on them, especially with the recent throughput of material. Of those listed in W&R10, only a couple need deletion : Tipsy Trainer G-AFVN was flying again by 1986; Emeraude G-BDDZ has moved on for rebuild, destination unconfirmed; IS.28M-2 G-BKAB has also moved on, again to an unconfirmed destination; McCulloch J2 N4329G became, in turn G-BKKL and G-BLGI, neither of which it has yet taken up, and moved to the Ipswich area, presumably for rebuild - more details?; the two former South African Djinns, ZS-HBA and 'HBB are thought to have been exported, possibly to the USA. Widgeon G-ANLW/'MD497' arrived here from Southend by 4/86, but was only here a short time, moving on via Little Staughton to Wellingborough. Whirlwind HAR.10 XP345/8792M arrived from Shawbury by 6/87, but left by road on 28/8/87 possibly for Storwood - which see. The following is thought to be the situation here, aircraft marked § have not been noted since W&R10 and may well have moved on or expired.

G-AEOH	HM.14 Pou du Ciel	ex South Woodford, Coventry. §
G-APMP+	Hiller UH-12C	ex Chilbolton, Southend. CoA expired 23/7/76. Arr by 9/86.
G-ASKJ	Terrier 1	ex Redhill, EI-AMC ntu, VX926, 664, AOPS, HS. Crashed 20/6/84.
G-ATHF	Cessna 150F	ex Cambridge, N6292R. Crashed 7/9/83.
G-ATJU	Cessna 150F	ex N8265S. Crashed 9/11/82.
G-AVVE+	Cessna F.150H	Crashed 14/5/83. First noted 3/85.
G-AXGA+	PA-18-95 S'Cub	ex PH-NLE, PH-CUB ntu, RNethAF R-51, 52-2447. Crashed 26/12/86. First noted 5/87.
G-AXRC	Cricket	Crashed 22/10/77.
G-AYFY	EAA Biplane	ex Cardiff, unfinished. §
G-AYJW+	Cessna FR.172G	ex Leavesden. Damaged 13/12/83. First noted 4/86.
G-AYVT	Brochet MB.84	ex Sunderland, F-BGLI. Damaged 28/6/77. §
G-AZVV+	Cherokee 180G	Crashed 8/11/85. First noted 4/87.
G-AZYJ	Wilga 35	ex Studley, Bickmarsh, SP-WEA. CoA expired 5/3/76.
G-BAYX+	Bell 47G-5	ex CF-XPN, N6216N. Crashed 7/6/86. First noted 8/87.
G-BDJG	Luton Minor	ex Biggin Hill. Crashed 8/6/83.
G-BDNE	Harker Hawk	ex Middlesborough, unfinished.
G-BFMS+	Rallye 180GT	Crashed 11/10/86. First noted 2/87.
G-BFON+	Turbo Navajo	ex SE-FHB. Crashed 11/6/86. First noted 4/87.
G-BHOC+	Commander 112A	ex N1378J. Crashed 1/10/85. First noted 9/86.
G-HASL+	AA-5A Cheetah	ex G-BGSL. Crashed 25/6/86. First noted 9/86.
G-PULL+	PA-18-150 S'Cub	ex PH-MBB, ALAT 18-5356. Crashed 13/6/86. First noted 4/87.
G-ROAN+	Stearman B75N-1	ex Shoreham, Yugoslavia, N4685N, BuAer 07790. Damaged 21/10/83. First noted 9/86.
C-GOEA+	Hughes 369HS	G-BMSP. For rebuild. First noted 9/86.
D-ECIU	Cessna F.172H	wreck. §
EI-BKL	Cessna FR.172F	ex D-EBTQ, F-WLIT. Damaged 11/84.
5X-UUX	Scout	G-BKLJ, ex Heysham, Panshanger, Uganda Police Air Wing. Spares for XT788.
WH991	Dragonfly HR.3	ex Tattershall, Wisbech, Taunton, Fleetlands, Culdrose SF, 705, 700, Eglinton SF, *Centaur* Flt, 705, *Illustrious* Flt.

WV703	Pembroke C.1	8108M, 'G-IIIM', ex Coningsby, St Athan, 32, MCS, El Adem SF, Levant CF, MECS. Poor state.
XJ407	Whirlwind HAR.10	G-BKHB, ex Northolt, 32, 103, 110, 22, 155, XD777. CoA exp 29/10/82.
XL735	Skeeter AOP.12	ex Manston, Wroughton, Detmold, Middle Wallop. Identity confirmed.
XP329+	Whirlwind HAR.10	8791M, ex Shawbury, Lee-on-Solent, Akrotiri, 84, 230, 110, 225. First noted 6/87.
XP346+	Whirlwind HAR.10	8793M, ex Shawbury, Lee-on-Solent, Akrotiri, 84, 22, 225. F/noted 6/87.
XP395+	Whirlwind HAR.10	8674M, ex Halton, SARTS, 22, 230. First noted 6/87.
XT788	Wasp HAS.1	G-BMIR, ex Wroughton. Arrived 19/12/85.

WADDINGTON

With the choice of the Boeing Sentry in place of the troubled Nimrod AEW.3, the latter lie all over the field awaiting an uncertain fate. Meanwhile the runway will be widened during 1988 to allow for the operation of the lower-slung CFM-56 powered Sentry AEW.1s and the Vulcan Display Flight will deploy to Scampton for the time being. On the dump Vulcan B.2 XH539 had expired by mid 1987. VDF Vulcan B.2 XL426 was stood down and offered for tender in 1986, eventually flying out to Southend 18/12/86, with XH558 taking on the role of 'flyer' - long may she continue. A Victor K.2 arrived for display purposes during 8/86, joining the station Vulcan. Of the Nimrod AEW.3 fleet there have been four departures :- XV261 (arrived 1987) flew out to Abingdon 14/7/87; XV262 (arrived 23/3/87 from Woodford) flew out to Abingdon 8/87; XV263 (arrived 2/86) flew out to Finningley 14/7/87; XZ286 (arrived 2/86) flew out to Abingdon 13/7/87.

XH558	Vulcan B.2A	ex Marham, Waddington, 50, Wadd Wing, A&AEE, Wadd Wing, 27, 230 OCU, 27, Wadd Wing, 230 OCU. VDF aircraft.
XJ825	Vulcan K.2	8810M, ex 50, Wadd Wing, 35, 27, 35, Akrotiri Wing, Cott Wing, Wadd Wing, Cott Wing, 35, 27. BDR.
XL189+	Victor K.2	8912M, ex Marham, 55, 57, 55, 232 OCU, VTF, Witt Wing, 232 OCU, Witt Wing, 232 OCU. Arrived 8/86. Display airframe.
XM607	Vulcan B.2A	8779M, ex 44, 101, 35. Display airframe.
XV259+	Nimrod AEW.3	arrived 2/87. Stored.
XZ280+	Nimrod AEW.3	arrived 1/87. Stored.
XZ281+	Nimrod AEW.3	arrived 4/ 2/87. Stored.
XZ282+	Nimrod AEW.3	arrived 19/12/86. Stored.
XZ283+	Nimrod AEW.3	arrived 1/86. Stored.
XZ285+	Nimrod AEW.3	arrived 12/84. Stored.
XZ287+	Nimrod AEW.3	arrived 10/ 3/87. Stored.

WICKENBY

Throughput of W&R-type aircraft here remains entertaining. Going back to W&R10 for a moment, Pawnee G-BEII was not used as a source of spares, but reflew following rebuild as far back as 1984! Three of the aircraft listed in W&R10 are now flying ; J/1N Alpha G-ARUY by 1987; Pawnee G-ATFR by 1987 and Pawnee G-BGFN by 1986. The hulk of Pawnee G-BHUV had gone by 1986, presumed scrapped. The other airframes remain unchanged and there have been two additions.

G-AIGM+	J/1N Alpha	damaged in hangar collapse 1/87, stored in poor shape.
G-ARLK	Comanche 250	ex EI-ALW, N7257P ntu. Crashed 29/3/81. Awaiting rebuild.
G-BEYS	Archer II	ex N2658Q. Crashed 20/6/81. Spares use.
G-DCAT+	Turbo AgCat	ex N8312K. Crashed 3/7/85. For spares.
PH-TPR	AgCat 450	ex N6882Q. For spares.

Greater London

BENTLEY PRIORY

A state of flux for the gate guardians. The plot as we left it in W&R10 was just Lightning F.1A XM173 valiantly doing its bit. During 1986 Spitfire XVI TB252 arrived from Leuchars to give the base its obligatory Spitfire and Hunter FGA.9 XE597/8874M arrived from Brawdy. The latter was not suitable, for one reason or another, and left for Halton by 5/87. Coming in the other direction was a Hunter F.6. Hurricane LF751, currently at Rochester will return here when restoration is complete, by which time the base hopes to have a large 'glass' hangar in which to display both it and the 'new' Spitfire.

TB252+	Spitfire XVI	8073M//7281M/7257M, ex Leuchars, Boulmer, Acklington, Odiham, 61 OTU, 350, 341, 329, 84 GSU. 'GW-H'. *Lucky Nine*. See notes above.
XG290+	Hunter F.6	8711M, ex Halton, Laarbruch SF, A&AEE. See notes above.
XM173	Lightning F.1A	8414M, ex Binbrook, Binbrook TFF, Leuchars TFF, 226 OCU, 56. Displayed within the grounds.

BIGGIN HILL

The Proctor is believed still stored in the general area. By early 1986 the hulk of Pup 100 G-AWDZ had gone from the yard of Biggin Hill Metals.

NP181	Proctor IV	G-AOAR, ex Headcorn, Biggin Hill. wfu 10/65.

BIGGIN HILL AIRPORT

RAF Memorial Chapel The strange vista of two Spitfires on an RAF gate came to an end during 1987 when both XVI SL674 and F.21 LA226 moved out (at different time) to Abingdon for refurbish. SL679 came back sporting new colours and continues to guard the chapel, but LA226 then moved to Shawbury for storage.

SL674	Spitfire XVI	8392M, ex Little Rissington, 501, 17 OTU. 612 Squadron colours as 'RAS-H'. See notes above.

Warbirds of Great Britain In late 1987 it became clear that *The Hill* was to be the new base for this well-known warbird collection, following the need to vacate Bitteswell. There are plans to build a hangar here to house the aircraft. Three aircraft, all airworthy, are so far present. Readers should also refer to the notes under Bitteswell.

NH238+	Spitfire IX	G-MKIX, ex Bitteswell, Blackbushe, N238V, Harlingen, Hemswell, Winthorpe, Southampton, Andover, COGEA OO-ARE, Coxyde, Belgian AF SM-36, Netherlands AF H-60, Sealand, 76 MU, 9 MU, 49 MU, 84GSU. Flew in 28/11/87.
PL983+	Spitfire PR.XI	G-PRXI, ex East Midlands, Stonebroom, Duxford, Old Warden, Vickers G-15-109, NC74138, PL983 2, 4, 1 PP. Flew in 10/87 ex Bournemouth auction.
NX49092+	F4U-4 Corsair	flew in 19/2/88 from Ipswich, ex Florida via Felixstowe Docks.

Airport Proper As usual, *The Hill* continues to be a hive of interest for the W&R merchant. One of the characteristics of the place from this point of view is the extreme longevity of some of the hulks. Of the aircraft listed in W&R10 a notable number have moved on/passed on/flown again, but the ranks have been swollen by a goodly gaggle of new aspiring hulks. Leaving the nest have been the following :- Civilian Coupe G-ABNT flew following restoration in 1987; DH.60G Moth G-ABYA believed to be parts only and best deleted; Tipsy Trainer G-AFWT flew again early 1988; TriPacer 150 G-ARBV was flying again by 1987; Apache 160 G-ARJW had moved to Bristol by 5/86; TriPacer G-AWLI was flying again by 1987; Air & Space 18A G-AYUE had gone by mid 1987, possibly going to join- ; Air & Space 18A G-BALB left, possibly for somewhere as geographically precise as 'Scotland' during 1986; Stampe G-EEUP was flying again by 1987. Additionally Tiger Moth G-BBRB transitted through here after a spell at Headcorn. It later moved to a nest off site. The current situation is therefore :-

G-AKVZ	Messenger IVB	ex RH427. CoA expired 18/8/72. Under rebuild.
G-AOGE+	Proctor III	ex BV651,Halton SF, 2 GCS, FAA. CoA expired 21/5/84. Stored.
G-AOKH	Prentice 1	ex VS251, 3 FTS, CFS, 2 FTS. CoA expired 2/8/73. Spares use.
G-APZR	Cessna 150	ex N6461T. Crashed 14/1/81. engine test-bed with Airtech.
G-AREE+	Aztec 250	CoA expired 6/6/81. External store.
G-ARWC+	Cessna 150B	ex Exeter, N1115Y. Crashed 28/4/84. Wreck, first noted 6/87.
G-ASDA	Queen Air 65-80	CoA expired 8/11/79. External storage.
G-ASJU	Commander 520	ex N4176B. CoA expired 22/7/73. Engineless.
G-AVWE+	Cherokee 140	CoA expired 22/4/82. External storage.

G-AWCO Cessna F.150H CoA expired 29/8/75. Fuselage, poor state.
G-AWEK Fournier RF-4D crashed 25/10/72. Fuselage, stored. Noted again 3/86.
G-AYRM Cherokee 140D crashed 12/1/84. Wreck.
G-BEAC+ Cherokee 140 ex 4X-AND. CoA expired 20/11/83. External storage.
G-BGAU Rearwin 9000L ex N18548. Stored.
G-BHYS+ Cherokee 181 ex N8218Y. Crashed 7/12/85. Wreck, first noted 6/87.
G-BLXX+ Aztec 250F ex G-BLVM ntu, G-PIED, N6534A. Damaged 16/1/87. Wreck.
EI-BEM+ Shorts SD.360 ex Aer Lingus, G-BLGC, G-14-3642. Crashed 31/1/86. Wreck, for spares. Arrived 15/2/88 from AAIU Farnborough.
Civilian Coupe ex Carmarthen. 7th unfinished example. Spares for G-ABNT.
XE998+ Vampire T.11 ex Warmingham, Wigan, Woodford, Chester, St Athan, 8 FTS, 4 FTS, 8 FTS. Arrived 20/12/86 for restoration to flying condition.
Scout AH.1 ex Southampton. Cockpit section. Noted again 8/82, still present 1/88.
Hunter F.51/T.7 ex Bournemouth, mostly former T.7 ET-272. Mounted outside Brencham building. Composite. All-red colour scheme.

CHESSINGTON

(On the A243 south of Surbiton) A virtual clear-out of W&R material at the strip here. Currie Wot G-ARZW flew again following rebuild 1/88, only to meet shortly with another accident; Zlin G-BLMA/F-BORS was airworthy by late 1987 as was Tomahawk G-BLNN. Parts from Tomahawks SE-GVH and G-CGFC have not been noted for some time and are thought to have been consumed in G-BLNN. Tiger Moth G-ANZZ and the anonymous Auster frame have not been seen since 10/85 and may be heading for *LOST!* before too long. The two anonymous Pitts S-1 fuselage frames written out of W&R10 are, in fact, still here, lurking in the rafters. (Pause for a reminder, always look up - it's good for your morale, and you may see something new!) By 5/87 another Zlin was under rebuild here.

G-AWJX+ Zlin Z.526 CoA expired 29/5/85. Under rebuild.
Pitts S-1 fuselage frame.) See notes
Pitts S-1 fuselage frame.) above.

COULSDON

(On the South Circular, north of Croydon) The Edwards Gyrocopter is still in the care of Bernie King.

G-ASDF. Edwards Gyrocopter stored.

ENFIELD

At the Lippitts Hill Police Helicopter Base the remains of Cessna 172 EI-AYH have not been reported since 11/83 and may well have passed on. At the St Ignatius Upper College in Turkey Street, the Chipmunk T.10 PAX Trainer is thought to be still extant. At the famous former MoD/Royal Ordnance Factory (now owned by BAe - or is it the Rover Group?) a Harrier GR.3 has been allocated for cannon trials. Please note the word *allocated*, as yet there has been no confirmed sighting.

WK587 Chipmunk T.10 PAX 8212M, ex Cambridge, Shawbury, Gatow SF, Bir UAS, Cam UAS, Edn UAS, Hul UAS, Lon UAS, Stn UAS, Oxf UAS, Lee UAS, Sta UAS, 11 RFS.
XW922+ Harrier GR.3 8885M, ex 233 OCU, 1, 233 OCU, 1. Crashed 19/11/85. See notes above.

GOLDERS GREEN

On the roof of the *Pizza Express* on the A502, not far east of Golders Green Underground station, Cessna 172C G-ARWH arrived from Fenland circa 10/86. Bearing the legend *PIZZA EXPRESS AEROBATIC TEAM* and suitably painted in *whizzo-prang-chaps* markings it caught many an eye until about mid March 1988 when it left.

HAMMERSMITH

The Cassutt that was listed here in W&R10 is in fact G-BGVM and is thought to have moved for rebuild.

HAMPTON

Roy Pullan's long term Tiger Moth rebuild 'G-ADNZ' is still kept here. His Chipmunk, G-ROYS, moved to Duxford and has been rebuilt as G-BNZC.

G-ADNZ" Tiger Moth ex Hayter, Christchurch, Tunbridge Wells, 6948M, DE673. No relationship to the original G-ADNZ.

HANWELL

(On the A4020 east of Uxbridge) There is some confusion relating to just how much of what Aeronca lies here. It would seem, however, that any spares recovery of G-AETG to G-AEFT was minimal and that the bulk of the former is still to be found here. As ever, further details much appreciated.

G-AETG	Aeronca 100	ex Booker. Crashed 7/4/69. Stored.
G-AEWV	Aeronca 100	Substantial components. wfu 1967. Stored.
G-AEXD	Aeronca 100	CoA expired 20/4/70. Composite, including parts from G-AESP.

HANWORTH

The little Kittiwake G-AWGM came here on 3/4/86 from Halton for another rebuild.

G-AWGM+	Kittiwake II	ex Halton. Accident 18/1/86. Arrived 3/4/86.

HAYES

(On the A4020 south east of Uxbridge) Science Museum Storage Facility The Short SC.1 XG900 left the store here for Wroughton 7/87, via a brief spell of stardom and dampness at IAT '87. The remainder of the store is thought unchanged.

G-ATTN	Piccard HAB	canopy only, basket and burner on display at South Kensington.
BAPC.52	Lilienthal Glider	ex South Kensington. Original.
	Gossamer Albatross	ex South Kensington.

HENDON

Royal Air Force Museum Complex

A much-needed overhaul of ideas relating to the three-museum, one site concept here was initiated in early 1988. Entry charges now relate to all three museum sites, making a visit to Hendon even greater value for money. Other plans are underway as we go to press, including more special exhibitions, 'inter-active' exhibits for kids of all ages and a much-needed overhaul of the renowned RAF Museum Shop. The museum complex is open 1000 to 1800 Monday to Saturday and 1400 to 1800 Sunday. Further details of the new arrangements, and all general enquiries can be had by sending an SAE to ; Royal Air Force Museum, Hendon, London, NW9 5LL. Telephone 01 205 2266 - four lines.

The RAF Museum storage facility at Henlow is being wound down, but the restoration workshop at Cardington continues to flourish. The 'out-stations' at Cosford and St Athan should also be referred to for a fuller picture of the extent of the RAF Museum.

Battle of Britian Museum Airframes within the impressive BBM remain unchanged :-

K8042	Gladiator II	8372M, ex RAFM, 61 OTU, 5 (P)AFU, A&AEE. 87 Squadron colours.
L8756"	Bolingbroke IVT	10001, ex Boscombe Down, RCAF. 139 Sqn Blenheim c/s as 'XD-E'.
N1671	Defiant I	8370M, ex RAFM, Finningley, 285, 307. 307 Sqn c/s as 'EW-D'.
P2617	Hurricane I	8373M, ex RAFM, 71 MU, 9 FTS, 9 SFTS, 1, 607, 615. 607 Sqn c/s 'AF-F'.
P3175	Hurricane I	ex 257. Shot down by Bf 110 near North Weald 31/8/40. Wreck.
R9125	Lysander III	8377M, ex RAFM, 161, 225. 225 Sqn colours as 'LX-L'.
X4590	Spitfire I	8384M, ex Cosford, Finningley, 53 OTU, 303, 57 OTU, 66, 609. 609 Sqn colours as 'PR-F'.
ML824	Sunderland V	ex RAFM, Pembroke Dock, *Aeronavale*, 330, 201. 201 Sqn colours as 'NS-Z'.
A2-4	Seagull V	ex Cardington, Wyton, VH-ALB, RAAF A2-4.
4101	Bf 109E-3	8477M, ex St Athan, Henlow, Biggin Hill, Fulbeck, Wroughton, Stanmore Park, DG200, 1426 (EA) Flt, A&AEE, de H, Hucknall, RAE. Force-landed 27/11/40.
360043	Ju 88R-1	8475M, ex St Athan, Henlow, St Athan, Biggin Hill, Fulbeck, Wroughton, Stanmore Park, 47 MU, CFE-EAF, 1426 (EA) Flt, RAE. Defected 9/5/43. 'D5+EV'.
494083	Ju 87D-3	8474M, ex St Athan, Henlow, St Athan, Fulbeck, Wroughton, Stanmore Park, Eggebek. 'RI+JK'.
701152	He 111H-23	8471M, ex St Athan, Henlow, Biggin Hill, Fulbeck, Stanmore Park, RAE, 56th FG USAAF Boxted. 'NT+SL'.
730301	Bf 110G-4/R6	8479M, ex St Athan, Biggin Hill, Stanmore Park, 76 MU, RAE, AM.34, Karup, I/NJG.3. 'D5+RL'.
MM5701	Fiat CR-42	8468M, ex St Athan, Biggin Hill, Fulbeck, Wroughton, Stanmore Park, AFDU, RAE, BT474, 95 SCT. Force-landed Orfordness 11/11/40.

Bomber Command Museum and United States Army Air Force Memorial As might be expected with the size of the majority of the exhibits in here, only one change has occurred since W&R10. Hart J9941 has migrated the short distance to the RAF Museum itself.

168	Tabloid replica	G-BFDE, ex Cardington, Hucknall.
F1010	DH.9A	ex Cardington, Krakow, Berlin War Museum, 110, 'C'.
F8614"	Vimy replica	G-AWAU, ex RAFM, VAFA Weybridge. *Triple First*.
R5868	Lancaster I	7325M, ex RAFM, Scampton, 467, 83. 467 Sqn c/s as 'PO-S'.
W1048	Halifax II	8465M, ex Henlow, Lake Hoklingen, Norway, 35, 102. Force-landed 9/4/44, recovered from lake bottom 1973.
MF628	Wellington T.10	ex RAFM, Abingdon, St Athan, Biggin Hill, Heathrow, Hendon, Wisley, Vickers, 1 ANS.
TW117	Mosquito T.3	7805M, ex RAFM, Henlow, 3 CAACU, 58, 264, HCF, Linton-on-Ouse SF, APS Acklington.
XD818	Valiant BK.1	7894M, ex Marham, 49 'A' Flt.
XL318	Vulcan B.2A	8733M, ex Scampton, 617, 230 OCU, Wadd Wing, 617, 230 OCU, Scamp Wing, 617.
429366	TB-25N-20-NC	ex Blackbushe, N9115Z, *Hanover Street*.
483868	B-17G-95-DL	ex Stansted, N5237V, Andrews AFB, TBM Inc, Butler Aircraft, Aero Union, USN PB-1W 77233.

Royal Air Force Museum of Aviation History A case of three in and three out at the 'main' museum on the site. Of the removals, all moved to Cardington in their own manner; Hart Trainer K4972 for restoration; Silver Dart BAPC.180 for storage and the BE.2 frame for use in the long-term complete BE.2 project. Of the inbounds, the Bristol F.2b restoration from Cardington is magnificent, and includes one side stripped back to show the interior. The Hart is a refugee from the Bomber Command Museum. The MiG 15 has apparently been on the 'wants' list of the RAFM for some time.

G-EBMB	Hawker Cygnet	ex Cardington, Henlow, Lympne Trials No 14.
BAPC.82	Afghan Hind	ex Kabul, Royal Afghan AF, RAF.
BAPC100	Clarke TWK	ex Cardington, Hayes. Science Museum loan.
164	Bleriot XI	BAPC.106, RAeS loan.
433	Bleriot XXVII	BAPC.107, ex Cardington, RAeS loan.
2345"	FB.5 Gunbus rep	G-ATVP, ex Cardington, Hendon, Weybridge.
3066	Caudron G.III	ex G-AETA, OO-ELA, O-BELA. RAeS loan.
A301	Morane BB	fuselage frame only.
E449"	Avro 504K	ex Henlow. Composite aircraft, including parts from 504K G-EBJE and 548A G-EBKN/E449.
F938	RAF SE.5A	ex Henlow, Heathrow, Colerne, 'B4563', Weybridge, Savage Skywriting G-EBIC.
A8226"	1½ Strutter rep	G-BIDW, ex Cardington, Land's End, '9382'. 45 Sqn colours.
E2466+"	Bristol F.2b	BAPC.165, ex Cardington, Weston-on-the-Green. Partially skeletal.
F6314	Camel F.1	ex Heathrow, Colerne, Hendon, Tring, Waddon. 65 Sqn colours as 'B'.
J9941"	Hart	G-ABMR, ex HSA, 'J9933'. See notes above.
K4232	Cierva C.30A	ex Cardington, SE-AZB, K4232 SAC.
K9942	Spitfire IA	8383M, ex 71 MU, 53 OTU, 57 OTU, 72. 72 Sqn colours as 'SD-V'.
N5182"	Sopwith Pup rep	G-APUP, ex Blackbushe, Old Warden.
N5628	Gladiator II	ex 263. Lost in Norway 4/40. Forward fuselage only.
N5912	Sopwith Triplane	8385M, ex Henlow, 49 MU, 5 MU, Cardington, SAF Redcar, SAF Marske.
T6296	Tiger Moth II	8387M, ex Yeovilton SF, BRNC, RNEC, Stretton, 7 EFTS, 1 EFTS.
KK995	Hoverfly I	ex Cranfield, 43 OTU, R-4B 43-46558. 'E'.
MN235	Typhoon IB	ex Shawbury, Smithsonian, USAAF evaluation FE-491, 47 MU, 51 MU.
NV778	Tempest V	8386M, ex Foulness Island, Middleton St George. Composite.
PK724	Spitfire F.24	7288M, ex Finningley, Gaydon, Norton, Lyneham.
RD253	Beaufighter TF.10	7931M, ex St Athan, Portuguese AF BF-13.
VT812	Vampire F.3	7200M, ex Cosford, Shawbury, Colerne, Cardington, 602, 601, 614, 32.
VX653	Sea Fury FB.11	ex Yeovilton, Lee-on-Solent, Lossiemouth, FRU, 811, 738, 736.
WE139	Canberra PR.3	8369M, ex Henlow, 231 OCU, 39, 69, 540.
WH301	Meteor F.8	7930M, ex Henlow, Kemble, 85, CAW, 609, DFLS/CFE. 'T'.
WP185	Hunter F.5	7583M, ex Henlow, 34, 1.
XA847	EE P.1B	8371M, ex RAE Farnborough, A&AEE, makers.
XG474	Belvedere HC.1	8367M, ex 66, 26, 66. 'O'.
XH124	Beverley C.1	8025M, ex Abingdon, Shawbury, 47, 242 OCU, 84, 30.
XP831	P.1127	8406M, ex RAE Bedford, Dunsfold.

	Beaufighter	ex Cranfield. Cockpit section.
920	Stranraer	ex CF-BXO Queen Charlotte Airlines, RCAF 920. 'QN'.
A16-199	Hudson IIIA	G-BEOX, ex Strathallan, VH-AGJ, VH-SMM, FH174, 41-36975.
HD-75	Hanriot HD.1	ex Cardington, N75 (US civil), G-AFDX, OO-APJ, Belgian AF.
HD5-1	Dornier Do 24T-3	ex N99225 ntu, Majorca, Spanish AF, HR5.1, 65-6, EC-DAF, '58-1'.
01120+	MiG 15bis	ex Middlesborough, Polish AF. Arrived 10/10/86.

HOUNSLOW

Not quite where you would expect to find a Mosquito. The Imperial War Museum have a store here and the Lambeth-based *Mossie* has moved here for temporary store while things are all cement and plaster.

TV959+	Mosquito T.3	ex South Lambeth, Bicester, 3 CAACU, HCEU, 228 OCU, 13 OTU. See above.

HOUNSLOW HEATH

At the Metropolitan Police Training Centre, the dark blue Trident 2E fuselage continues to train the boys-in-blue what to do with a Trident-in-blue.

G-AVFK	Trident 2E	ex Heathrow, BA, BEA. wfu 31/12/81.

KENLEY

The Cadet TX.3 is still based here, used by both 135 Squadron ATC and 1 MGSP at Halton as a travelling exhibit.

VM791"	Cadet TX.3	8876M/XA312. Travelling airframe.

KINGSTON-UPON-THAMES

At the British Aerospace plant here the Harrier T.4 forward fuselage that 'grew' a Sea Harrier radar nose has not been reported since. Adding to W&R10, it is now thought to have been XW272, not XW269.

LONDON AIRPORT

(Heathrow) There are plans, which hopefully will come to fruition, to remove the long-serving Comet 4 from here and take it to Hatfield for the nascent Heritage Centre there. As with W&R10, the bulk of the words under this heading deal with the world's most quietly charismatic jet airliner, the Trident. To clear up the disposal listing in W&R10 the following moved on, in one form or another :- G-AWZH broken up 6/86; G-AWZI fuselage left by road 27/6/87 for Reigate; G-AWZJ flew off to Prestwick 24/2/86; G-AWZK painted in 'proper' BA colours and used for anti-terrorist training by the police at 'LAP' - see below; G-AWZO flew to Hatfield 18/4/86; G-AWZP scrapped 6/86 with the nose going to Manchester 12/6/86; G-AWZR flying to Tees-side 19/3/86; G-AWZS did not fly off tae bonnie Glasgow, but to Tees-side 12/3/86; G-AWZU flew to Stansted 5/3/86; G-AWZV became 9Q-CTZ (the 2nd) and is presumably pulverising ears in Zaire.

G-APDT	Comet 4	ex XA-NAB, G-APDT. See notes above.
G-AVFG	Trident 2E	ex BA, BEA. Ground school airframe. wfu 30/4/85.
G-AWZK	Trident 3B-101	ex BA, BEA. Last flight 1/11/85. See notes above.

LONDON BRIDGE

To clear up the Paul Raymond/London War Museum saga. 'Heinkel' G-AWHB moved from here to a barn near Royston and recently became a film star with Aces High.

NORTHOLT

A clear-out of the dump during 1987 removed the remains of Devon C.2/2 VP976 and Argosy E.1 XR137. As yet there are no new candidates. Javelin nose XH837 moved to Caernarfon during mid 1987. This leaves the Spitfire guarding the gate :-

TE476	Spitfire XVI	7451M/8071M, ex Kemble, Henlow, 11 GCF, Martlesham Heath SF, North Weald SF, Biggin Hill SF, St Athan, Kemble, 1 CAACU.

ORPINGTON

(On the A224 in south east London) The Auster 3 is still stored in the area.

G-AHLI	Auster 3	ex Rush Green, NJ911. CoA expired 26/4/73. Stored.

PECKHAM RYE

During 12/87 a scrapyard near the railway station was noted as containing a Whirlwind HAR.10 minus boom and at least the booms of a Vampire T.11.

RUISLIP

Alan Allen continues to restore his Vampire T.11 pod and acquired one of the Bingley NF.10s during 1986, this too is under restoration.

WM729+	Vampire NF.10	ex Bingley, Bradford, Church Fenton, CNCS, 2 ANS, 25, 151. Pod only, arrived 5/9/86.
WZ581	Vampire T.11	ex Bushey, Keevil, 3/4 CAACU, 229 OCU, 233 OCU, 25. Pod only.
	Chipmunk T.10	cockpit section.

SOUTH KENSINGTON

The Science Museum There are large plans afoot relating to the Science Museum and the National Aeronautical Collection within, with refurbishing of the buildings underway and this may mean closure of sections and removal of exhibits. As W&R goes to press, these plans have been delayed, but readers should check up before visiting to make sure the aircraft will be on view. Other than the Fa 330 being moved into store at South Kensington, there have been no changes in the exhibits here. The Museum is open daily 1000 to 1800 and Sundays 1430 to 1800. Contact, The Science Museum, South Kensington, London SW7 2DD. Telephone 01 938 8000. See also : Hayes, store; London Colney, Mosquito Aircraft Museum; Southampton, Hall of Aviation; Wroughton, transport collection and large items store; Yeovilton, Concorde Exhibition.

G-AAAH	DH.60G Moth	*Jason*, Amy Johnson's aircraft.
G-ANAV	Comet 1A	ex CF-CUM. Nose section only.
G-ATDD	Beagle 206-1	ex Leeds-Bradford. Nose section only.
G-ATTN	Piccard HAB	basket and burner. *Red Dragon*. See also Hayes.
G-BBGN	Cameron A-375 HAB	gondola only. *Daffodil II*.
G-9-185	Hunter F.6	ex Kingston-upon-Thames, Dutch AF N-250. Nose section only.
BAPC.50	Roe No 1 Triplane	Roe's second, first flown 13/7/09.
BAPC.51	Vickers Vimy IV	Alcock and Brown's trans-Atlantic machine, 1919.
BAPC.53	Wright Flyer rep	Hatfield-built.
BAPC.54	JAP-Harding Mono	Bleriot-based design.
BAPC.55	Antoinette	1909 model.
BAPC.57	Pilcher Hawk rep	
BAPC124	Lilienthal	replica, built by the museum.
	Short Bros Gas	balloon basket.
	Airship No 17	*Beta II*. Gondola only.
OO-BFH	Piccard Gas	gondola only.
304	Cody Biplane	BAPC.62. With the Museum since 1913.
F939	RAF SE.5A	ex Hendon, Savage Skywriting G-EBIB. '6'.
D7560	Avro 504K	ex Waddon.
J8067	Pterodactyl 1	ex Yeovil, Farnborough.
L1592	Hurricane I	ex 615, 56. 615 Sqn colours as 'KW-Z'.
P9444	Spitfire IA	ex Sydenham, 53 OTU, 61 OTU, 58 OTU, 72. 72 Sqn colours as 'RN-D'.
S1595	Supermarine S.6B	ex RAFHSF. Schneider Trophy winner 1931.
W4041/G	Gloster E.28/39	ex Farnborough.
AP507	Cierva C.30A	ex Halton, Sydenham, 76 MU, 5 MU, 529, 1448 Flt, Duxford Calibration Flt, RAE, G-ACWP. 529 colours as 'KX-P'.
EE416	Meteor III	ex Martin Baker. Nose section only.
KN448	Dakota IV	ex Ottawa, RCAF, 436, 10, 44-76586. Nose section only.
VX185	Canberra B.8	7631M, ex makers. Nose section only.
XN344	Skeeter AOP.12	8018M, ex Middle Wallop, 654, 652.
XP505	Gnat T.1	ex RAE Bedford, MinTech, Dunsfold, CFS.
210/16	Fokker E.III	BAPC.56. Captured 8/4/16. Stripped airframe.
100509	Fa 330A-1	ex Farnborough. In store at the museum.
191316	Me 163B-1a Komet	ex Halton, 6 MU, Farnborough, Husum, II/JG.400.
442795	Fi 103 (V-1)	BAPC.199. Omitted from W&R10.

SOUTH LAMBETH

Imperial War Museum While the Science Museum is planning a refurbishment of some of its galleries, the Imperial War Museum is well into an ambitious re-arrangement. While the aviation galleries are all cement the following aircraft have moved to Duxford : Swordfish NF370; Halifax nose PN323; He 162

120235; Fw 190 733682 and the Typhoon and Zero cockpit sections. Mosquito T.3 TV959 has moved into store at Hounslow. The wherabouts of the museums Fi 103 (V.1) BAPC.198 are unknown, possibly at Hounslow. Several of these will return for display here in the fullness of time. The Museum is open 1000 to 1750 weekdays and 1400 to 1750 on Sundays. Contact : Imperial War Museum, Lambeth Road, London SE1 6HZ. Telephone : 01 735 8922.

N6812	Camel 2F1	ex 'F4043'. Culley's aircraft.
R6915	Spitfire I	ex Cardiff, RNDU, 57 OTU, 61 OTU, 609.
DV372	Lancaster I	ex 1651 CU, 467. SOC 4/1/45. Nose section only.

SOUTHALL

(On the A4020 south east of Uxbridge) The Technical College has added another instructional airframe to its already impressive fleet with the arrival of a Vampire T.11 from Reading in 1986.

G-AREF	Aztec 250	ex Biggin Hill. CoA expired 17/1/86.
G-ARMN	Cessna 175B	ex N8294T. CoA expired 16/12/77.
G-MBTY	American Eagle	bought from new 1982.
WB763	Chipmunk T.10	G-BBMR, ex 2 FTS, 4 FTS, AOTS, 1 ITS, 1 AEF, BRI UAS, 3 AEF, AAC, 652, Odiham SF, 24 RFS, 14 RFS.
XD536+	Vampire T.11	7734M, ex Reading, Oakington, 5 FTS, Geilenkirchen SF, 234.
XL763	Skeeter AOP.12	ex Wroughton, 15/19 Hussars, HQ 1 Wing, 654.

STAINES

Mike Vickery and Neville Jones imported an Auster from Saudi Arabia during 1986. It is stored locally.

VP-KKO+	J/5G Autocar	ex Saudi Arabia, AP-AHK, VP-KKO. Arrived 1986. Stored.

STANMORE PARK

(On the A4140 in north west London) The gate of this RAF Station is still guarded by the Javelin.

XA553	Javelin FAW.1	7470M, ex Yatesbury, Gloster.

SUNBURY-ON-THAMES

Sunbury Salvage Company, in Fordbridge Road, Lower Sunbury, still display the anonymous Adams-Wilson Hobbycopter at their premises.

UXBRIDGE

(On the A4020 south of the town) RAF Uxbridge is still guarded by its plinth-mounted Spitfire.

RW382	Spitfire XVI	7245M/8075M, ex Leconfield, Church Fenton, C&RS, 3 CAACU, 604.

WELLING

It is thought that the Edwards-Mitchell Group are still working on the Auster here.

XN437	Auster AOP.9	G-AXWA, ex Biggin Hill, Luton area, Oldham, Maghull, Hoylake, 19 MU, Kenya.

WEST DRAYTON

(Off the A4/M4 north of London Airport) The RAF 'end' of the London Air Traffic Control Centre is still guarded by a Lightning.

XN769	Lightning F.2	8402M, ex Leconfield, 92, 19, 92.

WOOLWICH

At The Rotunda the Royal Artillery Museum have acquired a Canberra B.6 to go with their more appropriate Auster AOP.9. Contact : Royal Artillery Institution, Old Royal Military Academy, Woolwich, London SE18 4JJ. Telephone 01 854 5533.

WH952+	Canberra B.6	ex RAE Bedford, BAe Warton, RAE. Arrived 1986.
XR271	Auster AOP.9	ex Larkhill, St Athan, Middle Wallop.

Greater Manchester

ALTRINCHAM

Long since abandoned by W&R, Alan Ellis still has the pod of Vampire T.11 XD595 here.

XD595+ Vampire T.11 ex Woodford, Chester, St Athan, 1 FTS, Oakington, 7 FTS, 4 FTS. Pod only.

ASHTON-UNDER LYNE

In Darnton Street, 247 Sqn ATC took delivery of Chipmunk T.10 PAX Trainer WP927 from Woodvale 3/86.

WP927+ Chipmunk T.10 PAX 8216M, ex Woodvale, Crosby, Hamble G-ATJK, MCS, Oxf UAS, Lon UAS, Detling SF, Lon UAS. Arrived 3/86.

BARTON AERODROME

The W&R situation has changed little. Kept for a long time in the rafters of the Barton Moss hangar, Colt 108 fuselage frame G-ARST was put into a rubbish skip 11/86 and left for another form of existence. The other two airframes listed in W&R10 are unchanged. Across the airfield in a former hangar, the Department of Fluid Mechanics of Manchester University still keep their Vampire.

G-APVV Mooney M.20A ex N8164E. Crashed 11/1/81. Under restoration.

G-AXWE Cessna F.150K Damaged 2/1/76. Hulk, poor state.

XD434 Vampire T.11 ex Woodford, Chester, St Athan, 5 FTS, 7 FTS.

BLACKLEY

(On the A664 north of Manchester) The Staravia yard in Ward Street was visited during 11/87, but contained nothing large enough to merit a mention here.

DROYLSDEN

The Unimetal yard here has closed. The pod of the anonymous Vampire T.11 was burnt by May 1986 and the centre section of Swift WK265 moved to the Midlands.

DUKINFIELD

MAPG moved their former Iraqi AF Vampire pod to their new workshop at Hadfield.

HEATON CHAPEL

Fairey Ultra-Light Helicopter G-APJJ has rejoined the Midland Air Museum at Coventry Airport 6/2/88.

LEVENSHULME

(On the A6 south east of Manchester) In St Oswald's Road, 1940 Sqn ATC keep their Tiger Moth fuselage.

N6720 Tiger Moth 7014M, ex Kings Heath, West Bromwich, 9 AFTS, 2 GS, LON UAS, QUB UAS, 11 RFS, 11 EFTS, 4 CPF, 206. Fuselage only.

MANCHESTER

Greater Manchester Museum of Science and Industry At the Air and Space Gallery a Trident 3B-101 nose section arrived 12/6/86 and it has been installed as a 'walk-in' exhibit. Otherwise, the aircraft contents have not changed. Frequent supplemental displays are held in the 'balcony' area. The Museum is open every day from 1030 to 1700 including Bank Holidays but excluding December 23-25. Contact : Greater Manchester Museum of Science and Industry, Liverpool Road, Castlefield, Manchester M3 4JP. Telephone 061 832 2244.

G-EBZM Avian IIIA ex Higher Blagdon, Peel Green, Lymm, Liverpool, Huyton, Manchester Airport, Hesketh Park, Giro Aviation, Merseyside Aero Club. TAC loan.

G-APUD Bensen B.7M ex Firbeck, Nostell Priory, Wigan, Biggin Hill. TAC loan.

G-AWZP+ Trident 3B-101 ex Heathrow, BA, BEA. Nose section only, arrived 12/6/86.

BAPC. 6 Roe Triplane rep ex London, Southend, Irlam, Peel Green, Old Warden, Woodford. TAC loan.

BAPC.89 Cayley Glider rep ex Hendon, Lasham.

BAPC.98 Ohka II 8485M, ex Henlow, Cottesmore.

BAPC175 Volmer VJ-23 ex Old Warden.

BAPC182 Wood Ornithopter ex Hale.

T9707" Magister I 8378M, ex Hendon, G-AKKR, T9708, 51 MU, 16 EFTS, 239.

BL614	Spitfire Vb	4354M, ex St Athan, 'AB871', Colerne, Credenhill, 118, 64, 222, 242, 611, 222 Squadron colours as 'ZD-F'.
WB440	Firefly AS.6	ex Heaton Chapel, Newton-le-Willows, Salford, Failsworth, Anthorn, 812. Forward fuselage only. On loan from Colin Waterworth.
WG763	EE P.1A	7816M, ex Henlow, RAE Farnborough, RAE Bedford, A&AEE, EE Warton.
WP270	Eton TX.1	8598M, ex Henlow, Hendon, 27 MU, 61 GCF.
WR960	Shackleton AEW.2	8772M, ex Cosford, 8, 205, A&AEE, 210, 42, 228. *Dougal*.
WT619	Hunter F.1	7525M, ex Henlow, St Athan, 233 OCU, 222, 43. Partially sectioned.
WZ736	Avro 707A	7868M, ex Waddington, Cosford, Finningley, RAE Bedford, A&AEE, Avros.
XG454	Belvedere HC.1	8366M, ex Henlow, Abingdon, A&AEE, makers, Old Sarum, B'dere Trials Unit.
XL703	Pioneer CC.1	8034M, ex Henlow, 209, 230.
XL824	Sycamore HR.14	8021M, ex Henlow, Wroughton, CFS, 1564 Flt, 103, 284.
100549	Fa 330A-1	ex Liverpool Airport, Liverpool, Blackpool, Lavenham, Hullavington, Biggin Hill, Farnborough. MASL loan.
J-1172	Vampire FB.6	8487M, ex Cosford, Colerne, Dubendorf, Swiss Air Force.

MANCHESTER AIRPORT

(Or Ringway) There have been a couple of changes with the long term W&R candidates at the airport. Meta-Sokol G-APVU had gone by 7/86, appearing in Wilmslow. Cessna 336 G-ASKS flew again 18/11/86 and Tomahawk G-BMSF had flown away by much the same date. Worthy of a mention, although now after the fact was the open storage of BAC 111-408 G-NIII which arrived during 4/85, leaving in 9/87 as 5N-AYV.

G-ARPK	Trident 1C	ex BA, BEA. wfu 27/3/82. Fire service.
G-BAWV+	Aztec 250B	ex Woodvale, G-BAWU ntu, 9J-REL, N5255Y. CoA expired 11/10/85. Engineless, external store.
G-BCCJ	AA-5 Traveler	accident 2/1/76. External stored by 8/87.

MOSTON

(On the B6393 north of Manchester) North Manchester College, Moston Centre, in Ashley Lane swopped instructional airframes during the summer of 1986. PA-22 G-ARHT was damaged by fire and was removed by the Pennine Aviation Museum 29/5/86 to Bacup. On 7/6/86 withdrawn Cherokee G-ATOO arrived. In the area, an Ekin Airbuggy is held as a source of spares for 'flyer' G-AXZA.

G-ATOO+	Cherokee 140	ex Cark. CoA expired 24/9/84. Arrived 7/6/86.
G-AXYX+	Ekin Airbuggy	dbr 30/7/83. Spares for G-AXZA.

PEEL GREEN

Correcting the mention in W&R10, both Luton Minor G-AFIU and Flea BAPC.13 did not go to Warmingham, but to Wigan.

ROYTON

(On the A627 north of Oldham) 1855 Squadron ATC still keep their two airframes (parented by RAF Sealand) at their headquarters in Park Lane.

WS726	Meteor NF.14	7960M, ex Kemble, 1 ANS, 2 ANS, 25. 'G'.
XK637	Vampire T.11	ex Woodford, Chester, St Athan, 4 FTS, 7 FTS. '56'.

STOCKPORT

The nose of Anson C.19 VP519 moved to the workshop at Hadfield. It is thought that the Jodel is still kept in the area by John Mott.

G-AXUY	SAN DR.100A	ex F-BIZI. Crashed 3/9/78. Stored.

TIMPERLEY

(On the A560 east of Altrincham) 145 Squadron ATC still keep their Chipmunk PAX Trainer here.

WD318	Chipmunk T.10 PAX	8207M, ex Chorlton, Sealand, Wrexham, Shawbury, DUR UAS, QUB UAS, Acklington, Ouston SF, 19 RFS.

WIGAN

The Aeroplane Collection Warmingham remains the main centre of TAC activity, but the storage facility here has seen some 'action' since W&R10. The aircraft listed here in the last edition remain in store. HM.14 Pou du Ciel BAPC.13 arrived from Peel Green 13/1/85, but was sold to Mr Handley and left by road for Derby 24/5/86. It stayed here only a short time before moving to Sheffield. Emeraude G-BLHL arrived here from Tattershall before settling upon Warmingham as its new home.

G-AFIU+	LA.4 Minor	ex Peel Green. Arrived 13/1/85.
G-ARDX	Auster 6A	ex Handforth, Cardiff, TW524, Austers, 1900 Flt, Austers. Crashed 1/1/64.
BAPC.17	Woodhams Sprite	ex Irlam. Incomplete.
BAPC.60	Murray Helicopter	ex Salford.
RA854	Cadet TX.1	ex RAFGSA, Woodvale, 41 GS.

Vampire T.11 XE998 was acquired by Ken Fern and moved to Warmingham 18/10/86.

WOODFORD

British Aerospace Avro Aircraft Restoration Society Restoration of the Avro XIX to flying condition comes on apace and there is a possibility that the Vulcan may also fly again. These two aircraft are not available for public inspection, but general enquiries about the Society can be made to : Harry Holmes, British Aerospace plc, Woodford, Cheshire SK7 1QR.

G-AHKX	Avro XIX Srs 2	ex Strathallan, Kemps Aerial Surveys, Treffield Aviation, Meridian Air Maps, Smiths Instruments. CoA expired 10/4/73.
XM603	Vulcan B.2A	ex 44, 101, Wadd Wing, Scampton Wing, 9.

British Aerospace Disaster struck on 12/8/87 when a hangar collapsed at Woodford. A man was killed in the incident and an aircraft took the major brunt of the roof's drop. The aircraft was Charle Church's Lancaster G-BCOH which had arrived by road from Strathallan on 9/4/87 for restoration to flying condition by BAe. The restoration project will continue, but it seems certain that another airframe will have to be procured and the exact future of the Woodford aircraft is undecided as W&R went to press. Of the aircraft listed in W&R10, there have been three departures ; sections of Comet 4C G-BDIU went to Kinloss for use in a simulator; Comet 3 fuselage XP915 moved to the care of the firemen and was scrapped by 3/87; Andover C.1 fuselage XS647 moved to Hatfield 15/8/86 for use as the ATP 'road show'. As well as the Lancaster, a damaged Nimrod and three HS.748s are in store.

TJ-CCD+	HS.748-2ALFD	ex Cameroon Airlines, TJ-AAN, Cameroon AF TJ-XAF. Flew in 16/12/85. Trade in, stored.
+	HS.748-2B	c/no 1808, Set 289, uncompleted airframe. Stored.
+	HS.748-2B	c/no 1809, Set 290, uncompleted airframe. Stored.
KB976+	Lancaster X	G-BCOH, ex Strathallan, CF-TQC, St Albert, Calgary, Rockcliffe, RCAF, 405. 405 Sqn colours as 'LQ-K'. Arrived 9/4/87. see notes above.
XV148	Nimrod prototype	ex A&AEE, makers. Fatigue testing. Minus nose by 1/88.
XV257+	Nimrod MR.2	ex St Mawgan Wing, Kinloss Wing, 203, Kinloss Wing. Cat 4 at St Mawgan 3/6/84, ferried here 7/11/85. Open store.
	Comet 4	fuselage, c/no 06402, ex Nimrod development work, stored.
	Andover	test shell, ATP ground tests.

WYTHENSHAWE

MAPG moved Vampire XD534 to Hadfield during 1987.

Merseyside

BIRKDALE

(On the A565 south west of Southport) Parented by RAF Sealand, 281 Squadron ATC's Chipmunk T.10 PAX Trainer is still to be found in Upper Aughton Road.

WG477	Chipmunk T.10 PAX	8362M, ex Hamble G-ATDP, G-ATDI ntu, Marham SF, MECS, 114, Bri UAS, Abn UAS, 11 RFS, 2 BFTS, 25 RFS, Liv UAS, 25 RFS.

LIVERPOOL AIRPORT

(Or Speke) Principal interest here lies with the Keenair Warbirds C-47 and the fleet of Nord 3202s. Martin Keen entered the C-47, the airworthy Nord G-BIZM and the non-flying G-BIZK into the Luton auction of October 1987 - see the appendix - but found no buyers. Of other W&R residents, Bell 47G G-AXKN was cancelled as being sold in West Germany 5/86 and has moved on.

G-AOJB	Viscount 802	ex BA, BEA. Fire service, poor state. wfu 1/4/76.
G-AVWF+	Cherokee 140	ex Caernarfon, PH-VRK, G-AVWF. CoA expired 23/5/81. Arr by 7/86.
G-BIZJ	Nord 3202	ex Fort Lauderdale, N22546, FAF No 70 'AIX'.
G-BIZK	Nord 3202	ex Fort Lauderdale, N2255E, FAF No 78. See notes above.
G-BIZL	Nord 3202	ex Fort Lauderdale, N2255Y, FAF No 85 'AJG'.
G-OCME+	Trislander	ex G-AYWI, G-51-262. Crashed 9/2/87. Arrived 10/2/87 for spares use.
N54607	C-47A-50-DL	ex Blackbushe, N9842A ntu, 20669/CNA-LM Moroccan AF, CN-CCL Royal Air Maroc, F-BEFA Aigle Azur, 42-24211 USAAF. *Maggie Mae*.

MEOLS

The current status of the Vampire here is unknown. It was last heard of near the *Railway Inn* in poor state.

WZ514	Vampire T.11	ex Irby, Bidston, Woodford, Chester, Shawbury, 5, 98.

WOODVALE

Since W&R10 the number of W&R inmates here has halved. Jim Cassidy's Provost G-BKOS moved initially to Kingsclere by 10/86. Chipmunk T.10 PAX Trainer WP927 moved by 3/86 to Ashton-under-Lyne. Leaving:

WA591	Meteor T.7	7917M, ex St Athan CCAS, Kemble, CAW, 8 FTS, 5 FTS, CAW, 12 FTS, 215 AFS, 208 AFS, 203 AFS, 226 OCU, CFE. Gate guardian.
WG418	Chipmunk T.10 PAX	8209M, ex Hamble, Jever SF, Lon UAS, 61 GCF, Qub UAS, Lon UAS, 3 BFTS, 16 RFS. 10 AEF trainer.

West Midlands

ALLESLEY

(On the A4114 north west of Coventry) Carl Butler's cache of aircraft is kept in the area.

G-AFHA	Mosscraft MA.1	uncompleted airframe, started 1938.
G-AFJV	Mosscraft MA.2	uncompleted airframe, started 1939.
G-AKUW	Super Ace 2	CoA expired 5/6/70. Under restoration.

BERKSWELL

(Between the A452 and the A45 west of Coventry) Ken Woolley still stores his two sequential classics in the area.

G-AFJA	Watkinson Dingbat	ex Headcorn. Crashed 19/5/75. Stored.
DR613	GM.1 Wicko	G-AFJB. CoA expired 12/7/63. Under restoration.

BIRMINGHAM

Museum of Science and Industry Located in Newhall Street, the three airframes held by the museum have not changed. Open Monday to Saturday 0930 to 1700 and Sunday 1400 to 1700.• Contact : Birmingham Museum of Science and Industry, Newhall Street, Birmingham B3 1RZ. Telephone 021 236 1022.

KX829	Hurricane IV	ex Loughborough, 631, 1606 Flt, 137. With wings of Z7015. 6 Squadron colours as 'JV-I'.
ML427	Spitfire IX	6457M, ex Castle Bromwich, St Athan, South Marston, Millfield, Hucknall, FLS, 3501 SU. 'IS-T'.
	Beaufighter I	ex Coventry. Cockpit section only.

Haslucks Green Barracks Located in Haslucks Green Road, Shirley, the barracks hosts 492 Squadron ATC (not as given in W&R10) and Training Ship *Gamecock*. The ATC unit added an anonymous JP nose to their Canberra nose section during 1987. The Sea Cadets took delivery of a Wessex early in 1987.

WT534	Canberra PR.7	8549M, ex Halton, St Athan, 17. Nose only.
XS886+	Wessex HAS.1	A2685, ex Lee-on-Solent, Wroughton, 771. Arrived 2/87.
+	Jet Provost	nose section, first noted 5/87.

2 Field Hospital, Kings Heath. A report to hand has this Birmingham-based unit receiving Wessex ,5 XS521 during March 1987 - further details much appreciated.

30 Squadron ATC still have their Meteor, parented by Cosford, at the Barrows Lane TAVR Centre, eldon.

646 Meteor TT.20 8189M, ex 5 CAACU, 3/4 CAACU, CSE.

71 Squadron ATC at the Wilfred Martineau Upper School in Gressel Lane, Tile Cross, maintain their mpire T.11 pod.

450 Vampire T.11 ex Sealand, Wrexham, Woodford, Chester, Shawbury, RAFC, 233 OCU, 202 AFS. Pod only.

hers Still stored at a private house in Shirley are Bensen G-ASLF and its anonymous friend.

ASLF Bensen B-7 ex Aston. Stored.

Bensen ex Aston. Stored.

RMINGHAM AIRPORT

r Elmdon) No change here, the Trident still serves the firemen and the MAM Humber still 'flies' in e terminal building.

AWZZ Trident 3B-101 ex BA, BEA. wfu 23/11/84.

PC.9 Humber Monoplane ex Yeovilton, Wroughton, Yeovilton, Coventry. MAM loan. In terminal.

OVENTRY

3 Squadron ATC In Smith Street, the unit still maintains its anonymous nose sections.

Valiant ex Cosford. Nose section, white scheme.

Jet Provost T.3 ex Kemble. Fuselage number PAC/W/10169. Nose section only.

hers Several individuals have aircraft in the area. Roy Nerou continues with the restoration of the ilton, as do Maurice and Peter Bayliss with their Spitfire Tr IX. Mike Abbey should still have his 'lea' in the area, although this has not been physically confirmed for some time.

-AFSV Chilton DW.1A CoA expired 12/7/72. Under restoration.

-BMSB Spitfire Tr IX ex Stockbridge, Andover, G-ASOZ, Elstree, IAAC 158, Gormanston, 1 Fighter Squadron, G-15-171, RAF MJ627 29 MU, 441, 83 GSU. Under restoration.

PC.27 HM.14 Pou du Ciel ex Stratford. Under construction using some original parts. See above.

OLIHULL

he Editor popped this into 'Warwickshire' in W&R10 - he apologises to the population for the chronic sorientation trauma thereby caused.) Norecrin G-BAYL stored here moved on to Rye. In the town rasive Development Ltd acquired an Aztec hulk from Ipswich during early 1987. It is used for trials plastic bead blasting!

-ASRE+ Aztec 250C ex Ipswich, Southend. CoA expired 6/11/77. Arrived 10/4/87.

TONNALL

n the A452 south east of Brownhills) The hulk of former Jersey-based Horizon G-AYOL arrived here uring 1986.

-AYOL+ Horizon 180 ex St John, N3788, F-BNQU. Poor state.

UTTON COLDFIELD

b Mitchell Continues to keep his Monarch here, along with his Whitney Straight.

-AEUJ+ Whitney Straight ex Marple, East Midlands, Bournemouth. CoA expired 4/6/70. Under restoration.

-AFRZ Monarch ex Shipdham, G-AIDE, W6463, Kemble, 10 GCF, FTCCF, 13 EFTS, G-AFRZ.

George's Barracks Is still guarded by its Scout, located in Rectory Road.

R777" Scout AH.1 XT625, ex 'XR625', Middle Wallop, TAD625.

5 Squadron ATC The unit's Vampire T.11 was put up for tender by the MoD in July 1987. The unit ere/are located in St Bernards Road, off Wylde Green Road.

602 Vampire T.11 7737M, ex Smethwick, RAFC, 125. See notes above.

Norfolk

COLTISHALL

On the dump, Canberra PR.3 WE173/8740M had perished by mid 1986. Two Hunters have arrived as possibl candidates for burning at some stage. Hunter F.6 XF386 had gone by late 1986 moving on to Otterburr Otherwise, little change here.

SL542	Spitfire XVI	8390M, ex Horsham St Faith, Duxford SF, 2 CAACU, 1 CAACU, 695, 595. Gate guardian, in 695 Squadron colours as '4M-N'.
WT745+	Hunter T.8C	8893M, ex St Athan, Shawbury, Kemble, FRADU, 764, Yeovilton SF, 14. Rear end of XL565. For the ASF. Arrived 1987.
XG254+	Hunter FGA.9	8881M, ex St Athan, 1 TWU, 2 TWU, TWU, 229 OCU, 54, HS, 54. Arrived 10/3/86. BDRT.
XM172	Lightning F.1A	8427M, ex 226 OCU, 56. Gate guardian.
XX109+	Jaguar GR.1	8918M, ex Warton. Arrived 21/10/86. weapons loading trainer.
XX734	Jaguar GR.1	8816M, ex Abingdon, Indian AF JI014, XX734. Fuselage only, BDRT.

FAKENHAM

Tiger Moth G-ANFL's restoration was completed during 1987 and it flew again. Jim O'Sullivan continue to work on his Terrier.

G-ASCH	Terrier 2	ex Hinton-in-the-Hedges, Enstone, VF565, 654, 12 ILF, 1912 Flt, 652. CoA expired 20/7/81. Under restoration.

FELTHORPE

Alpavia RF-3 G-BHLU was flying by 1986. The rebuild of the Nipper continues.

G-ARBG	Nipper II	crashed 16/5/84. Under rebuild.

FOULSHAM

Islander G-AXXG was rebuilt and flying again by late 1987.

LITTLE SNORING

There has been no news of the anonymous Tiger Moth reported to be under construction/reconstructic here. The little Alaparma Baldo G-BCRH moved back to Challock.

LUDHAM

A case of all change here. The Piaggio P.149D that was stored here, OO-MEL, had gone by 5/86. It i reported to have been moved by road to 'Lincolnshire' - anyone have a more precise location? Spitfir FR.XVIII HS649 (Indian serial), last reported at Hemel Hempstead, arrived here during 1986 and wa prepared for static display standard before being exported to Overloon, in the Netherlands. Arrivir in late 1986 was a former St Leonards Spitfire, which is now receiving attention. A Chipmunk is als under rebuild.

TE566+	Spitfire IX	G-BLCK, ex St Leonards-on-Sea, Israeli DF/AF 32, Czech AF, RAF TE566, 312. Arrived by 5/86.
+	Chipmunk T.10	rebuild, possibly frustrated, to *Supermunk* status. Using wings of WD334.

MARHAM

With respect to the *electric flick knives* based here, the Victors are still the main focus of attentic at the base, and dominate the W&R sphere. Victor K.1 XA932, in poor state, was put up for tender 8/8 and by 11/87 was cut up for scrap and removed. On the dump K.2 XL232 had expired by 1987. Former 5 Squadron K.2 XH673 has been mounted dramatically outside the Station Headquarters and carries joint 5 and 57 squadron markings. Another K.2 has been allocated for BDRT and spares recovery, other item mentioned in W&R10 are unchanged.

WH863	Canberra T.17	8693M, ex 360, RAE, IAM. BDRT.
XA917	Victor B.1	7827M, ex Wyton, 232 OCU, 15, 101, RAE, A&AEE. Cockpit section only, rescue trainer.
XH560	Vulcan B.2	ex Waddington, 50, Wadd Wing, 27, Akrotiri Wing, Cott Wing, Wadd Wing, Cott Wing, 230 OCU, 12, MoA, 230 OCU. Fire dump.
XH673+	Victor K.2	8911M, ex 57, Witt Wing, 139, MoA. Outside SHQ, 55/57 Squadron markings.
XL160+	Victor K.2	8910M, ex 57, 55, Witt Wing, 100, MoA. Wfu 6/86 BDRT and spares use.
XX947	Tornado P.03	8797M, ex Warton. Weapons loading trainer.

EATISHEAD

in between the A149, A1062 and A151 north east of Norwich) The Meteor still guards this RAF base.

(654	Meteor F.8	8092M, ex Kemble, 85, CFE, AWFCS, 247.

ORWICH AIRPORT

Or Horsham St Faith) City of Norwich Aviation Museum Recent developments have mainly involved nprovement of display and visitor facilities within the site. There have been three new additions, though the Grasshopper glider is on loan. The Museum is open on Sundays October to April 1000 to 300 and May to September 1000 to 1700 and on Thursday evenings during June, July and August from 1930 o dusk. Contact : City of Norwich Aviation Museum, Old Norwich Road, Horsham St Faiths, Norwich, orfolk.

-ASKK	Herald 211	ex Air UK, PP-ASU, G-ASKK, PI-C910, CF-MCK. wfu 30/3/85.
(228	Anson C.19	ex Duxford, Crawley, WCS, TCCF, Old Sarum SF, SLAW, FCCS, SLAW, Hucknall SF. Poor state, blown over 1/2/83.
0375	Vampire T.11	7887M, ex Cleethorpes, Elsham Hall, Duxford, Winterbourne Gunner, St Athan, 4 FTS, 1 FTS, 3 CAACU, 73.
.840+	Whirlwind HAS.7	ex Sibson, Blackpool Airport, Fleetwood, Wroughton, 705, Brawdy SF, Culdrose SF, 705, 820. Arrived during 1986.
1612	Vulcan B.2A	ex 44, Wadd Wing, Scampton Wing, 9.
355	Whirlwind HAR.10	G-BEBC/8463M, ex Faygate, 38 GCF, 21, MinTech, CFS.
458+	Grasshopper TX.1	ex Fakenham area. Arrived during 1986. On loan.
919	Sea Vixen FAW.2	8163M, ex Chertsey, Halton, 766, 899, A&AEE.
21	Mystere IVA	ex Sculthorpe, French AF.
5718+	T-33A-5-LO	ex Sculthorpe, Turkish AF ntu, French AF, 51-6718. Arrived 31/5/86.

irport At the airport itself, the Herald is still the dominant shape in the W&R listing. Series 401 -BEYK was flying again by late 1986, though not in maritime patrol guise.

-APWH	Herald 201	ex Air UK, BIA, BUA. wfu 11/7/80. Fire dump, poor state.
-AVEZ	Herald 210	ex Museum, Air UK, BIA, BUA, PP-ASW, G-AVEZ, HB-AAH. wfu 5/1/81. External store.
907	Varsity T.1	ex 6 FTS, AES, 3 ANS. Fire dump, poor state.

LD BUCKENHAM

On the B1077 south of Attleborough) Jim Avis of Howard Avis Aviation has expanded the number of irframes being worked on here, including two much-travelled Skeeters. The wreck of Pawnee G-AVXA moved ut to 'Lincolnshire' by 8/87.

-AODT+	Tiger Moth	ex R5250, Schwechat SF, 24 EFTS, 19 EFTS, 16 OTU. CoA expired 26/6/86. Under restoration, first noted 8/87.
-APOI+	Skeeter 8	ex Llandegla, Inverness, Blackpool, Southampton. CoA expired 30/3/61. First noted 7/87.
.812+	Skeeter AOP.12	G-SARO, ex Inverness, Leeds, Wroughton, 9 Flt, 652, Middle Wallop. CoA expired 4/11/84. First noted 7/87.

AVENINGHAM

On the B1136 north of Beccles) Both Stampes remain on rebuild, along with the composite Cub.

-AYDR	SNCAN SV-4C	ex Ipswich, F-BCLG. Damaged 16/6/73. Rebuild.
-BEPF	SNCAN SV-4A	ex F-BCVD. Rebuild.
30228	J-3C-65 Cub	under rebuild, using the wings of N2092M.

EYMERSTON HALL

ing Commander K H Wallis bases his fleet of autogiros here. The fleet is large and varied, and everal could well justify listing under W&R. However, aircraft are frequently returned to use so only onfirmed groundings are listed, in this case just one 'spares ship'. The Austers and Monsun are nchanged. See also Swanton Morley.

-ATHL	Wallis WA-116/F	ex Bury St Edmunds. Damaged 5/3/85. Spares use.
-AZBU	Auster AOP.9	XR246/7862M, ex Shipdham, Middle Wallop, Beagle, 651. Stored.
-AZVA	Monsun 150FF	ex D-EAAQ ntu. CoA expired 3/3/83. Stored.
-BGKT	Auster AOP.9	XN441, ex Shipdham, Scarning, St Athan, Aden, Kenya. Stored.

SCULTHORPE

T-33A 16718 departed by road for Norwich 31/5/86 leaving only the gate guardian.

42212	F-100D-11-NA	ex French AF. Displayed within the base.

SHIPDHAM

The Arrow Air Services store of Indian Tigers is undisturbed. Tiger G-ALUC was flying again by 1986 otherwise the listing for W&R10 holds.

G-AYAF	Twin Comanche 160C	ex N8842Y. CoA expired 8/5/77. Stored.
G-BINH	Tiger Moth	ex VT-DOW, Indian AF HU488. Crashed 19/6/84. Rebuild.
VT-CZV	Tiger Moth	ex G-AISY, N6740, 7 EFTS, 11 EFTS, 18 ERFTS.
VT-DOU	Tiger Moth	ex Indian AF HU483. Stored.
VT-DOX	Tiger Moth	ex Madras, Indian AF HU492. Stored.
VT-DOY	Tiger Moth	ex Madras, Indian AF HU498. Stored.
VT-DOZ	Tiger Moth	ex Indian AF HU504. US Mail colours. Stored.
VT-DPA	Tiger Moth	ex Madras, Indian AF HU511. US Mail colours. Stored.
VT-DPB	Tiger Moth	ex Madras, Indian AF HU708. Stored.
VT-DPC	Tiger Moth	ex Indian AF 'HU187'. Stored.
VT-DPE	Tiger Moth	ex Indian AF HU858. Stored.
VT-DPH	Tiger Moth	ex Indian AF HU887. Stored.
N9191	Tiger Moth	G-ALND, ex Panshanger, 5 SoTT, 19 EFTS, Duxford SF, 6 CPF. Crashed 8/3/81, under rebuild.

SWANTON MORLEY

The home of the Maintenance Data Centre of the Central Servicing Development Establishment, the tw airframes used by the unit remain unchanged. Additions relate to the civil side of the airfield, th Chipmunk cockpit section having been in need of an identity for some time. Ken Wallis's Wallbr Monoplane has been out of action here for some time, and is overdue for a mention.

G-BFIP+	Wallbro Monoplane	CoA expired 22/4/82. Stored.
WB626+	Chipmunk T.10	ex Hendon SF, 5 FTS, 18 RFS. Cockpit section, spares for G-BCXN.
WJ775	Canberra B.6RC	8581M, ex 51, 192.
XV152	Buccaneer S.2A	8776M, ex St Athan, 237 OCU, 208.

SWANTON NOVERS

Adding to W&R10, Cessna 310 G-ATCR turned up at Denham by 4/87.

THORPE ABBOTTS

(On the A143 east of Diss) The 100th Bomb Group Museum is based upon the former control tower here The Carvair cockpit section is believed to still be here.

CF-EPV	Carvair	ex Fitton Lake, Southend, EI-AMR, N88819, 42-72343. Cockpit section only.

WATTON

The gate guardian is still in place at the main gate of the RAF Station. The RAF Watton Mustan Restoration Group disbanded and their P-51D 28 (correcting W&R10) moved to Fowlmere for Robs Lamplough The Varsity WL628/8098M mentioned in W&R10 was acquired by a scrap merchant and removed.

WS807	Meteor NF.14	7973M, ex Kemble, 1 ANS, 2 ANS. 46 Squadron colours as 'N'.

WEST RAYNHAM

The gate at this RAF airfield and SAM site is still protected by the Javelin.

XH980	Javelin FAW.8	7867M, ex Stafford, Shawbury, 41. 85 Squadron colours as 'A'.

Northamptonshire

EAST HADDON

(North of the A428 north west of Northampton) The Brantly is still stored in the area.

G-AVIP Brantly B.2B CoA expired 19/11/81. Stored.

HINTON-IN-THE-HEDGES

It is thought that the Cessna hulk is still to be found here, but confirmation would be appreciated.

G-AWCJ Cessna F.150H Crashed 2/83. Wreck.

KINGS CLIFFE

(South of the A47, west of Peterborough) John Tempest and friends are rebuilding a Stampe in the area.

G-BEUS+ AIA SV-4C ex Gransden, Long Marston, F-BKFK, F-DAFK, French military.

NORTHAMPTON

Robin and Josephine Livett are rebuilding their Moth Minor in the area.

G-AFPR Moth Minor ex Woodley, X5122, Langham SF, 1 TTU, 5 OTU, 16, G-AFPR. CoA expired 15/4/56. Under rebuild.

NORTHAMPTON AIRPORT

(Or Sywell) The wreck situation here is remarkably stable, with the only addition to the listing below being a long-lost specimen. Going back to W&R10, Hiller G-APKY eventually surfaced at Wellingborough.

G-AIGR+ J/1N Alpha original fuselage frame, stored.
G-ARFG Cessna 175A ex Panshanger, N7005E. CoA expired 16/11/81. Fuselage only.
G-AWRA Pup 100 ex ZK-CYP ntu, G-35-020. Damaged 12/68. Stripped fuselage, in shed.
G-BKJR Hughes 269C ex VR-HHT, VR-HHM, N8969F. Crashed 13/7/84. Spares recovery.

WELLINGBOROUGH

By early 1987, two 'vintage' helicopters had gravitated here.

G-APKY+ Hiller UH-12B ex Northampton Airport, PH-NFL. CoA expired 7/5/74. Arrived here circa 1984. Stored.
MD497"+ Widgeon G-ANLW, ex Little Staughton, Tattershall Thorpe, Southend. CoA expired 27/5/81. Arrived during early 1987.

Northumberland

BOULMER

This RAF SAR base is guarded by a Lightning.

XP745 Lightning F.3 8453M, ex Leconfield, 29, 56. 29 Squadron colours.

CURROCK HILL

At the gliding site, it is believed the Chipmunk 'spares ship' is still in the rafters.

WK549 Chipmunk T.10 ex Kemble, BFWF, 651, 657, 63 GCF, 9 RFS, 5 BFTS. Stored.

OTTERBURN RANGES

(On the A696 north of Newcastle-on-Tyne) The ranges here have been combined with those of Spadeadam, at least in terms of airspace, and represent a vast tract of land. Accordingly, it is very difficult to confirm the status of aircraft and the main source of information is a confirmed delivery into the area, or a fleeting visit. For this issue, we have the luxury of an actual visit in 4/86 to the dummy airfield site, although other areas could well contain aircraft targets. Whirlwind HAR.10 XP302/8443M was reported as "burnt" and was certainly not visible by 4/86, also gone by that date were the other two Whirlwind HAR.10s, XP331/8649M and XR457/8644M. Present at that time were :-

XF386+ Hunter F.6A 8707M, ex Coltishall, Kemble, Laarbruch SF, 229 OCU, 92, 65.
XG264+ Hunter FGA.9 8715M, ex Brawdy, 2 TWU, TWU, 229 OCU, 58, 45, 54. Rear fuselage of XF445.
XP515+ Gnat T.1 8614M, ex Wattisham, Kemble, 4 FTS, CFS, 4 FTS, CFS, 4 FTS.
XS594 Andover C.1 ex Kemble, 84, St Athan Apps, A&AEE.
XS601 Andover C.1 ex Kemble, A&AEE, 46, Andover CU.

Nottinghamshire

BALDERTON

(On the A1 south east of Newark-on-Trent) In the compound used by A1 Commercial Vehicle Sales as a billboard, the Lightning is still causing cars to take a 'double-take' as they scream past!

XN728	Lightning F.2A	8546M, ex Coningsby, 92.

COSSALL

(Between the A6096 and the M1 north of Stapleford) The Auster continues to rot in Wheatley's scrapyard.

G-AJDY	J/1 Autocrat	ex Sherburn. CoA expired 9/7/71.

FIRBECK

(West of the A60 north of Worksop) South Yorkshire Aircraft Preservation Society At Home Farm, SYAS continue to work on their expanding airframe fleet, and on the establishment of what will be a first class museum display here. Major achievement here has been the salvage from Braemar of considerable sections of Wellington L7775. As yet insufficient for a 'main-line' entry, this is a major long term project and is also helping the Brooklands example. Visits are possible at weekends, further details from ; SYAS, Home Farm, Firbeck, near Worksop, Nottinghamshire. Telephone 0709 812168. The Cessna T.210L G-BAGE mentioned in W&R10 is only a rear fuselage and should be discounted. Dave Pope picked up TB-10 G-BGTB fuselage and moved it to Reading in January 1988.

G-AEKR"	HM.14 Pou du Ciel	BAPC.121, ex Nostell Priory, Crowle, Finningley.
G-ALYB	Auster 5	ex Bristol, White Waltham, RT520. wfu 5/63. Under restoration.
G-AWFH	Cessna F.150H	ex Netherthorpe. Crashed 16/12/79. Fuselage, with tail of G-AWTX.
A4850"	SE.5A scale rep	BAPC.176, ex Pontefract. Based on a Currie Wot airframe.
XE935+	Vampire T.11	ex Sibson, Hitchin, Woodford, Chester, St Athan, 8 FTS. Includes part of XE985. Arrived during 1986.
XM279	Canberra B(I).8	ex Nostell Priory, Cambridge, 16, 3. Nose section only.
+	Vampire FB.5	ex Malmesbury. Pod only, on loan from Paul Flynn. Arrived by 5/87.

HUCKNALL

Both of the aircraft that were listed here could be heading for *LOST!* Luton Minor G-ATWS is reported by one source to have been burnt. Cadet TX.1 RA897 has not been seen for a considerable period of time.

LANGAR

The para-trainer in use with the club here is now identified.

G-BATD	Cessna U.206F	ex Isle of Man, Sibson, Shobdon, N60204. Crashed 5/4/80. Para-trainer.

MANSFIELD

384 Squadron ATC still have their Canberra nose at their headquarters.

WT507	Canberra PR.7	8131M/8548M, ex Halton, St Athan, 31, 17, 58, A&AEE, 58, 527, 58. Nose.

MISSON

(Near Bawtry) There having been no up-to-date reports on the contents of Lew Jackson's yard and the continued existence of Jet Provost T.5 XW424 wreck, it is felt prudent in this edition to appeal for more information.

NEWARK-ON-TRENT

Cliff Baker's Auster hive continues to thrive as he supplies parts to Auster operators worldwide. The bulk of these aircraft are frames or withdrawn from use. There have been two additions.

G-AIJI	J/1N Alpha	ex East Midlands, Elsham Hall, Goxhill, Kirmington. Damaged 12/1/75.
G-AIKE	Auster 5	ex Portsmouth, NJ728. Crashed 1/9/65.
G-AJAS+	J/1N Alpha	CoA expired 17/4/86. Stored.
G-AKOT	Auster 5	ex North Denes, TJ433. Crashed 9/9/62.
G-AKWT	Auster 5	ex East Midlands, Elsham Hall, Goxhill, Stroxton Lodge, Tollerton, MT360. Crashed 7/8/48.

-ALNV+ Auster 5 ex Nottingham, Leicester, RT578. wfu 10/59.
-AMUJ J/5F Aiglet Tnr ex East Midlands, Winthorpe. Crashed 8/6/60.
-ANHW Auster 5D ex Shipdham, TJ320, 664. CoA expired 9/3/70.
-ANHX Auster 5D ex Leicester, TW519, 661, A&AEE. Crashed 28/3/70.
-AOCP Auster 5 ex TW462, 666. Damaged 4/70. Under rebuild.
-ARGB Auster 6A ex Waddington, VF635, 662, 1901 Flt. CoA expired 21/6/74.
-ARGI Auster 6A ex Chirk, Heathfield, VF530, 661. CoA expired 4/7/76.
-AROJ Airedale ex Leicester, Thorney, HB-EOC, G-AROJ. CoA expired 8/1/76.
-ARTM Terrier 1 ex Chirk, WE536, 651, 657, Schwechat SF. Damaged 6/70.
-ASWF Airedale ex Leicester. CoA expired 27/4/83.
C-AXR Auster 4 ex Shoreham, Spain, G-ANHU, MT255.
-BBSO Auster 5 ex Taunton, G-AMJM, TW452, 62 GCF. Frame only.
Auster D.6/180 ex White Waltham. Frame only.
Terrier 2 ex White Waltham. Frame only.

EWTON

ne missile loading trainer Lightning T.5 XS451 was put up for tender 6/87 and successfully bid for by eter Hoar of Militair. It made the journey to Cranfield by 4/88. The Jet Provost that was nidentified in W&R10 is now sewn up. Otherwise no change with the airframes here.

.627 Varsity T.1 8488M, ex 6 FTS, 2 ANS, 1 ANS, BCBS. Police Dog Training School.
N901 Hunter F.2 7543M, ex 9 SoTT, Melksham, 257. Fire dump, poor state.
T694 Hunter F.1 7510M, ex Debden, 229 OCU, DFLS, 54. Gate guardian, 43 Squadron colours.
N641 Jet Provost T.3 8865M, ex Shawbury, 1 FTS, RAFC, 3 FTS. Fire dump.

OTTINGHAM

uster 4 G-AJXV moved on to Leicester Airport.

OTTINGHAM AIRPORT

Or Tollerton) Auster 5 G-ALNV which was 'lost' in W&R10, has turned up at Cliff Baker's place at ewark. G-AGVJ, also 'mislaid', is still here, having never left! Pup 160 G-AVLM moved to Tatenhill 2/11/86. Globe GC-1 Swift G-BFNM arrived here by 2/86 and started restoration. It moved by road to atenhill 15/11/86.

-AGVJ J/1N Alpha wfu 8/64. Fuselage, stored.

OUTH SCARLE

In between the A46 and the A1133 south west of Lincoln) It is believed that the original fuselage of allye G-AZEE is still stored here.

-AZEE MS.880B Rallye ex Shipdham, F-BKKA. Original fuselage, stored in rafters.

TAPLEFORD

On the A453 south west of Nottingham) 1360 Squadron ATC still keep their camouflaged Vampire in Cliff ill Avenue.

J463 Vampire T.11 8023M, ex St Athan, CATCS, 3/4 CAACU, 5 FTS, 7 FTS.

YERSTON

he RAF Police School still uses its Sea Prince instructional airframe here and also uses the Varsity t Newton for similar instruction. Central Gliding School has continued to handle the disposal of a arge number of gliders, but all have been too transitory for inclusion within W&R. Three gliders have een given 'M' serials for display purposes at Syerston however and these are given below.

P314 Sea Prince T.1 8634M, ex Halton, Kemble, 750, Sydenham SF, 750, Lossiemouth SF, Shorts Ferry Flt, Brawdy SF, Lossiemouth SF, 750.
Z791+ Grasshopper TX.1 8944M, ex High Wycombe.
E799+ Cadet TX.3 8943M, ex CGS.
N185+ Sedburgh TX.1 8942M, ex CGS, 634 VGS, 4 MGSP, 635 VGS.

INTHORPE

On the A46 north east of Newark-on-Trent) Newark air Museum With only one acquisition and one eparture from the 'fleet', it would seem at first glance that NAM is slowing down. Far from it, the ctivity at the Newark Show Ground site is probably at the highest it has ever been, with a combination of part and full-time staff working on the restoration of exhibits and the development of the site general. The entrance hall and shop is complete and plans are underway to construct an engi exhibition building during 1988. Plans for a hangar are progressing well and the hunt is now on for suitable building. During late 1986 the owner of Magister T9738/G-AKAT removed the aircraft to t Sherburn area where it is under restoration to flying condition. The Museum is open April to Octob Monday to Friday 1000 to 1700, Saturday 1300 to 1700 and Sundays 1000 to 1800. November to Marc Sundays only 1000 to dusk. All buildings are available to the disabled, as are the toilets. Contact Mick Smith, Curator, Newark Air Museum, 35 Queen Street, Balderton, Newark, Notts, NG24 3NS. Muse telephone : 0636 707170.

G-AHMP	Proctor II	ex Honiton Clyst, BV631, Filton, Bristol, 758. Centre section only.
G-ANXB	Heron 1	ex Biggin Hill, Fairflight, BEA Scottish, G-5-14. Under restoration.
BAPC.20	Lee Richards rep	ex *Those Magnificent Men*. Dismantled.
BAPC183	Zurowski ZP.1	ex Burton-on-Trent. Homebuilt helicopter, unflown.
VH-UTH	Monospar ST-12	ex ex Australia. Stored.
KF532	Harvard IIB	cockpit section. Identity now confirmed.
TG517	Hastings T.5	ex 230 OCU, SCBS, BCBS, 202, 53, 47.
VL348	Anson C.19	G-AVVO, ex Southend, Shawbury, 22 GCF, 24 GCF, Colerne SF, 62 GCF, HCMSU, Reserve Command CF.
VR249	Prentice T.1	G-APIY, ex 1 ASS, RAFC. 'FA-EL'.
VT229	Meteor F.4	7151M, ex Duxford, Colerne, 12 FTS, 209 AFS, 207 AFS, 616, Lubeck SF.
VZ608	Meteor FR.9(mod)	ex Hucknall, Shoreham, MoS, Rolls-Royce. RB.108 test-bed.
VZ634	Meteor T.7	8657M, ex Wattisham, 5 MU, MoA, Leeming SF, Stradishall SF, 41, 141, 609, 247.
WF369	Varsity T.1	ex 6 FTS, AE&AEOS, AES, 2 ANS, 201 AFS.
WH904	Canberra T.19	ex Cambridge, 7, 85, West Raynham TFF, 228 OCU, 35, 207.
WK277	Swift FR.5	7719M, ex Cosford, Leconfield, 2.
WM913	Sea Hawk FB.3	8162M/A2510, ex Fleetwood, Sealand, Culdrose, Abbotsinch, 736.
WR977	Shackleton MR.3/3	8186M, ex Finningley, 203, 42, 206, 203, 42, 201, 206, 201, 220.
WS692	Meteor NF.12	7605M, ex Cranwell, Henlow, 72, 46, 38 MU, 33 MU.
WS739	Meteor NF.14	7961M, ex Misson, Church Fenton, Kemble, 1 ANS, 2 ANS, 25.
WT933	Sycamore 3	7709M, ex Sutton-in-Ashfield, Strensall, Halton, G-ALSW ntu.
WV606	Provost T.1	7622M, ex Halton, 1 FTS. 'P-B'.
WV787	Canberra B.2/8	8799M, ex Abingdon, A&AEE. Sapphire test-bed and other trials.
WW217	Sea Venom FAW.21	ex Cardiff-Wales, Ottershaw, Culdrose, Yeovilton, ADS, 891, 890.
XD515	Vampire T.11	7998M, ex Misson, Linton-on-Ouse, 3 FTS, 7 FTS, 1 FTS, 5 FTS, 206 AFS.
XD593	Vampire T.11	ex Woodford, Chester, St Athan, 8 ftS, CFS, FWS, 5 FTS, 4 FTS.
XE317	Sycamore HR.14	ex Portsmouth, CFS, G-AMWO ntu. 'S-N'.
XH992	Javelin FAW.8	7829M, ex Cosford, Shawbury, 85.
XJ560	Sea Vixen FAW.2	8142M, ex RAE Bedford, Farnborough, Halton, 893, 899, 892, 890. Arrived 10/8/86, not as given in W&R10.
XL149	Beverley C.1	7988M, ex Finningley, 84, 30, 84, 242 OCU. Cockpit section only.
XL764	Skeeter AOP.12	7940M, ex Nostell Priory, Rotherham, Middle Wallop, Arborfield, MoA, Middl Wallop.
XM594	Vulcan B.2A	ex 44, Scampton Wing, 617, 27.
XM685	Whirlwind HAS.7	ex Panshanger area, Elstree, Luton, G-AYZJ ntu, Fleetlands, Lee-on-Solent, 771, *Ark Royal* Ship's Flt, 847, 848.
XN819	Argosy C.1	8205M, ex Finningley, Shawbury, Benson Wing, 105, MoA. Cockpit section.
XN934+	Buccaneer S.1	A2600, ex Bruntingthorpe, East Midlands, Brough, Pershore, 807. Arrived 13/3/88.
XP226	Gannet AEW.3	A2667, ex Lee-on-Solent, Southwick, Lee, Lossiemouth, Ilchester, 849.
XT200	Sioux AH.1	ex Middle Wallop.
51-9036	T-33A-1-LO	ex Sculthorpe, French AF. Thunderbirds colours.
54-2223	F-100D-16-NA	ex Sculthorpe, French AF.
83	Mystere IVA	ex Sculthorpe, French AF. '8-MS'.
56321	Safir	G-BKPY, ex Norwegian AF.

Oxfordshire

ABINGDON

In previous editions Abingdon's entry has become a little fragmented, this is now remedied with fewer sub-headings.

Abingdon Maintenance Unit The skyline at Abingdon changed during 1987 with the scrapping of four of the Super VC-10s and the arrival of three forlorn Nimrod AEW.3s. Super VC-10s ZD231, ZD236, ZD237 and ZD238 were put up for tender during 2/87 and were snapped up by a scrappy who turned them into pots and pans during 4/87. It is rumoured that six of the remaining airframes will be converted to two-point tankers (K.4s?) sometime in the future, as the RAF strives to get over its tanker-debit. The arrival of the Nimrods also caused much rumouring. High in the ratings at present are ; tankers, flying classrooms, Nimrod crew trainers, ingots - in no particular order.

XV261+	Nimrod AEW.3	ex Waddington, Woodford, Kinloss Wing, St M Wing, 203. Flew in 14/7/87.
XV262+	Nimrod AEW.3	ex Waddington, Woodford, Kinloss Wing, St M Wing, 203, Kinloss Wing. Flew in 12/8/87.
XZ286+	Nimrod AEW.3	ex Waddington, JTU, Woodford. Flew in 13/7/87.
ZD230	Super VC-10 1151	ex G-ASGA, Prestwick, BA, BOAC.
ZD235	Super VC-10 1151	ex G-ASGG, Prestwick, BA, BOAC.
ZD239	Super VC-10 1151	ex G-ASGK, Prestwick, BA, BOAC.
ZD240	Super VC-10 1151	ex G-ASGL, Prestwick, BA, BOAC.
ZD241	Super VC-10 1151	ex G-ASGM, Prestwick, BA, BOAC.
ZD242	Super VC-10 1151	ex G-ASGP, Prestwick, BA, BOAC.
ZD243	Super VC-10 1151	ex G-ASGR, Prestwick, BA, BOAC.

Battle Damage Repair Flight As might be expected, the throughput of airframes with the BDR school is impressive. The normal procedure is to relegate an 'experienced' airframe to the dump, but other disposals do crop up. Departures since W&R10 include ; Whirlwind HAS.7 XK943 to the dump - see below; Jet Provost T.3A XN643 going to Cranwell; Whirlwind HAR.10 XP352 was put up for tender 8/87 and had gone by 1/88 - destination unknown; Phantom FGR.2 hulk XV436 was put up for tender 8/87 and was scrapped by 1/88; Jaguar GR.1 XX118 did not come here, and can be found under Halton. The example that did come here was XX115, and only in the form of a centre section; Hawk T.1 hulk XX300 moved to Valley by early 1987; the Valiant BK.1 nose turned out to be XD826, this was acquired by WAM and moved to Cardiff-Wales Airport by 6/86. After all that activity it is somewhat surprising to find that only two new airframes have arrived, a noseless Hunter (listed below) and the centre fuselage of Jet Provost T.5A XW315 which arrived by 10/86 and is mentioned here for completeness, being too small to list.

WJ678	Canberra B.2	8864M, ex Wyton, 100, 85, C(A).
WJ867	Canberra T.4	8643M, ex Newton, A&AEE, ETPS.
XG226+	Hunter F.6A	8800M, ex 1 TWU, TWU, 229 OCU, 92, 66, 92. Noseless fuselage and centre section, arrived by 4/86. Nose at Catterick.
XP541	Gnat T.1	8616M, ex 4 FTS. Camouflaged. Reported sold in the USA mid 1987.
XT274	Buccaneer S.2A	8856M, ex St Athan, 237 OCU, 12, 237 OCU, 208, 237 OCU, 12.
XT284	Buccaneer S.2A	8855M, ex St Athan, 237 OCU, 15, 208.
XV337	Buccaneer S.2C	8852M, ex A&AEE, 208, A&AEE.
XX344	Hawk T.1	8847M, ex Dunsfold, RAE. Crashed 7/1/82. Hulk.

Royal Air Force Exhibition Flight Parented by the resident Aircraft Salvage and Repair Unit, RAFEF is responsible for moving the RAF's fleet of static airframes around the country in their recruiting 'roadshows'. It has a mixture of whole (and real) airframes, real nose section and convincing, but nevertheless plastic, replica airframes. The plastic *thingies* regularly have their 'serials' changed, so beware! There have been a couple of disposals and a few additions to the fleet. Whirlwind HAR.10 XP359 moved to Stafford during late 1987; Jet Provost T.3 nose XN493 went to Camberley; JP T.4 nose section XP677 to Uckfield; JP T.4 nose section XR681 to Odiham; and Vulcan B.1 nose section XA893 to Cosford. That leaves :-

TB382	Spitfire XVI	7244M, ex Henlow, Ely, Middleton St George, 602.
TE311	Spitfire XVI	7241M, ex Henlow, Wattisham, 2/3 CAACU, 103 FRS, 102 FRS, 83 GSU, 421. In 421 Squadron colours as 'AU-Y'.
WH903	Canberra B.2	8584M, ex 100, 85, MoA, 85, West Raynham TFF, 228 OCU, 102, 617. Nose.

WJ876	Canberra T.4	ex 7, 13, 39, 13, 56, 13, Akrotiri SF, 39, Akrotiri SF, HS, 231 OCU, Waddington SF, 1 GCF, Binbrook SF, Scampton SF. Nose section.
WK146	Canberra B.2	ex 59, 102. Nose section.
XE643	Hunter FGA.9	8586M, ex 208, 56, 63, 66, 92. Accident 9/12/61. Nose section.
XE670	Hunter F.4	7762M/8585M, ex 93, 26. Nose section.
XM191	Lightning F.1	7854M/8590M, ex Wattisham, 111. Crashed 9/6/64. Nose section.
XN137	Jet Provost T.3	ex 3 FTS, CFS, makers. Nose section.
XN503	Jet Provost T.3	ex MinTech, 4 FTS, 2 FTS, MinTech, 6 FTS, A&AEE. Nose section.
XN962	Buccaneer S.1	8183M. Nose section.
XR658	Jet Provost T.4	8192M, ex 6 FTS, CAW, 7 FTS. Fuselage.
XT595+	Phantom FG.1	8851M, ex St Athan, Coningsby, A&AEE. Nose section - remainder can be found at Wattisham.
XV338	Buccaneer S.2A	8774M, ex St Athan, 237 OCU, 12. Nose section.
XX162"	Hawk T.1 replica	BAPC.152. 4 FTS/CFS colours.
XX262"	Hawk T.1 replica	BAPC.171. Red Arrows colours.
XX396	Gazelle HT.3	8718M, ex 2 FTS. Crashed 30/6/81. Nominally based at Henlow.
XX718"	Jaguar GR.1 rep	BAPC.150. 54 Squadron colours.
XX824"	Jaguar GR.1 rep	BAPC.151. 14 Squadron colours.
XZ135+	Harrier GR.3	8848M, ex 4. Nose section, truck mounted. First noted 4/86.
ZA322"	Tornado GR.1 rep	BAPC.155. TTTE colours as 'B-50'.
ZD472+"	Harrier GR.5 rep	BAPC.191. 1 Squadron colours as '01'. With unit by 7/87.
	'Nimrod MR.1'	G-ALYW, ex Farnborough, Heathrow, BOAC. Comet fuselage suitably converted and fitted out.

Others Under this heading, Abingdon's myriad airframes used for other reasons can be grouped. Dave Pope's Chipmunk T.10 PAX Trainer WP907 moved to Benson 3/86. The four fire dump aircraft listed in W&R10 have all gone : Canberra TT.18 WH856 was sectioned by 12/86 and had gone by 4/87; Sea Vixen FAW.2 XJ609 had gone by mid 1986; Wessex HAS.1 XS120 had moved to Wroughton by 1/87; Gazelle HT.3 ZA801 had gone by mid 1986. Whirlwind HAS.7 XK943 moved from the BDRF to become the sole fire training airframe by 1/86. The Vulcan is still 'preserved' on the field, and the Spitfire is immaculate on the gate.

PK624	Spitfire F.24	8072M, ex Northolt, Uxbridge, North Weald, 9 MU, 614. 614 Squadron colours as 'RAU-T'. Gate guardian.
WH869	Canberra B.2	8515M, ex St Athan, 7, 98, 245, 527, RAFC. AS&RU training airframe.
XH537	Vulcan B.2MRR	8749M, ex 27, 230 OCU, MoA. 'Preserved' on the airfield.
XK943	Whirlwind HAS.7	8796M/A2653, ex BDRF, Lee-on-Solent, Wroughton, 705, 848, 824. Fire dump from 1/86.

ARNCOTT

(South of the A41 south east of Bicester) By 9/86 an Auster had moved here for restoration.

G-ASEF+	Auster 6A	ex Somerton, Bicester, RAFGSA, VW985, 664. wfu 13/1/67.

BENSON

At the RAF Station the restoration of the Bf 109G to flying condition continues. Of the other airframes here there has been no change. Dave Pope brought his Chipmunk T.10 PAX Trainer WP907 here from Abingdon in 3/86, but it moved to Reading 11/10/86. Phil Dunnington's BAC Drone G-ADPJ, which was kept in the vicinity, moved to Bristol in late 1986.

G-ARRV	HS.748MF	8669M, ex Woodford, G-APZV. Fire dump, poor state.
PM651	Spitfire PR.XIX	7758M, ex Bicester, Andover, Hucknall, Leconfield, Church Fenton, C&RS, 3 CAACU, 604. Gate guardian.
XR509	Wessex HC.2	8752M, ex 72, 240 OCU, 72, 18. Crashed 16/10/81. BDR.
XS642	Andover C.1	8785M, ex Kemble, 84, SAR Flt, 84. Rescue training.
10639	Bf 109G-2	8478M/RN228, ex Northolt, Lyneham, Henlow, Wattisham, Stanmore Park, 47 MU, CFE-EAF, 1426 (EA) Flt, Sicily, I/JG.77. Under restoration.

BICESTER

The RAFGSA continues to develop its appetite for Chipmunk airframes and redundant devices that will provide it with a source of engines for the glider tugs. Having donated its engine to the cause, the hulk of Airedale G-ATAW was burnt during 1985. Chipmunk fuselage WB645 was scrapped that same year Two more Chipmunks have 'appeared', along with an Aztec for engine amputation.

;-ASRI+	Aztec 250B	ex Shoreham, N5287Y. CoA expired 30/8/87. Acquired for engines 2/88.
JB556+	Chipmunk T.10	ex Oxf UAS. SOC 12/9/73 and presumed here since. Spares for RAFGSA.
JG300+	Chipmunk T.10	ex Liv UAS, 19 RFS, 2 BFTS. Former RAFGSA engine test-bed, now used for spares recovery.
JG303	Chipmunk T.10	8208M, ex Gatow SF, Wittering SF, Marham SF, Bir UAS, 5 RFS, 2 BFTS. Fuselage, RAFGSA engine test-bed. Pink colour scheme.

3RIZE NORTON

'raining loadmasters, the Air Movements School fleet of airframes remains unaltered at this large base. 'ATE - Joint Air Warfare Training Establishment - has expanded its airframe fleet with the addition of another Wessex. VC-10 ZD234 was not scrapped as described in W&R10 and just about hangs on to an existence here. On the dump Andover C.1 XS595 had perished by mid 1986. The current situation here is accordingly :-

V-AEE	Cessna A.150M	ex N9860J. Spares ship for G-AYUY.
T684	Hunter F.1	7422M, ex Abingdon, Reading, 71 MU, 229 OCU, DFLS. Dump.
S479	Wessex HU.5	8819M, ex Wroughton, 845. JATE.
S598	Andover C.1	ex Andover CU, Andover SF, HS, A&AEE. Fuselage. AMS.
T141	Sioux AH.1	8509M, ex Middle Wallop. AMS.
T486+	Wessex HU.5	8919M, ex Wroughton, 845. JATE. Arrived 3/2/87.
T677	Wessex HC.2	8016M, ex Lyneham, Thorney Island, 18. Crashed 25/4/68. Fire dump. Identity now confirmed.
V638	Wasp HAS.1	8826M, ex Portland. AMS. Confirmed present.
X914	VC-10 1103	8777M, ex RAE Bedford, 9G-ABQ, G-ATDJ. Fuselage. AMS.
D234	Super VC-10 1151	8700M, ex Heathrow, G-ASGF, BA, BOAC. Nose for conversion to tanker simulator. Remainder to dump by 1/88.
D493	VC-10 1101	ex Heathrow, G-ARVJ, Gulf-Air, BA, BOAC. External store.

:HALGROVE

s ever, difficult to confirm what really is here at the Martin Baker test airfield. Of the aircraft isted in W&R10, only Meteor T.7 WA638 is still thought to be present. Accordingly, the nose of anberra WH854 and former WGAF T-33A nose BD+735 have been tentatively omitted this time in the hope hat more information will be forthcoming. 'Spares ship' Dove G-ASPA is also in doubt as the 'flyer' -AVVF has been sold off. What we *do* know is that the anonymous Vulcan nose was scrapped during 1986!

A638	Meteor T.7	ex ETPS, RAE. Spares ship for WL419.

:ULHAM

On the A415 south east of Abingdon) Part of the UKAEA, the Culham Lightning Studies Unit (should be t Binbrook?) is thought still to have its Hunter GA.11 in a shocking test rig.

V381	Hunter GA.11	ex Kemble, FRADU, FRU, FWS, 222. Fuselage only.

:NSTONE

akes a come-back to the pages of W&R, last listed when it held a solitary Terrier frame in 1980. Farm viation were working on a derelict Pawnee by 1985 and by early 1987 it had been joined by the classic nonymous Pawnee fuselage frame.

-BEIH+	Pawnee 235D	ex N54926. Under rebuild from 1985.
+	Pawnee	fuselage frame. First noted 1/87.

IENLEY-ON-THAMES

he Berkshire Aviation Group (see under Woodley) have established a store here for their cache of ormer Vintage Aircraft Team Geminis and Messengers. All arrived by 4/86.

-AHUI+	Messenger 2A	ex Cranfield, Bushey, Caistor, Elsham Hall, Goxhill, Handforth, Wolverhampton. wfu 9/60. Fuselage.
-AJFF+	Messenger 2A	ex Cranfield, Bushey, Caistor, Elsham Hall, Egham, Elstree, Swanton Morley. wfu 3/68.
-AKER+	Gemini 1A	ex Cranfield, Bushey, Elsham Hall, Tattershall. wfu 18/9/65. Cockpit.
-AKGD+	Gemini 1A	ex Cranfield, Bushey, 'Sussex', Southend. wfu 22/11/73. Sectioned.
-AKHZ+	Gemini 1A	ex Cranfield, Bushey, Elsham Hall, Handforth. Complex composite, including parts from G-ALMU, G-ALUG, G-AMME. wfu 1/64.

OXFORD

David Elvidge continues to work on the rear fuselage and other parts of Mosquito TT.35 TJ118. The nose section is to be found at London Colney.

OXFORD AIRPORT

(Or Kidlington) The contents of the CSE Aviation Ground Training School are thought unchanged. The unassembled Tomahawk 112 c/no 79A-1077 has not been noted for some time and is best deleted. Two fuselages were noted in store here late in 1987, possibly candidates for the GTS.

G-ARJR	Apache 160G	ex N4447P. CoA expired 24/10/78. GTS.
G-ARMA	Apache 160G	ex N4448P. CoA expired 22/ 7/77. GTS.
G-ASEW	Brantly B.2B	CoA expired 17/12/73. GTS.
G-AVBU+	Cherokee Six 260	Crashed 28/2/81. Fuselage. First noted 11/87.
G-BBVI	Enstrom F-28A	Crashed 19/6/78. GTS.
G-BDBZ	Whirlwind HAR.10	ex Luton, XJ398, XD768 ntu. GTS.
G-BFSK	Apache 160	ex OO-NVC, OO-HVL, OO-PIP. GTS.
G-SHOE+	Cessna 421C II	ex G-BHGD, D-IASC, OE-FLR, N3862C. Fuselage. First noted 11/87.
XT175	Sioux AH.1	ex TAD175, Middle Wallop. GTS.

SHOTTESWELL

(Off the A41 north of Banbury) The Cessna is still in open store at the strip.

G-BCLS	Cessna 170B	ex N8094A. CoA expired 27/1/83. External store.

SHRIVENHAM

(On the A420 north east of Swindon) Gremlins galore got into the reference to the Royal Military College of Science fleet of instructional airframes in W&R10. Skeeter AOP.12 XL770 should have been deleted as it moved to Middle Wallop as long ago as 1985. The Scout mentioned as arriving was not listed. Other than that, everything else was correct! Current situation :-

WZ706	Auster AOP.9	7851M, ex St Athan, 656, Far East.
XN263	Whirlwind HAS.7	ex Wroughton, Middle Wallop, Wroughton, 771, Brawdy SF, 705, 848. Stored from 1/86.
XT151	Sioux AH.1	ex Wroughton. Stored from 1/86.
XT621	Scout AH.1	ex Wroughton. Arrived 16/12/85. See notes above.

SOMERTON

Stored Auster 6A G-ASEF moved to Arncott by 9/86.

UPPER HEYFORD

The BDR airframes here were joined by a Texas ANG F-4C during 8/86. With the building of concrete monstrosities all over the place, it is very difficult to see just what is what in terms of grounded airframes here, but it is thought that the fleet is unchanged. The Mysteres all carry USAF type camouflage and EABDR numbers (which is thought to equate to Engineering and Battle Damage Repair). Inspection of one of these airframes has resulted in a 'serial' change.

36	Mystere IVA	EABDR.8, ex Chateaudun, French AF. 'UH36'.
46	Mystere IVA	assumed EABDR.9, ex Chateaudun, French AF.
127	Mystere IVA	EABDR.7, ex Sculthorpe, Chateaudun, French AF.
129	Mystere IVA	EABDR.6, ex Sculthorpe, Chateaudun, French AF.
62-4428	F-105G-RE	ex Davis-Monthan 'FK095', 128 TFS, Georgia ANG. 17th WWS colours as 'JB'.
63-7449+	F-4C-17-MC	ex 182 TFS, Texas ANG. Arrived 8/86. BDR.

Shropshire

BRIDGNORTH

Derek Leek acquired a Vampire T.11 pod from the Vintage Aircraft Team during 8/87 and is currently restoring it here.

XH330	Vampire T.11	ex Bushey, London Colney, Chester, Woodford, Chester, Shawbury, RAFC. Pod only, arrived 8/87.

CHETWYND

The airfield still has its para-trainer Cessna fuselage.

G-ATIE	Cessna 150F	ex Market Drayton, N6291R. Crashed 28/7/79. Para-trainer.

COSFORD

Aerospace Museum and British Airways Annex Hangar refurbishment at this dynamic museum is now complete and the main hangar boasts an overhead walkway allowing the public to see the exhibits from different angles. A similar high level system is proposed for the two top hangars. Major work is underway on the Belfast, and it will return to RAF markings. 'Cosford' represents a fabulous collection of aircraft, including the British Airways airliner collection. The Museum is open daily from April to October 1000 to 1600 and weekdays only 1000 to 1600 November to March. Closed Christmas and New Year for two weeks. Contact : Aerospace Museum, RAF Cosford, Wolverhampton, West Midlands WV7 3EX. Telephone 090 722 4872 or '4112.

Working in support of the collection is the Cosford Aerospace Museum Society, enquiries about their activities can be made via the above address. The Wartime Aircraft Recovery Group have a small display at Cosford. WARG can be contacted through : Joe Collier, 68 Woodhouse Lane, Horeshay, near Dawley, Shropshire TF4 3BN

Several airframes have moved on and there have been no less than six additions. Briefly going back to W&R10, Pitts S-2A G-BADW and Stampe G-AWIW were acquired by Bob Mitchell, the former is now airworthy and flies occasionally from Cosford, the latter is nearing completion of restoration. Vulcan B.1A XA900 was declared beyond economic saving and was scrapped during 1986; Gnat F.1 XK740 moved out late 1986 for refurbish at Hamble, prior to handing on to the Hall of Aviation at Southampton; Gnat T.1 XR571 left during 7/84 for Scampton. That leaves :-

G-AFAP"	CASA 352L	ex Spanish AF T2B-272. British Airways (the original lot!) colours.
G-AGRU	Viking 1	ex Soesterberg, Channel, Lasham, Kuwait Oil, BWIA, VP-TAX, G-AGRU, BEA *Vagrant*. BEA colours. wfu 1/64.
G-AJOV"	Dragonfly HR.3	WP495, ex Biggin Hill, Banstead, Warnham, Wimbledon. BEA colours.
G-AMOG	Viscount 701	ex Cardiff-Wales, BOAC, Cambrian, BEA *Robert Falcon Scott*, G-AMNZ ntu. BEA colours. wfu 5/76.
G-AOVF	Britannia 312F	ex Southend, Merchant Air, 9Q-CAZ, G-AOVF, Stansted, Donaldson, British Eagle, BOAC. BOAC colours. wfu 5/84.
G-APAS	Comet 1XB	8351M, ex Shawbury, XM823, G-APAS, Air France, F-BGNZ, G-5-23. BOAC colours.
G-APFJ	Boeing 707-436	ex British Airtours, BOAC. wfu 12/6/81. British Airtours colours.
G-ARPH	Trident 1C	ex Heathrow, BA, BEA. wfu 26/3/82. British Airways colours.
G-ARVM	VC-10 1101	ex BA, BOAC. wfu 22/10/79. British Airways colours.
BAPC.94	Fi 103 (V.1)	8583M.
BAPC.99	Ohka II	8486M, ex St Athan, Cosford.
K7271"	Fury I replica	BAPC.148. 1 Squadron colours.
DG202/G	F.9/40 Meteor	5758M, ex Yatesbury, Locking, Moreton Valance. Prototype Meteor, f/f 4/43.
KG374"	Dakota IV	KN645/8355M, ex Colerne, AFN CF, MinTech, AFN HQ, SHAPE CF, Malta CF, BAFO CS, 2nd TAF CS, 44-77003. 'YS'.
KN751	B-24L-20-FO	ex Colerne, Indian AF 6 Squadron HE809, RAF KN751, 99.
MT847	Spitfire XIV	6960M, ex Weeton, Middleton St George, Freckleton, Warton, 226 OCU, A&AEE.
RF398	Lincoln B.2	8376M, ex Henlow, Abingdon, CSE, BCBS.
TA639	Mosquito TT.35	7806M, ex CFS, 3 CAACU, Aldergrove TT Flt. 627 Squadron colours as 'AZ-E'.
TG511	Hastings T.5	8554M, ex 230 OCU, SCBS, BCBS, 202, 47.
TS798	York C.1	ex 'MW100', Shawbury, Brize Norton, Staverton, 'LV633', G-AGNV, Skyways, BOAC, TS798 ntu.

TX214	Anson C.19	7817M, ex Henlow, HCCS, MCS, RCCF, Staff College CF, 1 FU, 16 FU.
VP952	Devon C.2/2	8820M, ex St Athan, 207, 21, WCS, SCS, Upavon SF, TCCF, MCS, BCCS, HCCS, A&AEE, MCCF, AAFCE, TCCF, Hendon SF, HS.
VV106	Supermarine 517	7175M, ex St Athan, Colerne, Yatesbury.
VX272	Hawker P.1052	7174M, ex St Athan, Colerne.
VX573	Valetta C.3	8389M, ex Henlow, Wildenrath CF, Buckeburg CF. *Lorelei*.
WA634	Meteor T.7(mod)	ex St Athan, Martin Baker.
WB188	Hawker P.1067	7154M, ex St Athan, Colerne, Melksham. Hunter prototype.
WF408	Varsity T.1	8395M, ex 2 SoTT, 6 SS, 2 ANS, 1 RS, 11 FTS, 201 AFS.
WG760+	EE P.1A	7755M, ex Binbrook, Henlow, Bicester, St Athan, Warton, A&AEE. Arr 1/86.
WG768	Short SB.5	8005M, ex Topcliffe, Finningley, ETPS, A&AEE.
WG777	Fairey FD-2	7986M, ex Topcliffe, Finningley, RAE Bedford.
WK935	Meteor F.8(mod)	7869M, ex St Athan, Colerne, RAE Farnborough. Prone-pilot aircraft.
WL732	Sea Balliol T.21	ex Henlow, A&AEE, Lossiemouth, Anthorn.
WP912	Chipmunk T.10	8467M, ex Hendon, Kemble, Man UAS, RAFC, ITS, Cam UAS, CFS, 2 FTS, Lon UAS, FTCCS, HCCS, 8 FTS.
WT346	Canberra B(I).8	8197M, ex Shawbury, Colerne, 16, 3, 14, 88.
WT555	Hunter F.1	7499M, ex Locking, A&AEE, Dunsfold. *State Express*.
WV562	Provost T.1	7606M, ex Cranwell, Henlow, 22 FTS. 'P-C'.
WV746+	Pembroke C.1	8938M, ex 60, 207, 21, WCS, TCCF, FTCCS, BCCS, HS, 2 TAF CF. Arr 13/4/87.
WZ744	Avro 707	7932M, ex Topcliffe, Finningley, RAE, makers.
XA564	Javelin FAW.1	7464M, ex 2 SoTT, Locking, Filton.
XA893+	Vulcan B.1	8591M, ex Abingdon, Bicester, A&AEE, makers. Nose section. Arrived 4/86.
XD145	SARO SR.53	ex Brize Norton, Henlow, Westcott, A&AEE.
XD674	Jet Provost T.1	7570M, ex St Athan, Swinderby, Finningley, 71 MU, makers.
XF926	Bristol T.188	8368M, ex Foulness Island, RAE, A&AEE.
XG337	Lightning F.1	8056M, ex 2 SoTT, Warton, A&AEE, Warton.
XH592	Victor K.1A	8429M, ex 2 SoTT, St Athan, 232 OCU, TTF, 232 OCU, Marham Wing, 15.
XJ389	Jet Gyrodyne	ex Southampton, G-AJJP, makers. One time XD759.
XJ918	Sycamore HR.14	8190M, ex 2 SoTT, 32, MCS, Kemble, Wroughton, 110, Seletar, A&AEE, 275.
XK724+	Gnat F.1	7715M, ex Cranwell, Bicester, Henlow, makers. Arrived by 3/86.
XL993	Twin Pioneer CC.1	8388M, ex Henlow, Shawbury, 21, 78.
XM555	Skeeter AOP.12	8027M, ex Shawbury, Ternhill, CFS, HQ BAOR, 654.
XM598	Vulcan B.2A	8778M, ex 44, Wadd Wing, Cott Wing, 12.
XN714	Hunting 126	ex RAE Bedford, NASA Ames and Moffett, Holme-on-Spalding Moor, RAE.
XP299	Whirlwind HAR.10	8726M, ex 22, 230, 1563 Flt, Queen's Flt, 230, CFS, MoA. QF colours.
XP411+	Argosy C.1	8442M, ex 2 SoTT, 6 FTS, Kemble, 70. Joined museum 4/88.
XR220	TSR-2 XO-2	7933M, ex Henlow, A&AEE. Never flown.
XR371	Belfast C.1	ex Hucknall, Kemble, 53. Under restoration to RAF colours as *Enceladus*.
XR977	Gnat T.1	8640M, ex 2 SoTT, Red Arrows, 4 FTS. Red Arrows colours.
XS770+	Basset CC.1	ex Boscombe Down, A&AEE, 32, Queen's Flt, 26, TCCS, NCS. Arrived 10/86.
ZD485	FMA Pucara	ex A&AEE, Yeovilton, Stanley Airport, Argentine AF A-515. To be restored to Argentine AF colours.
204	SP-2H Neptune	ex Dutch Navy 320 Sqn, Valkenburg, 5 Sqn, 321 Sqn.
J-1704	Venom FB.4	ex Greenham Common and Swiss Air Force.
L-866	PBY-6A Catalina	8466M, ex Colerne, Danish AF ESK.721, 82-866, 63993.
191614	Me 163B-1a	8481M, ex Biggin Hill, Westcott, Brize Norton, Farnborough, Hussum, II/JG.400.
	Fa 330A-1	8469M.
17473	T-33A-1-LO	ex Sculthorpe, French AF.

2 School of Technical Training and Weapons School With some disposals of older stock, including the remainder of the Sea Vixens, the SoTT has seen a massive influx of airframes with Hunters and Jaguars dominating. The Weapons Squadron, located on the sports stadium side of the base also took delivery of a Jaguar and a Tornado. Disposals have been as follows ; Shackleton MR.2C WL798 moved to Lossiemouth for use as spares during 1987; Sea Vixen FAW.2 XJ571 was put up for tender in 6/87 along with the other three, it moved to Southampton 17/9/87; Sea Vixen FAW.2 XN691 went to Coventry 4/88; Sea Vixen FAW.2 XJ607 went to Southampton 15/10/87; Sea Vixen FAW.2 XN685 went to Chester 19/8/87; Argosy C.1 XP411 rolled across to the Aerospace Museum 4/88; Shackleton MR.2C WL801 was scrapped early in 1985; Hunter FGA.9 XG194 moved to North Luffenham by 3/88; Hunter FGA.9 XG252 moved to Hereford 2/2/88.

As with other entries in this edition, the listing is no longer being made by 'M' number, but in the traditional serial order. 2 SoTT codes are given at the end of each potted history.

Serial	Type	History
WH740	Canberra T.17	8762M, ex 360, RNZAF, Upwood SF, 40, 18. 'X'.
WH775+	Canberra PR.7	8868M/8128M, ex 100, 13, 31, 17, 31, 13, 82, makers. Arrived 1985. 'O'.
WH957+	Canberra PR.7	8869M, ex 100, 98, Akrotiri Wing, 32, Hemswell SF, Upwood SF, 21, 542, 617. Arrived 1985. 'N'.
WH960	Canberra B.15	8344M, ex Akrotiri Wing, 32, 9, 12. 'A'.
WH964+	Canberra E.15	8870M, ex St Athan, 100, 98, Akrotiri Wing, 32, 12. Arrived by 6/87.
WH984	Canberra B.15	8101M, ex RAE, HS, 9, Binbrook SF, 9. 'E'.
WJ565+	Canberra T.17	8871M, ex St Athan, 360, CA. Arrived by 6/87. 'C'.
WJ640	Canberra B.2	8722M, ex 100, 85, 51, 192, 231 OCU.
WK102	Canberra T.17	8780M, ex 360, 45, RNZAF, 207.
WR971	Shackleton MR.3/3	8119M, ex 120, Kinloss Wing, 201, 120, Kinloss Wing, CA. 'Q'.
WR974	Shackleton MR.3/3	8117M, ex Kinloss Wing, 203, 42, 203, ASWDU, MinTech, ASWDU, MinTech, CA. 'K'. RAF Museum allocated airframe.
WR982	Shackleton MR.3/3	8106M, ex 201, 206, MoA, 205, 203, 206. 'J'.
WR985	Shackleton MR.3/3	8103M, ex 201, 120, 206, 203, 206, A&AEE, 206. 'H'.
WT532+	Canberra PR.7	8890M/8728M, ex RAE Bedford, 13, Wyton SF, 58, 31, 13, 80. Arrived 2/6/86.
WT536	Canberra PR.7	8063M, ex 80, 31, 13, 17. 'F'.
XG225	Hunter F.6A	8713M, ex 2 SoTT, Kemble, 229 OCU, 92, 74, 20. Weapons Squadron.
XH136	Canberra PR.9	8782M, ex 1 PRU, A&AEE, 39, 13, 58, MoA.
XH171	Canberra PR.9	8746M, ex 39, 13, 39, MoA, 58.
XH593	Victor K.1A	8428M, ex St Athan, 232 OCU, TTF, Marham Wing, 57, 15. 'T'.
XL569+	Hunter T.7	8833M, ex 2 TWU, 1 TWU, 12, 216, 237 OCU, Laarbruch SF, 15, 237 OCU, 12, MinTech, 2 TWU, 1 TWU, TWU, 229 OCU. Arrived 1986.
XL572+	Hunter T.7	8834M, ex 1 TWU, 2 TWU, TWU, 229 OCU. Arrived 1985.
XL576+	Hunter T.7	8835M, ex 2 TWU, 1 TWU, TWU, 229 OCU. Arrived 1985.
XL617+	Hunter T.7	8837M, ex 1 TWU, 237 OCU, 1 TWU, TWU, 229 OCU, 54, 229 OCU, Gutersloh SF, Jever SF, 4. Arrived 1985.
XL623	Hunter T.7	8770M, ex 1 TWU, 74, 19, 1, 43, 92, 208, 65.
XM351	Jet Provost T.3	8078M, ex Halton, Shawbury, 3 FTS, 7 FTS, 2 FTS.
XM367	Jet Provost T.3	8083M, ex Halton, Shawbury, 3 FTS, 2 FTS. 'W'.
XN492	Jet Provost T.3	8079M, ex Halton, 6 FTS, RAFC.
XN501+	Jet Provost T.3A	ex CFS, 1 FTS. Flew in 2/88.
XN816	Argosy E.1	8489M, ex 115, MoA. 'G'.
XP338	Whirlwind HAR.10	8647M, ex Shawbury, 2 FTS, CFS, HDU, CFS, 225. 'J'.
XP444	Argosy C.1	8455M, ex Kemble, 70. 'D'.
XP514	Gnat T.1	8635M, ex Cranwell, Red Arrows.
XP533+	Gnat T.1	8632M, ex Halton, Cosford, Kemble, Red Arrows, 4 FTS. Arrived by 6/87
XP538+	Gnat T.1	8607M, ex Halton, 4 FTS, CFS, 4 FTS. Arrived by 6/87.
XR107	Argosy T.2	8441M, ex Kemble, 70. 'B'.
XR537	Gnat T.1	8642M, ex Red Arrows, 4 FTS. 'T'.
XR987	Gnat T.1	8641M, ex Red Arrows, Yellowjacks. 'S'.
XS102+	Gnat T.1	8624M, ex Halton, 4 FTS. Arrived by 6/87.
XS104	Gnat T.1	8604M, ex Kemble, 4 FTS.
XS105	Gnat T.1	8625M, ex Kemble, 4 FTS, CFS, 4 FTS. 'V'.
XS107	Gnat T.1	8639M, ex Red Arrows, 4 FTS. 'U'.
XT277	Buccaneer S.2A	8853M, ex Shawbury, 237 OCU, 12. 'M'.
XT466+	Wessex HU.5	8921M, ex Wroughton, 847. First noted 6/87.
XW544	Buccaneer S.2C	8857M, ex Shawbury, 16, 15. 'Y'.
XX110+	Jaguar GR.1	8955M, ex Shawbury, 6. Arrived early 1988.
XX727+	Jaguar GR.1	8951M, ex Shawbury, 6. Arrived early 1988.
XX730+	Jaguar GR.1	8952M, ex Shawbury, 6. Arrived early 1988.
XX751+	Jaguar GR.1	8937M, ex 226 OCU. Arrived by 2/87.
XX756+	Jaguar GR.1	8899M, ex 14. Arrived by 8/86.
XX819+	Jaguar GR.1	8923M, ex Shawbury, 20. First noted 6/87.
XX948	Tornado P.06	8879M, ex Warton. Weapons Squadron.
XX959+	Jaguar GR.1	8953M, ex Shawbury, 20. Arrived early 1988.
XX969+	Jaguar GR.1	8897M, ex 226 OCU. Arrived 17/7/86.

XZ368+ Jaguar GR.1 8900M, ex Coltishall, 14. Arrived 27/10/86.
XZ371+ Jaguar GR.1 8907M, ex Shawbury, 14. First noted 7/87. Weapons Squadron.
XZ383+ Jaguar GR.1 8901M, ex Coltishall, 14. Arrived 27/10/86.
XZ384+ Jaguar GR.1 8954M, ex Shawbury, 17. Arrived early 1988.
Lightning F.2A cockpit section. Weapons Squadron.
Lightning F.3 cockpit section. Weapons Squadron. 29 Squadron colours.
Buccaneer S.2 cockpit section. Weapons Squadron.

Others The Vampire is still displayed on a plinth near the sports stadium. It is thought the former ATC Vampire is still kept on the base. Gnat T.1 XM698/8497M arrived here from Leeming by 6/84. It was held by the Museum on a 'caretaker' basis until put up for tender in 1986. It wa sold in the USA and became N698XM.
XD377 Vampire T.11 8203M, ex Birmingham, Shawbury, 48 MU, 66.
XD613 Vampire T.11 8122M, ex CATCS, CNCS, Odiham SF. Displayed.

LUDLOW

Three aircraft have recently moved into storage in the area.
G-ABUS+ Comper Swift ex Heathfield. CoA expired 19/6/79.
G-AHLT+ Tiger Moth ex Heathfield, Manston, Rochester, N9128, 19 FTS, 11 EFTS, 5 CPF. CoA exp 24/6/58.
G-BADV+ MB.50 Pipistrelle ex Dunkeswell, F-PBRJ. CoA expired 9/5/79.

OSWESTRY

It is believed that the Cessna cockpit still survives with Mr D Higgins here, but confirmation would be appreciated.
G-AYOV Cessna FA.150L ex Sleap. Crashed 11/2/79. Cockpit section.

SHAWBURY

Storage Site The Shawbury Storage Site is the principal long term storage unit for the RAF and continues to provide a lot of material for W&R. In the past, W&R has undertaken a type-by-type look at the aircraft held here, from this edition, the book will list all aircraft by serial. As W&R goes to press, the news is out that the Army Air Corps have ordered BN-2 Islanders to take over from the venerable Beavers, so it is possible that more of the type will come here before too long. In 11/86 the MoD put the bulk of the stored Beavers up for tender and they were all snapped up by North American buyers ; XP774 became N9067F; XP780 became N9063G; XP804 sold in Canada; XP808 became N9066P; XP816 became N9063V; XP818 became N1215; XP822 moved to Middle Wallop by 7/87; XP823 sold in Canada; XP827 moved to the dump at Netheravon by 10/87. XP817 came to Shawbury from the Britannia Park, Ilkeston, debacle and was sold off, becoming N9063Q. With a former BTF machine coming into store by 9/87, that leaves four in Shawbury's care. By contrast, the Buccaneer store is undisturbed. The Bulldogs have also experienced a clear-out, with just one of those listed in W&R10 remaining, with a new example coming in by 9/87. Disposals here have been ; XX518 to Cam UAS 28/1/87; XX550 to Tees-side by 11/86; XX692 to CFS in 1986; XX709 to St Andrews UAS by 6/87; XX710 to Woodvale by 9/87. Once very static, the Chipmunk store has also experienced a great deal of 'trade' since W&R10. Leaving the fold have been the following ; WG466 left by road 7/5/87 bound for Gatow; WG478 left for St Athan 13/7/87 then joining EFTS; WG486 left by road 7/5/87 for Gatow; WK638 joined 9 AEF in 1986; WP844 joined 10 AEF 7/87; WP871 to BFWF at Middle Wallop by 2/88. Additionally WK554 was omitted from the listing in W&R10, but left, destination unknown, during 9/86. That leaves seven in long term store. One Hunter is all that remains of the long term store ; T.8 WT745 to St Athan; GA.11 XE682 left by 6/86 for Culdrose; T.7 XL566 left by road 9/10/86 to Bruggen; T.7 XL618 left by road 19/11/86 for Cottesmore; and T.66 XX466 left by road 14/5/86 for Culdrose. The Jaguar store has taken on new airframes and released the first substantial numbers into the world of instructional airframe work to Halton and Cosford, as follows ; XX110 to Cosford early 1988; XX726 to Halton by 1/88; XX727 to Cosford early 1988; XX729 flown out to Abingdon by 9/87; XX730 to Cosford early 1988; XX739 left by 7/86 for Halton; XX743 to Halton early 1988; XX747 left by 6/87 for Halton; XX757 out by 1/88 to Halton; XX818 to Halton early 1988; XX819 to Cosford by 6/87; XX956 to Halton early 1988; XX959 (ex 20, first noted 9/85) to Cosford early 1988; XX976 to Halton by 12/86; XZ369 to 6 Squadron as 'EE' by 3/87; XZ382 to Halton by 12/86; XZ384 (ex 17, arrived 20/2/85) to Cosford early 1988; XZ389 to to Halton by 1/88; XZ394 left by road 17/12/86 for refurbish at Abingdon, going on to join 6 Squadron. Additionally, XX966 escaped from the W&R10 listing but moved to Cosford by 12/86; XX975 arrived here by 3/86, moving on to Halton by 6/87; XZ371 arrived by 1986 and left fairly quickly for Cosford. As well as those held over from

W&R10, there are nine new inmates to record. The stored Jet Provost population halved during 11/85 when T.3A XN641 moved to Newton. The Meteor remains in store and was joined during 1987 by the former Biggin Hill gate guardian Spitfire F.21. Four Whirlwind HAR.10s previously on Cyprus arrived here (via Lee-on-Solent) and were put up for tender during 11/86. Three, XP329, XP345 and XP346 were moved to Tattershall Thorpe. The fourth, XP398/8794M is thought to have been acquired by Warbirds of Great Britain, but has yet to surface anywhere.

LA226+	Spitfire F.21	7119M, ex Abingdon, Biggin Hill, South Marston, London, South Marston, Little Rissington, 3 CAACU, 122. Arrived during 1987.
VZ467	Meteor F.8	ex 1 TWU, 229 OCU, 500, 54, A&AEE. *Winston.*
WG458	Chipmunk T.10	ex 1 AEF, 5 AEF, Cam UAS, 3 BFTS.
WK511	Chipmunk T.10	ex Kemble, BRNC, Wittering SF, Lon UAS, 61 GCF, Bri UAS, 22 RFS, 5 BFTS.
WK586	Chipmunk T.10	ex Kemble, 6 AEF, FSS, 3 FTS, 6 AEF, 2 SoTT, 2 FTS, RAFC, 1 AEF, Abn UAS, Oxf UAS, South Cerney SF, Nicosia SF, 114, StA UAS, 11 RFS. Omitted from W&R10.
WP786	Chipmunk T.10	ex FSS, 10 AEF, Liv UAS, Mcr UAS, Lee UAS, StA UAS, 6 RFS, 17 RFS.
WP803	Chipmunk T.10	ex Kemble, BRNC, Oxf UAS, 1 ANS, 6 FTS, Benson SF, Hul UAS, 15 RFS.
WP872	Chipmunk T.10	ex Kemble, Bri UAS, 3/4 CAACU, Dur UAS, QuB UAS, Stn UAS, 1 CAACU, QuB UAS, Lon UAS, 14 RFS.
WP891	Chipmunk T.10	ex Kemble, 2 FTS, Lon UAS, 6 AEF, FTCCF, Binbrook SF, FTCCF, Binbrook SF, FTCCF, Biggin Hill SF, 61 GCF, Cam UAS, Mcr UAS.
WT799	Hunter T.8	ex Kemble, FRADU, FRU, 759, RAE Bedford, 4, 111.
XN977	Buccaneer S.2B	ex St Athan, 15, 237 OCU.
XP775	Beaver AL.1	ex Kemble, St Athan.
XP810	Beaver AL.1	ex Kemble, St Athan.
XP814	Beaver AL.1	ex Kemble, St Athan.
XS231	Jet Provost T.5	ex A&AEE, RAE, G-ATAJ ntu.
XT270	Buccaneer S.2B	ex St Athan, 208, 237 OCU, 12.
XT275	Buccaneer S.2B	ex St Athan, 15, 208.
XT276	Buccaneer S.2B	ex St Athan, 16, 15.
XV157	Buccaneer S.2B	ex St Athan, 12, 208, 237 OCU, 12.
XV268+	Beaver AL.1	ex BTF. Arrived by 9/87.
XV334	Buccaneer S.2B	ex St Athan, 15, 237 OCU, 12, 237 OCU, 208, 12.
XV336	Buccaneer S.2B	ex St Athan, 12, 208, 237 OCU.
XV349	Buccaneer S.2B	ex St Athan, 12, 237 OCU, 15, 12.
XV356	Buccaneer S.2B	ex St Athan, 15, 208, 237 OCU, 12.
XV866	Buccaneer S.2B	ex St Athan, 16, 809.
XX121	Jaguar GR.1	ex 6.
XX140	Jaguar T.2	ex 226 OCU.
XX150	Jaguar T.2	ex 14.
XX538	Bulldog T.1	ex Ems UAS.
XX539+	Bulldog T.1	ex CFS. Into store by 9/87.
XX722+	Jaguar GR.1	ex 6. First noted 9/85.
XX744	Jaguar GR.1	ex 31.
XX753	Jaguar GR.1	ex 226 OCU.
XX763	Jaguar GR.1	ex 226 OCU.
XX764	Jaguar GR.1	ex 226 OCU.
XX825	Jaguar GR.1	ex 17.
XX826	Jaguar GR.1	ex 2.
XX837+	Jaguar GR.1	first noted 9/87.
XX839+	Jaguar GR.1	first noted 9/87.
XX841+	Jaguar GR.1	first noted 9/87.
XX847+	Jaguar GR.1	first noted 9/87.
XX887	Buccaneer S.2B	ex Laarbruch, 16, 15.
XX888	Buccaneer S.2B	ex St Athan, 16, 15.
XX896	Buccaneer S.2B	ex St Athan, 12.
XX958	Jaguar GR.1	ex 17.
XX967	Jaguar GR.1	ex 14.
XX968	Jaguar GR.1	ex 14.
XX977	Jaguar GR.1	ex 31.

XZ370	Jaguar GR.1	ex 17.
XZ374+	Jaguar GR.1	ex 14. First noted 9/87.
XZ381	Jaguar GR.1	ex 17.
XZ390	Jaguar GR.1	ex 2.
XZ392+	Jaguar GR.1	ex 54.

Airfield By comparison with the Storage Site, things have been tranquil at the 'operational' side of the base. Whirlwind HAR.10 XP351 had graduated to gate guardian by 12/87. Otherwise things are much as they were in W&R10.

WH724	Canberra T.19	ex 100, 85, West Raynham TFF, 228 OCU, 15. Nose section only. Dump.
XD382	Vampire T.11	8033M, ex Syerston, CATCS, CNCS, RAFC, 5 FTS, 206 AFS, 208 AFS. Gate guardian.
XG540	Sycamore HR.14	7899M/8345M, ex 'XJ385', Ternhill, MCS, CFS. 'S-Y'. Gate guardian.
XM927	Wessex HAS.3	8814M, ex Wroughton. Dump.
XP351	Whirlwind HAR.10	8672M, ex 2 FTS, SAR Wing, 22. Gate guardian by 12/87, ex BDRT.

SHREWSBURY

To answer the question posed in W&R10, the Jet Provost T.3 fuselage XM474 moved to Warrington.

SLEAP

Not having been reported for a long time, it is thought that the hulk of Cessna F.172H G-AVAS has been scrapped here.

TERNHILL

The Vampire hulk is still visible on the former dump. Its identity is widely believed, but not confirmed.

XH274	Vampire T.11	ex CATCS, 8 FTS, 4 FTS, 8 FTS. Hulk on dump.

TILSTOCK

Manchester Free Fall Club still use their Cessna para-trainer at the airfield.

G-ASNN	Cessna 182F	ex N3612U. CoA expired 3/5/85. Para-trainer.

WHITCHURCH

There have been no reports concerning the progress of Mr R G A Mansell with the restoration of his former London Colney Vampire T.11. It is, however, believed still to be here.

XD452	Vampire T.11	7990M, ex London Colney, Shawbury, 3 FTS, 7 FTS, 1 FTS, 8 FTS, 5 FTS.

Somerset

CHILTON CANTELO

(Just south of Yeovilton) By 3/87 the Sea Cadets at Chilton Cantelo House received their Sea Hawk back from the Hunter One Collection. Now very much a hybrid, the aircraft is essentially XE489/G-JETH, fitted with the wings and tail of the original WM983. Having said that, it is marked up as 'WM983'.

WM983+"	Sea Hawk FGA.6	ex Bournemouth. Composite of WM983 and XE489/G-JETH - see notes above. Arrived 3/87.

GLASTONBURY

Tor View Garage still has its Whirlwind as an inducement to buy Datsun cars....

XP399	Whirlwind HAR.10	ex Hadfield, Pryton Hill, 32, 1563 Flt, 230.

HENSTRIDGE

At Tony Young's airstrip W&R material remains much as it was, although two airframes have not been physically reported for some time. Tipsy Trainer 1 G-AFSC moved on during 1986, possibly to the Dunkeswell area. Otherwise the situation is as overleaf :-

G-AHSD	T'craft Plus D	ex Wincanton, LB323. CoA expired 10/9/62. Not noted since 8/85.
G-AISC	Tipsy B Srs 1	ex Yeovil area. CoA expired 23/5/79. Under restoration.
G-ALYG	Auster 5D	ex Charlton Mackrell, London Airport, Irby-on-Humber, MS968. CoA expired 19/1/70. Stored.
G-ANEW	Tiger Moth	ex NM138. CoA expired 18/6/62. Stored.
G-ARJD	Colt 108	crashed 17/11/71. Frame stored. Not noted since 8/85.

STALBRIDGE

Auster J/1N G-AGXU moved on to Northampton Airport in late 1986 and was flying shortly afterwards.

TEMPLECOMBE

A tender document 4/87 raised a few eye-brows when Wessex HAS.3 XS149 was offered for grabs at Plessey Naval Systems here. Presumably it served for trial installations. What became of it and how long it had been there will doubtless be revealed in W&R12!

WELLS

1955 Squadron ATC in Webbs Close have a Chipmunk T.10 fuselage which is wrongly painted. W&R10 had it as WD355, which is does indeed proclaim to be. It is, however, WD335 and was acquired from a local scrappy.

WD355"	Chipmunk T.10	WD335, ex Dur UAS, Oxf UAS, G&S UAS, Not UAS, Lon UAS, G&S UAS, Abn UAS, StA UAS, G&S UAS, 11 RFS, 23 RFS.

WESTBURY-SUB-MENDIP

The hulk of JetRanger G-BFCY travelled to Whinmoor by 1987.

WINCANTON

Restoration of the Auster continues in this area.

G-AJIS	J/1N Alpha	CoA expired 9/11/78. Under restoration.

YEOVIL

The Westlands plant continues to use the SH-3D import XV372 for installation trials and this can be found within the plant. Of the two Argentine Lynx Mk 87s held in store and listed in W&R10, the legalities appear to have been overcome during 1987 when the pair where sold to the Danish Navy. (G-BKBL/ZE388/249 becoming Mk 90 S-249 and 256 becoming Mk 90 S-256.) Clearing up W&R10, Scout AH.1 XP857 was unaccounted for, it joined the AETW at Middle Wallop. Locally, Simon Darch is thought to be still working on his Tiger Moth.

G-AOXN	Tiger Moth	ex Houghton-on-the-Hill, Burnaston, EM727. CoA expired 3/8/73.
XV372	SH-3D Sea King	ex Lee-on-Solent. See notes above.

YEOVILTON

Fleet Air Arm Museum Developments at the FAAM have continued following the appeal launched in 1985. The major planned exhibitions have been built on schedule, WRNS during 1986, and Swordfish and TAGS during 1987. The major exhibition about the RNAS is due to open during the summer of 1988. It is hoped that the Albatros and the Pup will fly on occasional weekends during the summer, joined by Robin Bowes' Fokker Triplane, which is frequently resident at Yeovilton. The Albacore fuselage arrived from Land's End in immaculate condition during 4/87. Wings are being made by the Society of Friends. The Barracuda has not gone to Land's End, despite W&R10's efforts to move it there. Restoration of this requires the location of substantial sections of wing and tail and a goodly injection of finance. Please note that projected re-arrangements within the museum will mean that some of the aircraft listed below may well not be on public show. FAAM is open every day (other than Christmas) March to October 1000 to 1730 and November to February 1000 to 1630. Contact : Fleet Air Arm Museum, RNAS Yeovilton, Ilchester, Somerset, BA22 8HT. Telephone : 0935 840 565.

Since W&R10 there have been no less than eight arrivals at FAAM, two of them being Phantoms! There have been five departures : Bensen B.8 G-AZAZ withdrawn from display circa 1986, and thought stored elsewhere; Eclipse Eagle G-BGWZ removed from display; Gannet COD.4 XA466 left by road for Wroughton 25/3/87; SARO P.531 XN332 left by road 8/4/87, also for Wroughton; finally Wasp HAS.1 XT427 left for the CAP at Helston 23/9/86. FAAM has its main store at Wroughton. FAAM aircraft can also be found at the following locations : Cardiff-Wales Airport, Coventry, Helston, Southampton, Strathallan and Weston-super-Mare. Currently held at Yeovilton are the following :-

BAPC.58	Ohka II	ex Hayes, South Kensington. Science Museum loan.
BAPC149	Short S.27 replica	ex Lee-on-Solent.
8359	Short 184	ex Duxford, South Lambeth. Forward fuselage. IWM loan.
B6401"	Camel replica	G-AWYY, ex Leisure Sport, N1917H, G-AWYY. CoA expired 1/9/85.
L2301	Walrus I	ex Arbroath, Thame, G-AIZG, Aer Lingus EI-ACC, IAAC N18.
L2940	Skua I	ex Lake Grotli, Norway, 800. Remains only.
N1854	Fulmar II	ex Lossiemouth, Fairey's 'hack' G-AIBE, A&AEE.
N2078"	Sopwith Baby	ex Nash Collection. composite of 8214 and 8215.
N4389+"	Albacore	N4172, ex Land's End, Yeovilton. Arrived 4/87 - see notes above.
N5226"	Gladiator II	N5903, ex Old Warden, 61 OTU. 804 Sqn colours as 'H'.
N5492+"	Sopwith Triplane	BAPC.111, ex Chertsey. Arrived 25/3/87. Replica.
N6452	Pup replica	G-BIAU, ex Whitehall. CoA expired 1/9/85.
P4139"	Swordfish II	HS618/A2001, ex 'W5984', Manadon, Donibristle.
AL246	Martlet I	ex Loughborough, 768, 802.
EX976	Harvard IIA	ex Portuguese AF 1657, EX976, 41-33959.
KD431	Corsair IV	ex Cranfield, 716, 731. 'E2-M'.
KE209	Hellcat II	ex Lossiemouth, Stretton, Anthorn.
LZ551/G	Sea Vampire I	ex CS(A), DH, A&AEE, RAE. Science Museum loan.
SX137	Seafire F.17	ex Culdrose, Stretton, 759, 1831, Culham.
VH127	Firefly TT.4	ex Culdrose, FRU, 700, 737, 812.
VR137	Wyvern TF.1	ex Cranfield. Eagle-powered prototype, never flown.
WA473	Attacker F.1	ex Abbotsinch gate, 736, 702, 800.
WJ231	Sea Fury FB.11	ex 'WE726', Yeovilton SF, FRU. '115/O'.
WN493	Dragonfly HR.5	ex Culdrose, 705, 701, A&AEE.
WT121	Skyraider AEW.1	ex Culdrose, 849, USN 124121. '415/CU'.
WV856	Sea Hawk FGA.6	ex RAE, 781, 806. '163'.
WW138	Sea Venom FAW.22	ex AWS, 831, 809. '229/O'.
XA127	Sea Vampire T.22	ex CIFE, 736. Nose section only.
XA864	Whirlwind HAR.1	ex RAE Bedford, A&AEE, RAE, CA, G-17-1.
XB446	Avenger AS.4	ex Culdrose SF, 831, 751, 820, USN 69502. '992/CU'.
XB480	Hiller HT.1	A2577, ex Manadon, 705.
XD317	Scimitar F.1	ex FRU, RAE, 800, 736, 807. '112/R'.
XJ402	Whirlwind HAS.3	A2572, ex Manadon, XD772 ntu.
XK488	Buccaneer S.1	ex BSE Filton and makers.
XL503	Gannet AEW.3	ex RRE, 849 'D', 'A' Flts, A&AEE, 849 HQ Flt, C(A), 849 'A' Flt.
XL717	Tiger Moth	ex G-AOXG, T7291, 33 MU, 24 EFTS, 19 EFTS.
XN957	Buccaneer S.1	ex 736, 809. '630/LM'.
XP142	Wessex HAS.3	ex 737. *Humphrey*. Falklands exhibition.
XS527+	Wasp HAS.1	ex Wroughton, *Endurance* Flt. Arrived 31/7/86.
XS590	Sea Vixen FAW.2	ex 899, 892. '131/E'.
XS881	Wessex HAS.1	A2675, ex Culdrose. '046/CU'.
XT176	Sioux AH.1	ex Coypool, 3 CBAS.
XT596+	Phantom FG.1	ex BAe Scampton, Holme-on-Spalding Moor, A&AEE. (YF-4K). Arr 19/1/88.
	Gannet AS	anonymous cockpit section.
A-522	FMA Pucara	8768M, ex St Athan, Stanley, Argentine AF. Falklands exhibition.
AE-422	UH-1H Iroquois	ex Stanley, Argentine Army, 74-22520. Falklands exhibition.
0729	T-34C-1 T'Mentor	ex Stanley, Pebble Island, Argentine Navy. '1-A-411'. Falklands exhibition.
0767	MB.339AA	ex Stanley, Argentine Navy. Composite airframe. '4-A-116'. Falklands exhibition.
S.3398+	SPAD XIII replica	G-BFYO, ex Land's End, Chertsey, D-EOWM. Arrived 18/9/86.
D.5397"	Albatros D.Va rep	G-BFXL, ex Leisure Sport, Land's End, Chertsey, D-EGKO. CoA exp 24/9/82.
102/17"	Fokker Dr I rep	BAPC.88, scale replica, based on a Lawrence Parasol.
155848+	F-4S-MC	ex Lee-on-Solent (transit), VMFA-232, USMC. Arrived 6/11/86. 'WT-11'.
159233+	AV-8A-MC	ex VMA-231, USMC. Arrived 6/6/87. 'CG-03'.
01420+	MiG 15bis (LIM-2)	G-BMZF, ex North Weald, Gamston, Retford, Polish AF. Arrived 14/5/87.

Concorde Exhibition An integral part of the FAAM, the Concorde exhibition is set in its own superb hangar, with an overhead walkway to allow inspection of the British prototype *Hotrod*. Two development aircraft and a wide array of *Concordelia* are on show.

G-BSST Concorde 002 UK prototype, first flew 9/4/69.
WG774 BAC 221 ex East Fortune, RAE Bedford, Filton, Fairey FD-2.
XP841 HP.115 ex Cosford, Colerne, RAE Bedford.

Fleet Air Arm Historic Aircraft Flight Also based at Yeovilton is the FAAHAF, whose aircraft can be seen frequently displaying at air events. At Yeovilton the aircraft of the FAAHAF are not available for public inspection.

T8191 Tiger Moth ex Yeovilton SF, Culdrose SF, Yeovilton SF, BRNC, Lossiemouth SF, Arbroath SF, Culdrose SF, Bramcote, Gosport, 3 FF, 22 EFTS, 4 FIS, 3 EFTS.
LS326 Swordfish II ex Westlands, Fairey G-AJVH, Worthy Down, 836.
TF956 Sea Fury FB.11 ex HSA G-9-395, Dunsfold, FRU, 738, 807, 799, 805. 807 Squadron colours as '123/T'.
WB271 Firefly AS.5 ex RAN Nowra, 723, 725, 816/817, 814. '204/R'.
WG655 Sea Fury T.20S ex DLB D-CACU/ES3616, HSA Dunsfold G-9-65, Anthorn, Eglinton SF. '910/GN'.
WV908 Sea Hawk FGA.6 ex Culdrose SF, Halton 8154M, Sydenham A2660, 738, 806, 898, 807. 806 Squadron colours as '188/A'.

Others Going back to W&R10, the Tiger Moth clear out is a little clearer in one aspect, but murkier in another. NL750/G-AHUF moved to Lower Upham. DE373/A2127/A680 is certainly no longer here - fate required. There have been several departures from the ever-active dump area and two arrivals. Whirlwind HAS.7 XL846 left by road on 19/2/86 for Predannack; Wessex HAS.3 XM919 had perished on the dump by 1986; Wessex HAS.1 XS125 left by road on 21/2/86, also for Predannack. That makes the current situation as follows :-

WJ677 Canberra B.2 ex St Mawgan, 7, 231 OCU, 50, 40, 103. Nose section only.
WP309 Sea Prince T.1 ex 750, Arbroath SF. Dump, poor state.
XE369 Sea Hawk FGA.6 A2580/A2633, ex Culdrose, Lee-on-Solent, Halton 8158M, Arbroath. Dump.
XM845 Wessex HAS.1 A2682, ex Lee-on-Solent, Wroughton. Dump, very poor state.
XN308+ Whirlwind HAS.7 A2605, ex Corsham, Lee-on-Solent, Wroughton, Lee-on-Solent, Arbroath, 771, 847, 848, 846, 814. Dump, lying on its side. Arrived by 8/87.
XN692 Sea Vixen FAW.2 A2624, ex Culdrose, 893. External store.
XS128+ Wessex HAS.1 A2670, ex Lee-on-Solent, 737. Arrived 7/10/86 for BDR.

Staffordshire

BALDWINS GATE

(On the A53 south west of Newcastle-under-Lyme) Despite the Colt/TriPacer craze in the UK, G-ARKN remains dismantled at a farm here.

G-ARKN Colt 108 ex N10F. CoA expired 3/9/85. Dismantled and stored.

BURNTWOOD

It is thought that the Vulcan nose is still to be found at a private house here.

XM652 Vulcan B.2A ex Sheffield, Waddington, 50, 35, 44, 9. Nose section.

HALFPENNY GREEN

Previously derelict, the Airedale here is now undergoing restoration. The local Air Scouts keep a T.31 glider at their building.

G-AVKP Airedale ex SE-EGA. CoA expired 31/7/83. Under restoration.
BGA.1346 T.31 ex Bickmarsh, RAFGSA.297. wfu 1/79. Air Scouts.

LICHFIELD

In Cherry Orchard Road (near Lichfield City Railway Station) 1206 Squadron ATC keep their Chipmunk PAX Trainer. A local scrappy handled much of Gannet AEW.3 XL471 when it was broken up for spares by Neil Moffat. The wings can be found at Tinwald Downs.

WK576 Chipmunk T.10 PAX 8357M, ex AOTS, 3/4 CAACU, Cam UAS, Oxf UAS, Lon UAS, Cam UAS, Lon UAS, Cam UAS, Hul UAS, Cam UAS, Bir UAS, Cam UAS, 22 RFS.
XL471+ Gannet AEW.3 ex Farnborough, 849 'B', HQ, 'D', HQ, 'A', 'D', A', 'B', HQ and 'C' Flts.

PENKRIDGE

(On the A449 south of Stafford) In Grange Road, off Bungham Lane, 2415 Sqn ATC keep their Vampire.

XD528	Vampire T.11	8159M, ex Wolverhampton, Stafford, Shawbury, FECS, RAFC, 9 FTS, 10 FTS.

ROCESTER

(On the B5030 north of Uttoxeter) At the JCB factory, the company's first aircraft is kept, minus only the starboard outer wing.

G-ARJB	Dove 8	ex East Midlands. CoA expired 10/12/73.

STAFFORD

Home of the RAF's Tactical Supply Wing, the number of airframes here has doubled since W&R10.

XA801	Javelin FAW.2	7739M, ex St Athan, 46. Gate guardian.
XP359+	Whirlwind HAR.10	8447M, ex Abingdon, RAFEF, Wroughton, 103, 110, 103, 225. Arr 1987.
XS572	Wasp HAS.1	8845M, ex Wroughton. On its side, rescue training.
XT469+	Wessex HU.5	8920M, ex Wroughton. Arrived 10/12/86.

STOKE-ON-TRENT

City Museum and Art Gallery Open daily 1030 to 1700 Monday to Saturday and Sundays 1400 to 1700 the museum has a large display devoted to its home-spun lad, R J Mitchell, including a Spitfire XVI. Contact : Stoke-on-Trent City Museum and Art Gallery, Bethesda Street, Hanley, Stoke ST1 3DE. Tel 0782 273173.

RW388	Spitfire XVI	6946M, ex Kemble, 71 MU, 19 MU, 5 MU, Andover, Benson, FC&RS, 612, 667. In 667 Squadron colours as 'U4-U'.

Ken Fern Collection Ken Fern took delivery of Whirlwind HAR.9 XN298 during 1986 and has since taken the opportunity to establish his own aircraft collection in the area. Co-operating closely with TAC at Warmingham (which see) Ken is due to take on the Chrislea Airguard from TAC. At present visiting is by appointment only, but Ken is looking for bigger premises with a view to opening up more regularly. Contact ; Ken Fern Collection, 311 Congleton Road, Scholar Green, Stoke-on-Trent ST7 3JQ. Telephone : 0782 773140.

BAPC200+	Bensen B.7	composite airframe.
XN298+	Whirlwind HAR.9	ex Bournemouth, Yeovilton, Wroughton, Lee-on-Solent SAR Flt, Fleetlands, Lee-on-Solent, 846, 848. Arrived 16/3/86.

SWYNNERTON

(East of the A519 south of Newcastle-under-Lyne) The Whirlwind is still inside the Army camp here - possibly only wing-borne sleuths will find this one!

XK987	Whirlwind HAR.10	8393M, ex Stafford, Brize Norton, 103, 110, 228, 22, 217, 1360 Flt, 22.

TATENHILL

During November 1986 two aircraft moved in by road from Nottingham Airport for rebuild.

G-AVLM+	Pup 160	ex Nottingham Airport, Cippenham. CoA expired 24/4/69. Arrived 22/11/86.
G-BFNM+	GC-1B Swift	ex Nottingham Airport, N78205. Arrived 15/11/86.

Suffolk

BAWDSEY

(At the end of the B1083, south east of Woodbridge) The RAF base should still have its Hunter.

XE673	Hunter GA.11	8846M, ex Wattisham, Shawbury, FRADU, FRU, 234, 112. Fitted with the rear end of XE689. BDRT.

BENTWATERS

The BDR airframes at the USAF base are unchanged.

80260	F-101B-105-MC	ex Woodbridge, Davis-Monthan, Oregon ANG. BDR.
104	Mystere IVA	ex Woodbridge, Sculthorpe, French AF. '004/WR'.

BURY ST EDMUNDS

In Northgate Street, the headquarters of 301 Squadron ATC still hold the Chipmunk and Vampire.

VV217	Vampire FB.5	7323M, ex 'VV271', Oakington, makers.
WK575	Chipmunk T.10	ex Wyton SF, Oxf UAS, Cam UAS, Hul UAS, Bir UAS, Cam UAS, Bri UAS, 22 RFS, Oxf UAS, 22 RFS. Crashed 13/7/70. Wreck.

FLIXTON

(On the B1062 west of Bungay) Norfolk and Suffolk Aviation Museum Located behind the *Flixton Buck* public house, N&SAM have continued to develop and refine their collection. More buildings are planned and, as ever, this excellent collection of aircraft and artefacts is well worth a visit. Opening times have changed slightly ; April, May, September and October open Sundays and Bank Holidays 1000 to 1700; July and August open Wednesdays and Thursdays 1900 to 2100; June, July and August on Sundays 1000 to 2100 and in July and August on Thursdays 1100 to 1700. Contact : The Secretary, Norfolk and Suffolk Aviation Museum, Flixton, Bungay, Suffolk.

BAPC147	Bensen B.7	ex Loddon. 'LHS-1'
N99153	T-28C Trojan	ex East Ham, France, Zaire/Congo AF FG-289, USN VT-3 146289. Crashed 14/12/77. Fuselage only, combined Zaire/USN colours.
P9390"	Spitfire replica	BAPC.71. 'KL-B'.
VL349	Anson C.19	ex Norwich Airport, N5054 (US civil ntu), G-AWSA, SCS, NCS, North Coates SF, WSF, FCCS, HCCS, HCEU, 116, CSE, 1 FU.
VX580	Valetta C.2	ex Norwich Airport, MCS, MEAFCS, 114, HS. On loan.
WF128	Sea Prince T.1	8611M, ex Honington, Kemble, Sydenham SF, A&AEE, 750.
WF643	Meteor F.8	ex Coltishall, Kemble, 29, Nicosia SF, 611, 56. Composite. 'X'.
WV605	Provost T.1	ex Henlow, Higher Blagdon, 6 FTS, 3 FTS, 22 FTS. 'O-V'.
XH892	Javelin FAW.9R	7982M, ex Duxford, Colerne, Shawbury, 29, 64, 23. On loan.
XJ482	Sea Vixen FAW.1	A2598, ex Wimbourne Minster, 766, 700Y. '713/VL'.
XK624	Vampire T.11	ex Lytham St Annes, Blackpool Airport, CFS, 3 FTS, 7 FTS, 1 FTS, 23 GCF, CFS, 7 FTS.
XN304	Whirlwind HAS.7	ex Bedford, Henlow, Wroughton, Shrivenham, Wroughton, 705, Old Sarum, 848.
XR485	Whirlwind HAR.10	ex Wroughton, 2 FTS, CFS. 'Q'.
42196	F-100D-11-NA	ex Sculthorpe, French AF. USAF colours, tail code 'LT'.
54433	T-33A-5-LO	ex Sculthorpe, French AF. 'WD'.
79	Mystere IVA	ex Sculthorpe, French AF. '8-NB'.

HONINGTON

Much to talk of here, with Tornados making a valiant effort to equal the number of Buccaneer W&R airframes here. To add further detail to W&R10, when Vulcan B.2 XL388 was scrapped here, the nose went to Walpole, the remainder to a scrappy in the Newmarket area. Several departures to chronicle from the listing as given in W&R10, the first of which is less 'concrete' than the others. After many editions of listing Grunau Baby VT921 as being here it has been decided to remove it *LOST!* from W&R12 unless we hear otherwise) as it has not been physically reported here for a decade! Baron N1365Z was crated and shipped to the USA 5/87. Canberra PR.7 WJ825 left by 12/85, taking up a dodgy posting at Catterick. Buccaneer S.2B XW546 flew out 9/11/85 to Woodford to join the BAe new-*Bricks*-for-old line. There is a compound here holding Tornados that have lost during experimentation with gravity, and to date have been fairly long term.

XK526	Buccaneer S.1	8648M, ex RAE Bedford. Gate guardian.
XN930	Buccaneer S.1	8180M, ex St Athan, 736. Dump by 4/86, ex BDRT.
XV338+	Buccaneer S.2A	8774M, ex 237 OCU, 12. Cockpit section only.
XW541	Buccaneer S.2B	8858M, ex St Athan, 12, 16, 15. Spares for XW546 - see above.
XX886	Buccaneer S.2B	ex 208, 16. Weapons loading trainer for IX Sqn by 11/87.
XX946+	Tornado P.02	8883M, ex Warton. UK prototype. Weapons loading trainer. Arrived 5/2/86.
ZA408+	Tornado GR.1	ex TWCU. Crashed 7/87. Wreck.
ZA494	Tornado GR.1	ex 27. Crashed 18/7/84. Wreck.
ZA555+	Tornado GR.1	ex TWCU. Crashed 11/86. Wreck.

IPSWICH

At the TAVR centre on the A12, 188 Squadron ATC keep their Chipmunk PAX Trainer.

WG463	Chipmunk T.10 PAX	8363M, ex Hamble G-ATDX, Stn UAS, Not UAS, StA UAS, Cam UAS, Colerne SF, Oxf UAS, Abn UAS, Oxf UAS, 24 GCF, Cottesmore SF, 3 BFTS, 16 RFS.

IPSWICH AIRPORT

Much activity to record here, with the most interesting being the arrival of two Grumman Widgeons from Hal Far, Malta, for rebuild into one aircraft. The Hibernian Dakota Flight C-47 arrived 2/10/86 and has remained ever since, suffering in the January 1987 gales. It was entered in the October 1987 Luton auction - see the appendix. Three departures to record ; Cessna 182F G-ASLH left on 31/8/87 for Bournemouth Airport; Aztec 250C G-ASRE left by road 10/4/87 for an interesting career at Solihull; Tiger Moth D-EDON was crated up and exported back to West Germany 1/86. MS.892A Rallye hulk G-AYET arrived 6/8/86 for use as spares in G-BKGA. The hulk left again 4/87.

G-ARKM+	Colt 108	Damaged 27/11/83. Arrived 27/2/86 for rebuild.
G-ATES	Cherokee Six 260	Crashed 8/2/81. Para-trainer with Ipswich Parachute Centre.
PH-NLK	Apache 160	ex OY-DCG, SE-CKW. Abandoned Geronimo conversion. Derelict.
N750M+	Widgeon	ex Hal Far. Spares for N3103Q. Arrived 29/4/87.
N3103Q+	Widgeon	ex Hal Far. For restoration, possibly as G-DUCK. Arrived 29/4/87.
N4565L+	DC-3-201A	ex Dublin, LV-GYP, LV-PCV, N129H, N512, N51D, N80C, NC21744. Flew in 2/10/86 - see notes above.

KESGRAVE

Adding to W&R10 the Super Cub frame that was at Kesgrave High School is now thought to have been MM542372 'EI-184' ex Woodbridge and Italian Army. It is equally thought that it moved to Feltwell and from there to the Boston area for rebuild. Confirmation required.

LAKENHEATH

This USAF base has also been blessed with the F-4 hand-out, an aircraft arriving in 1985 and 1986. The plinth-mounted F-100 has received yet another identity. Of the huge fleet of Mystere IVA decoys, 60 coded '12' was burnt on the dump by 12/87. The aircraft that migrated to Mildenhall was 97, code '4'. As will be seen from the listing below a few of the Mysteres have had their codes 'cracked'.

14060	T-33A-1-LO	ex French AF, EC.10, SLVSV. BDRT. 'LN'.
24434	F-105G-RE	ex Davis-Monthan, 562 TFS. 'LN'.
37471+	F-4C-18-MC	ex 163 TFS/122 TFW, Indiana ANG. Arrived by 5/86. BDRT. 'LN'.
37610+	F-4C-20-MC	ex 171 FIS, Michigan ANG. Arrived 16/7/86. BDRT.
63319"	F-100D-16-NA	42269, ex '54048', French AF. Gate guardian. 'FW-319'.
16	Mystere IVA	ex Chateaudun, via Cambrai, French AF. Decoy.
75	Mystere IVA	ex Sculthorpe, Chateaudun, French AF. '11'.
99	Mystere IVA	ex Sculthorpe, Chateaudun, French AF.
113	Mystere IVA	ex Chateaudun, via Cambrai, French AF.
126	Mystere IVA	ex Sculthorpe, Chateaudun, French AF.
145	Mystere IVA	ex Chateaudun, French AF.
241	Mystere IVA	ex Chateaudun, French AF. '2'.
285	Mystere IVA	ex Chateaudun, via Cambrai, French AF.
300	Mystere IVA	ex Sculthorpe, Chateaudun, French AF. '5'.
309	Mystere IVA	ex Sculthorpe, Chateaudun, French AF.

MILDENHALL

Another base receiving a Phantom for BDR work. The T-33A lives on, although it looks like a patchwork quilt! In September 1987 a JetStar flew in and this will be used for non-destructive ground training. The Mystere IVA that came in during 1985 for BDR here is now known to be No 97, it was dismantled by 7/87 and appeared shortly thereafter at Molesworth.

16769	T-33A-1-LO	ex French AF, CIFAS-328. BDRT.
24198+	VC-140B-LM JetStar	ex 58 MAS, Ramstein. Flew in 23/9/87. See notes above.
40707+	F-4C-22-MC	ex 171 FIS, Michigan ANG. Arrived during 1986. BDRT. 'MI'.

MONEWDEN

(South of the A1120, north of Ipswich) The Cessna hulk is retained for spares use.

G-BENF	Cessna T.210L	ex Ipswich, N732AE, D-EIPY, N732AE. Crashed 29/5/81.

NEWMARKET

A scrapyard in this general area took the bulk of Vulcan B.2A XL388 from Honington in 1985, with much of it surviving up to at least 8/86. Also present was the forward section of a Concorde test-shell.

PARHAM

(Or Framlington, on the B1116 north of Woodbridge) A former Lakenheath Aero Club Cessna is stored here.

N11824+	Cessna 150L	Stored, dismantled. First noted 8/87.

STOWMARKET

1331 Squadron ATC have had a Chipmunk T.10 PAX Trainer here since at least 1984.

WG471+	Chipmunk T.10 PAX	8210M, ex Leeming, Abn UAS, 1 FTS, 6 FTS, 229 OCU, Aston Down CF, MCCS, 4 SoTT, Not UAS, Lee UAS, 19 RFS, 24 RFS, 3 BFTS, 16 RFS, 4 BFTS.

WALPOLE

(On the B1117 south east of Halesworth) The nose section of the former Honington Vulcan came to a private house here during 1985.

XL388+	Vulcan B.2A	8750M, ex Honington, 50, Wadd Wing, Scampton Wing, 9. Nose section.

WATTISHAM

The Lightning content here was dramatically reduced on 27/8/86 when the two long-serving decoy F.1As, XM139/8411M and XM147/8412M left by road - destination unknown. Sensing the imbalance, an LTF F.3 flew in early in 1987 for BDR. Gnat T.1 XP515 had gone by 4/86, joining the targets at Otterburn. Noseless Phantom FG.1 XT595 arrived from St Athan for BDR by 12/85. Its nose is with RAFEF at Abingdon.

EP120	Spitfire Vb	5377M/8070M, ex Boulmer, Wilmslow, St Athan, 53 OTU, 402, 501. Gate guardian, in 19 Squadron colours as 'QV-H'.
WJ603	Canberra B.2	8664M, ex 100, 85, 98, 85, 98, 6, 35, 115, 18. Dump, poor state.
XM192	Lightning F.1A	8413M, ex Wattisham TFF, Binbrook TFF, 226 OCU, 111. Gate guardian.
XR718+	Lightning F.3	8932M, ex LTF, 11, LTF, 11, 5, LTF, 5, 11, LTF, 5, LTF, 5, 226 OCU, 29, 56. Flew in 5/2/87. BDR.
XT595+	Phantom FG.1	8851M/8550M, ex St Athan, Abingdon, St Athan, Coningsby, A&AEE. Noseless. Arrived by 12/85 for BDR. See notes above.
XV154	Buccaneer S.2A	8854M, ex 12, 237 OCU. BDR.

WOODBRIDGE

An above average performance in the listing as given in W&R10 - the Voodoo here is as given below and not in the previous work. Mystere IVA '134' should have read 133 and Mystere IVA 104 was missed out all together! Other than that, the report was immaculate! With few sightings of the Mystere fleet here in recent times, their presence should be open to confirmation. The base was also a party to the Phantom world dispersal programme.

37414+	F-4C-15-MC	ex New York ANG. Arrived 16/7/86. BDRT.
70270	F-101B-80-MC	ex Davis-Monthan, Texas ANG. See notes above.
9	Mystere IVA	ex Sculthorpe, Chateaudun, French AF. Decoy.
25	Mystere IVA	ex Sculthorpe, Chateaudun, French AF. Decoy.
50	Mystere IVA	ex Sculthorpe, Chateaudun, French AF. Decoy.
104	Mystere IVA	ex Sculthorpe, Chateaudun, French AF. Decoy. See notes above.
133	Mystere IVA	ex Sculthorpe, Chateaudun, French AF. Decoy. See notes above.
276	Mystere IVA	ex Sculthorpe, Chateaudun, French AF. Decoy.

Surrey

BANSTEAD

(On the A217 north of Reigate) Bearing in mind the problems of identifying what aircraft are really *here* - ie which are as near as damn it fuselages or even whole airframes, and which are just panels and a lot of hope, little has changed at this salvage yard. Adding to W&R10, Tomahawk G-CGFC was not scrapped, but became G-BLNN instead at Chessington. The hulk of Cessna F.150L G-BLAL moved to Bredhurst by 7/87.

G-APZE	Apache 160	ex Chessington. CoA expired 21/12/81. Hulk.
G-ATLN	Cessna F.172G	crashed 1/83. Wreck.
G-ATRD	Cessna F.150F	ex Southend. Crashed 14/4/78. Wreck.
G-AXXA	Cherokee 180E	crashed 31/5/82. Wreck.
G-AZDB	Pup 100	crashed 8/10/77. Wreck.
G-AZWU	Cessna F.150L	dbr 3/4/80. Hulk.
G-BAXW	Cessna F.150L	ex Booker. Crashed 16/9/80. Wreck.

BROOKLANDS

(Or Weybridge) Brooklands Museum Work continues towards opening this ambitious project to the public - still some way off yet. The museum will be a centre for motor racing and aviation, reflecting the combination that Brooklands offered in its heyday. Several items have been acquired since W&R10, the most impressive being the arrival by air of the VC-10 - the last flight by a civil VC-10. Another large airliner arrived in early April 1988, Roger Hargreave/Proteus Engineering's Britannia G-ANCF, by road from Manston. The Museum have been good enough to let this lodge in open storage until Roger can find a permanent location for it. Viewing is possible by prior application, contact : Brooklands Museum, The Clubhouse, Brooklands Road, Weybridge, Surrey KT13 0QN. Telephone 0932 57381.

G-ACTF	Comper Swift	ex Booker, VT-ADO. On loan from Alan Chalkley - airworthy, may not always be present. CoA expired 6/10/87.
G-ADRY"	HM.14 Pou du Ciel	BAPC.29, ex Aberdare, Swansea. Loan Mike Beach.
G-AEKV	BAC Drone	BGA.2510/DZQ, ex Booker, Colerne, Bicester. CoA expired 6/10/60. Loan Mike Beach.
G-ANCF+	Britannia 308F	ex Manston, Merchant Air, Invicta, 5Y-AZP, G-ANCF, LV-GJB, LV-PPJ, G-ANCF ntu, G-14-1, G-18-4, N6597C ntu, G-ANCF. Arrived by road 5/4/88 - see notes above.
G-BJHV+	Voisin replica	ex Old Warden. Arrived during 1987. On loan.
G-LOTI	Bleriot XI replica	CoA expired 19/7/82. Loan Mike Beach.
G-MJPB	Manuel Ladybird	On loan from Bill Manuel.
BAPC187	Roe I Biplane rep	Under construction.
BAPC194	Demoiselle replica	ex Henlow, Gatow. Arrived 29/1/87.
	Curtiss Pusher rep	Loan Mike Beach.
	Slingsby Gull 3	prototype. Loan Mike Beach.
A40-AB+	VC-10 1103	ex Sultan of Oman, G-ASIX. Flew in 6/7/87.
G1381+"	Avro 504K replica	BAPC.177, ex Henlow. Arrived 29/1/87.
N2980	Wellington 1A	ex Loch Ness, 20 OTU, 37, 149. Ditched 31/12/40. Under extensive restoration. Many parts elsewhere, eg wings at Luton.
R4+"	Vickers Viking	BAPC.114, ex Chertsey. Arrived early 1988.

Brooklands Technical College Both instructional airframes are unchanged at the College.

XJ772	Vampire T.11	ex Wisley, Shawbury, CATCS, 1 FTS, 8 FTS, RAFC. 'H'.
E-421	Hunter F.51	ex Kingston-on-Thames, Dunsfold, G-9-443, Danish AF, Aalborg, ESK.724.

BYFLEET

(The Editor put this in Essex in W&R10. It has now moved back of its own accord.) The Proctor is believed to be still under restoration here.

NP303	Proctor IV	G-ANZJ, ex Caterham, Kenley, Nottingham, Royston, London Bridge, Southend. wfu 9/70.

CAMBERLEY

Both of Barry Parkhouse's aircraft have moved on ; Harvard IIB KF435 moving to Booker 1/3/87 and Provost T.1 WV686/G-BLFT moving to Cranfield 20/2/88. Coming the other way from Cranfield was his latest project, a Terrier for restoration to flying condition. Ted Tootel and C Sawyer are still busy restoring their 'Austers' (G-JETS and G-AJUD respectively). The Jet Provost nose with 1075 Squadron ATC (located on the A30 near the town centre) is now identified.

G-AJUD	J/1 Autocrat	ex Tongham. CoA expired 18/5/74. Under restoration.
G-AYDW+	Terrier 2	ex Cranfield, Bushey, G-ARLM ntu, TW568, LAS, AOPS, 227 OCU, 43 OTU. CoA expired 1/7/73. Arrived 20/2/88.
G-JETS	Terrier 2	ex G-ASOM, Chirk, G-35-11, VF505, AAC, 652, 1909. Damaged 8/1/78. Under restoration.
XN493	Jet Provost T.3	ex Abingdon, 3 FTS, 7 FTS, RAFC. Nose section only.

CHERTSEY

Thorpe Park As part of a major rethink at the leisure park, first the flying fleet and now the static fleet of replicas have been sold off. The bulk were auctioned by Christie's at their Bournemouth auction on 1/10/87, all but the airworthy G-BFCZ being 'hammered' *in absentia*. Of those auctioned, only three have turned up since and it is thought quite a few have found their way to the USA. Prior to the auction, the FAAM at Yeovilton acquired Sopwith Triplane replica BAPC.111/N5492 and the Brooklands Museum took the Vickers Viking R4/BAPC.114 off to Brooklands. The auction aircraft are listed below, along with 'high bids'. All of this leaves the Hansa-Brandenburg W.39 2292/BAPC.138 unaccounted for.

3/BAPC.140	Curtiss R3C-2 rep	built by FEM Displays, 1978	Fetched £ 6,000.	
5/BAPC.141	Macchi M.39 rep	built by Westward A/W, 1979	Fetched £ 2,800,	to North Weald.
19/BAPC.136	Deperdussin rep	built by FEM Displays, 1979	Fetched £ 600,	to North Weald.
5125/BAPC.110	Fokker D.VII rep	built by Harvestair, 1975	Fetched £ 2,700.	
8151/BAPC.137	Sopwith Baby rep	built by FEM Displays, 1978	Fetched £ 1,100.	
B4863/BAPC.113	SE.5A replica	built by Harvestair, 1975	Fetched £ 5,000.	
B7270/G-BFCZ	Sopwith Camel rep	built by Westward A/W, 1977	Fetched £32,000.	
C4912/BAPC.135	Bristol M.1C	built by FEM Displays, 1976	Fetched £ 4,800.	
S1595/BAPC.156	Supermarine S.6 rep	built by FEM Displays, 1979	Fetched £ 3,200,	to North Weald.
Dr.I/17/BAPC.139	Fokker Dr.I rep	built by FEM Displays, 1978	Fetched £ 2,800.	

CHOBHAM

Vampire T.11 XE950/8175M moved to Northolt in 10/86 and on 14/11/86 was picked up by a French Air Force C-160 Transall and flown to Toulouse for a museum. Press reports said that it was a gift from a Croydon ATC unit.

DUNSFOLD

The Trident is still the only W&R candidate at the BAe airfield. It is used for trials by RFD Ltd.

G-ARPZ	Trident 1C	ex Heathrow, BA, BEA. wfu 7/4/83.

EGHAM

It is believed that the Auster AOP.9 restoration continues here with Peter Neilson.

XN435	Auster AOP.9	G-BGBU, ex Amersham, Heston, St Athan, 6 Liaison Depot Flt, MoA.

FAIROAKS

Has always been problematical for W&R! Going back to the review of Sioux AH.1 disposals from here, XT508 became G-BGAI, XT196 became HP-789 and XT243 became HP-850 - not as given in W&R10. Twin Otter VP-FAW was dismantled and stored here by 12/84. It left by 6/87 for the USA. Otherwise there are no long termers here.

GODALMING

Canberra B.2 WH657 moved to Brenzett by 5/87 from the RFD Ltd plant. In Hallam Road at the TAVR Centre, 1254 Squadron ATC still have their Hunter nose.

WV332	Hunter F.4	7673M, ex Dunsfold G-9-406, Halton, 234, 112, 67. Nose.

REDHILL

Redhill Technical College The two airframes used by the college are unchanged.

G-ANOA Hiller UH-12A ex Redhill Aerodrome, F-BEEG, N8170H. CoA expired 12/6/70.
G-AWTU Musketeer A23-19A ex Deanland, AP-AWT, G-AWTU, N2769B. wfu 21/5/85.

East Surrey Technical College The Sea Devon is still used at this location. Note that both colleges are part of the same complex, but are located in different parts of the town.

G-KOOL Sea Devon C.2 ex Biggin Hill, VP967, Kemble, 781, 21, 207, SCCS, SCS, WCS, SCS, NCS, SCS, MCS, MoA, MCS, CCCF, 38 GCF, TTCCF, FCCS, 2 TAF CS, MCCS, RAFG CS, 2 TAF CS, Wahn SF, RCCF.

REDHILL AERODROME

Plans here are underway that look set to ruin the character of the airfield as it seems to be striving for the world of biz-jets and not Tiger Moths. Bristow Helicopters continue to supply the main W&R interest here. Of the aircraft listed in W&R10, Condor G-ASRB moved off site by 1986 for continued restoration; AB.204B VR-BDX had also gone by 1986, destination unknown; Wessex 60s 5N-AJN and 5N-ALO had gone by 1987, reportedly to the Isle of Wight. Going back to W&R10, the Servotec Grasshopper G-ARVN did not go to Shoreham, but ended up at Weston-super-Mare. Tiger Moth G-AOBO arrived here from Fareham early in 1986, but left, destination unknown, by mid 1987. Current situation here is :-

G-AODA+ Whirlwind Srs 3 ex Bristow, 9Y-TDA, EP-HAC, G-AODA. CoA expired 27/11/86. Stored.
G-ASKP Tiger Moth ex N6588, 9 EFTS, 9 ERFTS. Crashed 27/1/85. Restoration complete 1/88.
G-ASYW Bell 47G-2 ex Bristow, VR-BBA, CP-704, VP-TCF, CP-671, VR-BBA. CoA expired 23/11/85.
G-AXGS Condor ex Billingshurst. CoA expired 4/12/77. Stored.
G-AYNP+ Whirlwind Srs 3 ex Bristow, ZS-HCY, G-AYNP, XG576. CoA expired 27/10/85. Stored.
G-BGWT+ Wessex 60 Srs 1 ex Bristow, Ghana AF G-631. CoA expired 3/1/83. Stored.
G-TIGD Super Puma ex Bristow, G-BJYI. Crashed 4/7/83. Derelict.
5N-AJH Whirlwind Srs 3 ex G-ATLZ, EP-HAK, French AF F8, XK933 ntu, Arbroath, 737, 815, 820, 845. Forward fuselage with Apprentices.

REIGATE

The Fire Brigade Headquarters took delivery of a large package in the form of Trident 3 fuselage G-AWZI from Heathrow in June 1987. It is for non-destructive training.

G-AWZI+ Trident 3B-101 ex Heathrow, BA, BEA. Fuselage, arrived by road 28/6/87.

SMALLFIELD

(East of the M23, at Junction 9) The Cessna is still stored here.

N41836 Cessna 150A ex Redhill, G-ARFI. Stored.

TONGHAM

(On the A3014 south of Aldershot) The three 'Austers' are still to be found at Air Farm.

G-AHUG T'craft Plus D ex Aldershot, LB282. CoA expired 12/7/70.
G-AJAB J/1N Alpha CoA expired 3/10/75. Stored.
G-ASEE J/1N Alpha ex I-AGRI. Crashed 9/2/74. Stored.

VIRGINIA WATER

(On the A30 south west of Egham) The Machine Music Cessna 210 is to be found at a house near here.

G-OILS Cessna T.210L ex G-BCZP, N1736X. Crashed 29/1/82.

WOKING

In Westfield Avenue 1349 Squadron ATC avidly keep hold of their Gnat.

XM697 Gnat T.1 ex HSA, A&AEE, HSA. Red Arrows colours.

East Sussex

HAILSHAM

Still acting as 'pad guardian' for Grenville Helicopters at the Boship Manor Hotel is the composite Bell 47.

G-AYOE Bell 47G ex F-OCBF. Crashed 16/7/77. Composite, including Sioux parts.

HASTINGS

As predicted in W&R10, the Bo-Peep Garage did indeed have to move and is now to be found on the Castleham Estate, along with its Meteor 'pump guardian'. John Wakefield is still working on the Klemm in the area.

G-ACXE L-25C-1 Swallow CoA expired 7/4/40. Under restoration.
WL345 Meteor T.7 ex Hastings, Kemble, CAW, 8 FTS, 5 FTS, CFE, 229 OCU.

HEATHFIELD

Both the Comper Swift G-ABUS and the Tiger Moth G-AHLT moved to Ludlow by 1987.

LEWES

Paul Penn-Sayers is rebuilding his Linnet here.

G-APNS Linnet ex Chessington. CoA expired 6/10/78. Under rebuild.

ROBERTSBRIDGE

(On the A21 north west of Hastings) Robertsbridge Aviation Society RAS have added a substantial Hurricane cockpit section, including engine, to their collection at the Bush Barn. The museum is open to the public every Thursday evening from 1700 and on the last Sunday afternoon of each month except December. Contact : Dennis Woodgate, RAS, *Cwmavon*, Northbridge Street, Robertsbridge, East Sussex, TN32 5NY. RAS also own the Mystere IVA on show at Headcorn.

G-AIVW Tiger Moth ex Redhill, T5370, 20 AFU, SAN, 10 EFTS, 25 PEFTS, 1 PFTS. Wrecked 27/8/82. Remains.
V7350+ Hurricane I ex 85. Shot down by Bf 109s over Kent 29/8/40. Forward fuselage.
WZ822 Grasshopper TX.1 ex Syerston.
Horsa substantial fuselage section.

RYE

Ian Addy has acquired a Norecrin for restoration.

G-BAYL+ Norecrin VI ex Solihull, Bodmin, F-BEQV. Arrived 1987, for restoration.

ST LEONARDS-ON-SEA

The Vintage Airworks Spitfire restoration project has wound down. MJ730/G-BLAS moved to East Midlands and TE566/G-BLCK to Ludham. Steve Atkins' own machine, G-TRIX, is still in the area underway. With Guy Black's Aero Vintage, restoration of Bristol F.2b G-AANM is coming on nicely, and the former Nigel Ponsford/Anne Lindsay frame has arrived from Leeds.

BAPC.19+ Bristol F.2b ex Leeds, Wigan, Weston-on-the-Green. Frame only, arrived 1987.
D7889 Bristol F.2b G-AANM/BAPC.166, ex Old Warden. Under restoration.
PV202 Spitfire Tr IX G-TRIX, ex Saffron Walden, G-BHGH ntu, Strathallan, IAAC 161, G-15-174, PV202, 412, 83 GSU, 84 GSU, 33, 84 GSU. Under restoration.

SEAFORD

On the Cradle Hill Industrial Estate, Riverside Metals have an Aztec fuselage mounted to lure in customers. It has been here since circa 1982.

G-BHNG+ Aztec 250E ex Shoreham, N54125. Crashed 19/12/81. Fuselage only.

SEDLESCOMBE

(North of Hastings) Bill Cole still has his cache of stored aircraft in the area.

G-AWFT Jodel D.9 ex Hazeleigh Grange. CoA expired 22/7/69.
G-AXPG Mignet HM.293 ex Hazeleigh Grange, Southend. CoA expired 20/1/77.
F-BSIL Cessna F.150K dismantled, for spares.

UCKFIELD
During 1986 2530 Squadron ATC at Headley Court took on a former RAFEF Jet Provost nose. It is parented by RAF Biggin Hill.

XP677+ Jet Provost T.4 8587M, ex Abingdon, RAFEF, 2 FTS. Nose section only.

West Sussex

CHARLWOOD
(West of Gatwick) Sea Hawk G-JETH was acquired by Vallance Byways and moved to their unit on the Charlwood Industrial Estate in October 1987.

G-JETH+ Sea Hawk FB.5 ex Bournemouth, Southend, 'XE364', XE489, FRU, 899. Composite, with WM983 - see Chilton Cantelo. Arrived 10/10/87.

CHICHESTER
Spitfire FR.XVIII HS649 moved from here to Ludham and was then exported to Holland.

CRAWLEY
Crawley College of Technology have taken on the restoration of a SARO P.531 for the British Rotorcraft Museum (and on loan from the FAAM).

XN334+ SARO P.531 A2525, ex Weston-super-Mare, Yeovilton, Arbroath, Lee-on-Solent. Arrived 18/9/87 for restoration.

CUCKFIELD
Warden Park County School had to give up its airframes and they were disposed of as follows : Whirlwind VR-BEP to East Midlands and Widgeon 5N-ABW to Weston-super-Mare.

FAYGATE
(On the A264 between Horsham and Crawley) Park Aviation Supply's yard has expanded in terms of contents and has taken on its first piece of civilian scrap. All of the aircraft listed in W&R10 live on, other than the nose of Jet Provost T.3 XN597 which has not been noted since 12/84. Please remember that only substantial airframes are included in W&R. The Hunter F.51 is whole and lives at a private house not too far away.

G-BFTD+	AA-5A Cheetah	crashed 30/3/79. First noted 8/87. Hulk.
WH911	Canberra E.15	ex St Athan, 98, 35. Forward fuselage.
XG226+	Hunter F.6A	8800M, ex Catterick, 1 TWU, TWU, 229 OCU, 92, 66, 92. First noted 12/87.
XP568	Jet Provost T.4	ex Hatfield, Hatfield Tech, Shawbury, RAFC. Fuselage.
XP976+	Hawker P.1127	ex Wittering, Foulness Island, Farnborough, Sevenhampton, Aston Down, 71MU, BLEU, Dunsfold. First noted 8/87. Hulk.
XT866	Phantom FG.1	ex Leuchars, 43, Phantom TF. Crashed 9/7/81. Hulk.
XX114	Jaguar GR.1	ex 226 OCU. Crashed 19/9/83. Hulk.
XX137	Jaguar T.2	ex 226 OCU. Crashed 5/2/76. Hulk.
XX293+	Hawk T.1	ex 4 FTS. Crashed 17/4/85. First noted 8/87. Hulk.
XZ120	Jaguar GR.1	ex 2. Crashed 25/2/77. Hulk.
XZ438	Sea Harrier FRS.1	ex BAe. Crashed 17/5/82. Hulk.
+	F-4D	ex 32 TFS. Forward fuselage. First noted 2/87.
E-430	Hunter F.51	ex Chertsey, Dunsfold, G-9-448, Danish AF, Aalborg, ESK.724. FAA colours. See notes above.

GATWICK
Airport There has been no change with the airframes at the airport, which is just as well, as everything else seems to have changed!

G-APMB	Comet 4B	wfu 21/11/78. Cabin trainer with Gatwick Handling.
G-AWZX	Trident 3B-101	ex Heathrow, BA, BEA. wfu 1/10/84. Fire crews.
SX-BBD"	Aztec 250E	G-BBBD, ex Shoreham, N40292. Crashed 8/12/82. Fire crews.

Heliport The famous 'Beehive' has closed down and stored Sikorsky S-61N G-AWFX travelled to Aberdeen by road 27/11/85.

Gatwick Hilton Hotel Amy Johnson's *Jason* still does circuits in the lobby.

G-AAAH"	DH.60G Moth rep	BAPC.168.

GOODWOOD

The crated Tiger Moth is thought still stored here.

ZS-BCU Tiger Moth ex South Africa, SAAF 2267, T6741. Stored.

SHOREHAM-BY-SEA

Tiger Moth G-ALVP is known to be still under restoration in the area. Auster 5 G-AJGJ moved to Southampton for restoration.

G-ALVP Tiger Moth ex Shoreham Lighthouse, R4770, 4 RFS, 4 EFTS, 10 FIS, 7 EFTS, 11 EFTS. wfu 2/61. Under restoration.

SHOREHAM AIRPORT

This lovely airfield continues to be a hive of activity with Air South (AS) under the guidance of John and Jenny Pothecary holding an amazing array of airframes and artefacts. (See also under Slinfold.) Chelsea College's (CC) airframes have not changed, being housed in their own hangar. Southern Air deal in Enstroms and the throughput of frames and rebuilds is too quick to merit inclusion within W&R most of the time. Both Beagle aircraft are held in careful store with a view to using them as part of a Shoreham Airport museum. The two aircraft can be inspected by written appointment with Air Traffic.

Going back to a question posed in W&R10, the Auster AOP.9 XP283 turned up at Cranfield by 7/87. The following airframes have moved on since W&R10 ; Whatever came here from Redhill of Grasshopper II G-ARVN (the second) could not have been much and should be discounted. (The first G-ARVN is now at Weston-super-Mare.) Jim Wilkie took on Grasshoppers G-AWRP, G-AXFM (omitted from W&R10) and G-AZAU and took them all northbound to Heysham 4/9/87; Provost T.51 G-BLIW/177 flew again following restoration on 4/9/87 and continues to be based; Stearman wreck G-ROAN moved back to Tattershall Thorpe; Enstrom F.28A SE-HIY became G-BNNV and healthy during 1987. Current situation is as follows :-

G-ABNX+	Robinson Redwing	ex Slinfold. CoA expired 30/3/82. Under restoration.
G-ADXT+	Tiger Moth	CoA expired 27/5/84. Composite. Stored. AS.
G-AMNN"	Tiger Moth	ex Redhill. Composite airframe, real identity unknown. CC.
G-AOIS	Tiger Moth	ex R5172, West Malling SF, 22 SFTS, 15 EFTS, 9 EFTS. CoA expired 7/6/81. Under restoration.
G-APNJ	Cessna 310	ex EI-AJY, N3635D. CoA expired 28/11/74. CC.
G-APTH+	AB 47J Ranger	ex Southend, 5N-ACP, G-APTH. CoA exp 17/8/79. On rebuild.
G-ARBO+	Comanche 250	crashed 27/4/83. For rebuild. First noted 3/87.
G-ARRM	Beagle 206-1X	ex Duxford, Shoreham. Prototype. CoA expired 28/12/64. Stored.
G-ASFD	Morava L-200A	CoA expired 12/7/84. Stored.
G-AVDF	Pup 200	ex Duxford, Shoreham. Prototype. Stored.
G-AVUK	Enstrom F.28A/UK	ex Thruxton, N4460. Crashed 3/12/75. Wreck. Stored.
G-BBFF	Seneca 200	ex Coventry, N1077U. Crashed 25/5/74. CC.
G-BDJP+	J-3C-90 Cub	ex OO-SKZ, PH-NCV, NC3908K. CoA expired 18/5/84. Stored. AS.
G-BJAP+	Tiger Moth	ex Slinfold. Composite, under construction. AS.
+	Tiger Moth	fuselage frame with AS. First noted 2/88.
EC-AIU+	Tiger Moth	ex Spain. Under restoration, first noted 2/88. AS.
VQ-SAC	BN-2A Islander	crashed 4/9/76. Forward fuselage. CC.
EM-01+"	DH.60G Moth	G-AAOR, ex Slinfold, EC-AAO. Dismantled. First noted 2/88. AS.

SLINFOLD

Air South's other base (see also Shoreham Airport) has had a considerable clear-out with several airframes moving on to 'Shed Eleven' at Shoreham. DH.60 Moth G-AAOR and the lovely Redwing G-ABNX have both gone to Shoreham. Pup 100 G-AXBE hulk is presumed scrapped, the remains of Pawnee 235C G-BEAE are thought to have been exported to Sweden. Current situation here is as follows :-

G-AMKU+	J/1B Aiglet	ex ST-ABD, SN-ABD, G-AMKU. CoA expired 21/9/84. Stored.
G-ARLO	Terrier 1	ex TW642, 663, deH. Crashed 10/7/79. Spares use.
G-BBHJ	J-3C-65 Cub	ex OO-GEC. Under rebuild.

TANGMERE

Tangmere Military Aviation Museum Major new item with the museum is former Spanish Air Force Bf 109E C4E-88 on loan from Robs Lamplough. The museum is open daily 1100 to 1730 from March 1 to early November. Contact : Tangmere Military Aviation Museum, PO Box 50, Tangmere Airfield, Chichester, West Sussex PO20 6ER. Telephone 0243 775223.

XF314"	Hunter F.51	E-412, ex Dunsfold, G-9-439, Danish AF, Aalborg, ESK.724. 43 Squadron colours as 'N'.
19252	T-33A-1-LO	ex Hailsham, Sculthorpe, French AF. USAF colours.
C4E-88+	Bf 109E	ex Stubbington, Spain. Arrived by 3/87. Poor state.

WARNHAM

With the closure of the museum, Auster G-ANRP/TW439 moved to Dorchester for rebuild.

WEST CHILTINGTON

The Tri-Traveler G-ARAS reflew during 1987 as a Traveler.

Tyne & Wear

GATESHEAD

'Saltwell Airways' continues to provide entertainment in their Viscount fuselage at Saltwell Park.

G-WHIZ"	Viscount 701	G-AMOE, ex Chester-le-Street, Newcastle, Northest, Cambrian, British Eagle, Channel, BEA. wfu 6/1/72. Rear fuselage of G-AOHJ.

NEWCASTLE AIRPORT

(Or Woolsington) Acorn Aviation Services are undertaking the rebuild of a Baladou.

G-ATSY+	Super Baladou IV	CoA expired 22/7/85. Under rebuild.

SUNDERLAND

North East Aircraft Museum Located on the former Sunderland Airport (Usworth) NEAM continue to go from strength to strength. As if to underline NEAM's confidence the museum is now open every day from 1100 to 1800. During the winter period a 'phone call in to check times is advisable. Group visits are welcome with prior notice. NEAM are currently raising cash for a large hangar on their site and also to see if it would be possible to move Trident 1E G-AVYE from Wroughton (it served with Northeast). The F-86D has arrived from Greece, completing a very long range recovery operation. Contact : North East Aircraft Museum, Old Washington Road, Sunderland, Tyne & Wear SR5 3HZ. Telephone 091 5813602.

G-ANFU	Auster 5	ex Bristol, Netheravon, TW385, 663, 227 OCU, 13 OTU. dbr 1/76.
G-AWRS	Avro XIX Srs 2	ex Strathallan, Kemps, Junex, Hewitts, TX213, WCS, 22 GCF, OCTU, 18 GCF, 2 TAF CS, 527, CSE, RCCF. CoA expired 10/8/73.
G-SFTA+	Gazelle 1	ex Carlisle, HB-XIL, G-BAGJ, XW858 ntu. Arrived 11/86.
BAPC.96	Brown Helicopter	ex Stanley.
BAPC.97+	Luton LA-4 Minor	ex Sibson, Sunderland, Stanley. Returned 1986.
BAPC119	Bensen B.7	ex Stanley.
RH746	Brigand TF.1	ex Failsworth, CS(A), ATDU Gosport, Bristols, ATDU, A&AEE, makers. Fuselage, under restoration.
VX577	Valetta C.2	ex Northern Parachute Centre, MCS, 70, Malta CF, 70, MECS, Gibraltar CF, Malta C&TTS, 2 TAF CS, 30.
WA577	Sycamore 3	7718M, ex Kings Heath, Shirley, St Athan, A&AEE, G-ALST ntu.
WB685+	Chipmunk T.10	ex Leeds, Irlam, Edn UAS, Lyneham SF, 8 RFS, 1 RFS. Composite, rear fuselage of WP969/G-ATHC. Arrived 1986, on loan from Nigel Ponsford.
WD790	Meteor NF.11	8743M, ex Darlington, Leeming, RAE Llanbedr, RS&RE, RRE, TRE. Nose.
WD889	Firefly AS.5	ex Failsworth. With rear fuselage of VT409.
WG724	Dragonfly HR.5	ex Chester-le-Street, Moor Monkton, Blackbushe, Lossiemouth SF, Ford SF.
WK198	Swift F.4	7428M, ex Failsworth, 10 SoTT, Aldergrove, MoS. Fuselage.
WL181	Meteor F.8	ex Chester-le-Street, Acklington, Kemble, CAW, 604.
WL405	Meteor T.7	ex Farnborough, BCCS, 1 GCF, 231 OCU, Wittering SF, JCU, Hemswell CF. Major components, other than nose, for possible use in a restoration.
WN516	Balliol T.2	ex Failsworth, RAFC. Cockpit section.
WZ518	Vampire T.11	ex Chester-le-Street, Handforth, Pomona Dock, 5 FTS, Oldenburg SF, 2 TAF CF, 14. Composite, wings of WZ608.

Z767	Grasshopper TX.1	ex Syerston.
G518	Sycamore HR.14	8009M, ex Balloch, Halton, Wroughton, CFS, Khormaksar SF, El Adem SF, Habbiniya SF, Amman SF.
G680	Sea Venom FAW.22	ex Sydenham, ADS. Under restoration.
L319	Vulcan B.2A	ex 44, Wadd Wing, 35, 230 OCU, 617, 230 OCU, Scampton Wing, 617.
M660	Whirlwind HAS.7	ex Almondbank, Fleetlands, Lee, Lossiemouth SAR Flt, 737, 700H, 824.
P627	Jet Provost T.4	ex London Colney, Hatfield, Shawbury, 6 FTS, 3 FTS, 1 FTS.
46	Mystère IVA	ex Sculthorpe, French AF.
-419	Hunter F.51	ex Dunsfold, G-9-441, Danish AF, Aalborg, ESK.724.
2157	F-100D-16-NA	ex Sculthorpe, French AF.
4439	T-33A-1-LO	ex Sculthorpe, French AF.
51+	F-86D-35-NA	ex Hellenikon, Greek AF, USAF 51-6151. Arrived mid 1987.
41	F-84F-40-RE	ex Hellenikon, Greek AF, USAF 52-6541.
	Canberra	nose section, possibly from XH583.
	Auster AOP.6	ex Bristol. Frame only.
	Sycamore HR.14	ex Hayes, Middle Wallop. Nose section only, arrived 1987.

214 Squadron ATC Located next door to NEAM, the unit still has their Vampire T.11, parented by eeming.

D622	Vampire T.11	8160M, ex Leeming, Barkston Ash, Shawbury, 118, RAFC.

VALLSEND

et Provost T.3 XM426 moved on to Liversedge.

Warwickshire

LCESTER

ea Venom XG692 moved to Ragley Hall during 9/86 until moving on to its new home at Long Marston in id 1987.

COVENTRY AIRPORT

Or Baginton) Midland Air Museum Now on a 4½ acre site with its 10,000 square foot Sir Frank Whittle et Heritage Centre the Museum is aiming to upgrade its appearance - highlighting the better exhibits nd seperating the worst out of view in an open store. Aircraft from the Museum continue to travel nto Coventry to undergo restoration by MSC Community Programme teams. SAAB J.29 29640 returned on 2/11/86. Meteor F.4 EE531 left the same day returning on 13/11/87. Sea Hawk FGA.6 WV797 left on 2/11/87 and will return about June 1988. As well as the expansion and refinement of the site, ighlights in aircraft acquisition have to be the two flying arrivals, the Argosy under its own steam nd the Starfighter hitching a lift in a C-130. MAM also have a display in the form of its Humber onoplane in the terminal at Birmingham Airport. MAM is open from April (or Easter if it is in March) o October, Mondays to Fridays 1000 to 1600, Sundays and Bank Holidays 1100 to 1800. November to March undays only 1100 to 1800 or dusk (except Christmas). Contact : Midland Air Museum, Baginton, oventry, CV8 3AZ - please enclose SAE. Telephone 0203 301033.

-EBJG	Pixie III	ex Coventry, Stratford-on-Avon. CoA expired 2/10/36. Stored.
-ABOI	Wheeler Slymph	ex Coventry, Old Warden. Stored. On loan.
-ACCB	Fox Moth	ex Redhill, Blackpool, Southport. Ditched 25/9/56. Stored.
-AEGV	HM.14 Pou du Ciel	ex Coventry, Knowle, Northampton, Northampton Airport. Stored.
G-ALCU	Dove 2	ex airfield, VT-CEH. wfu 8/9/78.
G-APRL+	Argosy 101	ex ABC/Elan, Saggitair, N890U, N602Z, N6507R, G-APRL. Flew in from EMA 20/1/87. *Edna*.
G-APWN	Whirlwind Srs 3	ex Cranfield, Redhill, Bristow, VR-BER, G-APWN, 5N-AGI, G-APWN. CoA expired 17/5/78.
G-ASOK"	Cessna F.172E	D-EDCU, ex Denham, Chirk. Stored following gale damage.
G-BAPC	Luton LA.4 Minor	long term project. Stored.

G-SHIP	Aztec 250F	ex airfield, Birmingham, N62490. Crashed 4/12/83.
BGA.804	T.7 Cadet 1	ex Oxford, Coventry, Solihull, Perranporth, XE761, VM589.
BAPC.32	Crossley Tom Thumb	ex Coventry, Bewdley, Coventry, Banbury. Unfinished. Stored.
BAPC.67	Bf 109 replica	ex North Weald, Newark. On loan. Stored.
BAPC126	Turbulent	ex Shoreham, Croydon. Static display airframe.
VP-KJL	Messenger 4A	ex G-ALAR, RH371. Stored.
H3426"	Hurricane replica	BAPC.68, ex Wembley, Newark. On loan. Stored.
EE531	Meteor F.4	7090M, ex Bentham, Coventry Airport, Birmingham, Weston Park, Birmingham, RAE Lasham, A&AEE, makers.
VF301	Vampire F.1	7060M, ex Stoneleigh, Debden, 208 AFS, 595, 226 OCU.
VM325	Anson C.19	ex Halfpenny Green, WCS, NCS, WCS, TCCF, Upavon CF, 173, 4 FP.
VS623	Prentice T.1	G-AOKZ, ex Shoreham, Redhill, Southend, VS623, CFS, 2 FTS, 22 FTS.
VT935	BP-111A	ex Cranfield, RAE Bedford.
WF922	Canberra PR.3	ex Cambridge, 39, 69, 58, 82.
WS838	Meteor NF.14	ex Cosford, Manchester, Cosford, Shawbury, Colerne, RAE Bedford, RRE, MoS, 64, 238 OCU. Arrived 15/3/86.
WV797	Sea Hawk FGA.6	A2637, ex Perth, Culdrose, Halton 8155M, Sydenham, 738, 898, 899, Fleetlands, 787.
XA508	Gannet T.2	A2472, ex Yeovilton, Manadon, 737. '627/GN'.
XA699	Javelin FAW.5	7809M, ex Cosford, Locking, Shawbury, Kemble, Shawbury, 5, 151.
XA862	Whirlwind HAS.1	A2542, ex Wroughton, Lee-on-Solent, Seafield Park, Haslar, Lee-on-Solent, Fleetlands, 781, 771, 700, *Protector* Flt, 700, *Prot* Flt, 705, G-AMJT ntu.
XD626	Vampire T.11	ex Bitteswell, Shawbury, CATCS, CNCS, 5 FTS, RAFC, CFS. 'Q'.
XE855	Vampire T.11	ex Upton-by-Chester, Woodford, Chester, 27 MU, 22 MU, 10 MU, AWOCU. Stored.
XE872	Vampire T.11	ex Long Itchington, Woodford, Chester, St Athan, 5 FTS, 3/4 CAACU, 8 FTS, 7 FTS, CFS. Stored.
XF382+	Hunter F.6A	ex Brawdy, 1 TWU, TWU, 229 OCU, FCS, 65, 63, 92. Arrived 1/12/86.
XK741	Gnat T.1	ex Leamington Spa, Fordhouses, Dunsfold, Hamble, Boscombe Down, Dunsfold.
XK907	Whirlwind HAS.7	ex Bubbenhall, Panshanger, Elstree, Luton, ETPS, RRE, Alvis. Stored.
XL360	Vulcan B.2A	ex 44, 101, 35, 617, 230 OCU, Wadd Wing, 230 OCU, Scampton Wing, 617.
E-425	Hunter F.51	ex Dunsfold, G-9-446, Danish AF, Aalborg, ESK.724.
R-756+	F-104G	ex Alaborg, Danish AF. Flew in (inside a C-130H) 30/4/87.
14419	T-33A-1-LO	ex Sculthorpe, French AF. '30-QC'.
42174	F-100D-16-NA	ex Sculthorpe, French AF. '11-YI'.
70	Mystere IVA	ex Sculthorpe, French AF.
24535	HH-43B Huskie	ex Woodbridge, 67 ARRS Upper Heyford.
82062	U-6A Beaver	ex Mannheim, US Army.
28368	Fl 282V-20 Kolibri	ex Coventry, Cranfield, Brize Norton. Frame only.
29640	SAAB J.29F	ex Southend, R Swedish AF.

Aircraft Radio Museum and Percival Collection John Coggins' extensive collection of airborne radio gear can be inspected by prior arrangement. The Percival Collection is housed at the airfield and not normally available to public view. Contact : John F Coggins, Aircraft Radio Museum, Baginton, Coventry, Warwickshire. The collection is unchanged :-

G-AMLZ	Prince 6E	ex VR-TBN ntu, G-AMLZ. CoA expired 18/6/71.
G-AOKO	Prentice 1	ex Southend, VS621, CFS, 2 FTS, 22 FTS. CoA expired 23/10/72. Spares.
G-APIU	Prentice 1	ex VR200, 1 ASS, 2 ASS, CFS, 2 FTS. CoA expired 23/2/67. Spares use.
G-APJB	Prentice 1	ex VR259, 1 ASS, 2 ASS, RAFC. CoA expired 4/9/77.

Airport As usual, much activity to chronicle here. Visionair moved most of their aircraft over onto the far side, known as the 'AW Site' from the days when it was the Armstrong-Whitworth plant. Several Visionair aircraft were used in the making of *Empire of the Sun*. The following Coventry-based aircraft were entered in the 10/87 Luton auction ; CASA 352L G-BECL, TB-25N NL9494Z, Nord 3400s 37 and 124/N9048P; Viscounts G-BAPF and G-BMAT - see the Appendix. The following aircraft have moved since W&R10 :- JetRanger hulk G-AZRU, not noted since 2/85, thought scrapped; Cessna F.172H G-BAKK was under conversion into a para-trainer, thought left - to Long Marston?; Bell 47G G-BGHO and the anonymous Bell 47 frame, both thought moved on; Lynx ground rig RG-05, left on 25/6/86 for Lancaster; Lama C-GDAX became G-AZNI again and was flying in 1986; Lama C-GJVI was trans-shipped to Canada; Provost T.1 WW444 left by road 10/86 for Sibson; the Gunbus, Pfalz and Camel replicas held by Visionair all moved to La Ferte Alais, France. Viscount 812 G-BAPF flew in 4/8/87 for storage by BAe, but flew out again

/10/87, for Exeter, reportedly sold in Eire. Viscount 813 G-BMAT flew in 10/12/86 likewise, but left e day after 'PF, again for Exeter and then Eire. The current situation here is :-

ASUS	MJ.2B Tempete	crashed 18/5/80. Dismantled, stored.
AYKZ+	SAI KZ-8	ex HB-EPB, OY-ACB. CoA expired 17/7/81. Stored.
AWSH"	Luton LA.5 Major	G-ASWH, ex Sywell, Yeovilton. Crashed 3/7/77. Stored.
-ACQ	Fleet 80 Canuck	ex Rochester, Blackbushe, Portugal, CF-DQP.
	Nord 3400	ex La Ferte Alais, ALAT 'MAB'. See notes above.
	Nord 3400	ex Rochester, ALAT 'MOC'.
	Nord 3400	ex Rochester, ALAT 'MHA'.
1	Nord 3400	ex La Ferte Alais, ALAT 'MJA'.
4	Nord 3400	N9048P, ex Rochester, ALAT 'MOO'. See notes above.
4700+	T-6G-NH Texan	ex La Ferte Alais, FAF. In Japanese colours by 8/87.
1632"	TB-25N-NC	NL9494Z, ex Blackbushe, USAAF 44-30925. *Gorgeous George-Anne*. See notes above.
+AA"	CASA 352L	G-BECL, ex Blackbushe, Spanish AF T2B-212. CoA exp 4/11/85. See above.

AWFORD HEATH

ear Church Lawford) The Hunter is still on guard at the headquarters of 8 Group ROC. (Reached from e A428 on the road signed to Church Lawford Industrial Estate.)

651	Hunter F.1	7532M, ex Halton, Credenhill, 229 OCU, 233 OCU, 229 OCU, 222.

EAMINGTON SPA

other entrant in the 10/87 Luton auction was Skeeter AOP.12 XL765. It is not known if it returned re.

765	Skeeter AOP.12	ex Leeds, Rotherham, Wroughton, 17 Flt, 654, 651, makers.

ONG MARSTON

ratford Aircraft Collection David Cotton and friends established SAC during 1987 at the airfield. present the aircraft are not available for inspection, but enquiries can be made to SAC, 32 Flaxley ose, Winyates Green, Redditch, Worcs, B98 0QS. SAC co-operated with the Midland Warplane Museum, who ved their Sea Venom in here during late 1987.

AHRI+	Dove 1B	ex East Kirkby, Tattershall, Little Staughton, 4X-ARI, G-AHRI. wfu 1/71. Arrived 2/88.
798+	Grasshopper TX.1	ex Syerston. Arrived by 11/87.
293+	Cadet TX.3	ex Redditch. Arrived by 11/87.
447+	Vampire T.11	ex East Kirkby, Tattershall, Woodford, Chester, St Athan, 8 FTS, RAFC, 5 FTS. Arrived by 2/88.
692+	Sea Venom FAW.21	ex Alcester, Wellesbourne Mountford, Sydenham, Castlereagh, Sydenham, 750. Arrived late 1987. MWM.

rfield By 5/86 the local parachute club had gained a Cessna para-trainer. A likely candidate is G-KK from Coventry Airport.

UNEATON

ith's Scrapyard in Attleborough Road handled the hulk of Pilatus Porter G-BHCR, which was part of the ortive Loughborough Leicester museum.

BHCR+	PCPC.6-B2/H2	ex East Midlands, Sibson, HB-FFT, ST-AEW, HB-FFT. Crashed 15/2/81. Arrived circa 12/85.

TRATFORD-ON-AVON

mes Rowe is thought still to store his Auster Arrow here.

-AIJK	Auster J/4	wfu 8/68. Stored.

TUDLEY

In the A435 south of Birmingham) In Evesham Road, 480 Squadron ATC keep their Vampire.

E864	Vampire T.11	ex Chester, Woodford, Chester, St Athan, 8 FTS, 7 FTS, 1 ANS, CFS, 4 FTS. Composite airframe, wings from XD435.

ARWICK

ohn Berkeley's Seafire fuselage is stored in the area.

K300	Seafire F.17	A646/A2054, ex Leamington Spa, Bramcote.

WELLESBOURNE MOUNTFORD

Wellesbourne Aviation Group Restoration of the Vampire is nearly complete, WAG having produced a firs class job. The underground control rooms and strongpoint are still underway and work has begun o WAG's latest project; a D4 Link Trainer. WAG is open to visitors all day every Sunday and at othe times by appointment. Contact : Dell Paddock, 2 Longford Close, Bidford-on-Avon, Alceste Warwickshire, B50 4EB. Telephone 0789 778816.

XK590	Vampire T.11	ex Witney, Brize Norton, CATCS, 4 FTS, 7 FTS.

Others The Vulcan was restored to the UK register and entered in the 10/87 Luton auction where i attracted no bids. Roy Jacobsen also has another Vulcan at Southend - which see. The dismantled Se Venom turned out to be XG692 from Castlereagh and it moved on to Alcester initially. Locally, th restoration of the Super Cub is proceeding.

G-BJTP	PA-18-95	ex Kingsclere, MM51-15302, I-EICO, MM51-15302, USAF 51-15302. Under restoration.
XM655	Vulcan B.2A	G-VULC, ex N655AV, 44, 101, 50, 44, 9.

Wiltshire

BOSCOMBE DOWN

With just one removal and several additions things are expanding again on the W&R front at t Aeroplane and Armament Experimental Establishment. One of the additions fills a hole left 'vacant' a Little Rissington as far back as 12/9/73 when this particular item left the base by road, never to b seen again! This is Harvard IIB FS890 and there is now every reason to believe it has been here eve since, acting as spares for the A&AEE Harvards that are employed as chase-planes. Canberra PR.9 nos section (now thought to be from XH177) was put up for tender 10/87 and the Wales Aircraft Museu snapped it up, it left by road for Cardiff-Wales 5/2/88.

G-ALRX	Britannia 101	ex WB473 ntu, VX447 ntu. Crashed 4/2/54. Nose section, with Aeromedical and Safety Training School.
FS890+	Harvard IIB	7554M, ex Little Rissington. See notes above.
VP968	Devon C.2/2	ex Northolt, 207, 26, TCCS, NCS, SCS, FCCS. Dump.
VZ345	Sea Fury T.20S	ex DLB D-CATA, D-FATA, ES.8503, G-9-30, Hawkers, Dunsfold, 1832. Accident 19/4/85. Rebuild commenced early 1988.
WD496	Hastings C.2	ex A&AEE. Fire dump, poor state.
WH876+	Canberra B.2(mod)	ex A&AEE, 73, 207, 115. In store by 10/86.
WT309+	Canberra B(I).6	ex A&AEE, HS. In store by 10/86.
XL472	Gannet AEW.3	ex 849 'B', HQ and 'A' Flts. Rescue training.
XL629	Lightning T.4	ex ETPS, A&AEE. Gate guardian.
XL898	Whirlwind HAR.9	8654M, ex Abingdon, Wroughton, *Endurance* Flt, 847, 825, 824, 820.
XN923	Buccaneer S.1	ex RAE West Freugh. Electro-magnetic tests.
XR717	Lightning F.3	ex A&AEE, 56, 29, 56. Fire dump, poor state.
XV373+	Sea King HAS.1	ex A&AEE. wfu 10/86. Reported to be bound for a firing range.
	Canberra B.6	nose section. Put up for tender 10/87.

CHILMARK

(South of the A303 between Wylye and Cricklade) The Wessex at the armaments depot had come outside b 9/87. It is probably here for rescue training.

XP140	Wessex HAS.3	8806M, ex Wroughton.

CHIPPENHAM

1304 Squadron ATC still have their Chipmunk T.10 PAX Trainer. The unit is located near the *Thr Crowns* in The Causeway. The unit is parented by Lyneham. There have been no recent reports concerni the contents of the G Flowers scrapyard in the town.

WP863	Chipmunk T.10 PAX	8360M, ex Shawbury, Hamble G-ATJI, RAFC, 664, RAFC.

:ORSHAM

On the B3353 south west of Chippenham) HMS *Royal Arthur* took on Whirlwind HAS.7 XN308 from Lee-on-olent 30/6/86, only to lose it again to Yeovilton by 8/87.

:RUDWELL

On the A429 south of Kemble) No reports on the continued existence of the Whirlwind in the scrapyard. he yard is on the A429 coming south out of the town.

K912 Whirlwind HAS.7 ex Notton, Wroughton, 705, *Centaur* Flt, *Hermes* Flt, 737, 815, 824, 820, 845.

.EEVIL

aving given what looked like a very concise run-down of who-went-where-and-why on the Vampire store ere, there is more to add. All of the booms extant here moved on to Cranfield during 1987, but all of he wings are still to be found here. Thanks once again to Alan Allen, herewith a brief resume of the ircraft that were here, and the few that still are : WZ415 to Bushey then to Croxley Green and thence o Leavesden; WZ581 to Alan Allen at Ruislip; WZ616 to Bushey to Cranfield and to the USA during 1987; Z620 still at Keevil; XD459 to Bushey and to Cranfield; XE860 to Stone; XE921 still at Keevil; XE928 till at Keevil; XH328 to Bushey then to Cranfield; XH329 still at Keevil; XK632 to Bushey to Croxley reen and then Hemel Hempstead. Having got that off our chest, herewith the four that are still in tore here :-

Z620	Vampire T.11	ex Exeter, 3/4 CAACU. '68'. Stored.
E921	Vampire T.11	ex Exeter, 3/4 CAACU, 1 FTS, CFS. '64'. Stored.
E928	Vampire T.11	ex Exeter, 3/4 CAACU, 74. '76'. Stored.
H329	Vampire T.11	ex Exeter, 3/4 CAACU, Acklington SF, Biggin Hill SF. '70'. Stored.

YNEHAM

n response to the increased mail bag, the 2491 Squadron ATC Meteor T.7 did not leave as W&R10 would ave readers believe. It is still very much here. Two airframes that have gone are Hunter F.6A XJ676 nd Vulcan K.2 XL445, both of which had perished on the dump by 1987. Great news was the arrival of he Comet C.2 from Henlow and its placing on the gate here.

F825	Meteor T.7	8359M, ex Kemble, CAW, 33, 603. See notes above.
K699+	Comet C.2	7971M, ex Henlow, Lyneham, 216. Arrived 10/86 and mounted on gate 6/87.
T472	Wessex HU.5	ex Wroughton, 845. 47-Para Brigade instructional.

MARLBOROUGH

uster AOP.9 XP248 moved to Wroughton by 1/87.

MELKSHAM

ackaroo G-APAP became Tiger Moth G-APAP and was flying again by 1987. The Auster 6A frame has not een noted since 8/83 and is thought to have moved on.

ETHERAVON

n the fire dump Whirlwind HAS.7 XK906 had perished by mid 1987. Wessex HU.5 XT470 moved briefly to ullavington and then to the BRM at Weston-super-Mare. A Beaver joined the dump from late 1987. It is elieved that the Islander fuselage still serves the parachutists.

-BBRP	BN-2A-9 Islander	crashed 20/2/82. Para-trainer, fuselage only.
P827+	Beaver AL.1	ex Shawbury, Kemble. Arrived by 12/87, for the dump.

OLD SARUM

ampire T.11 XD453 moved to Elvington, probably via Harrogate, early in 1987.

PORTON DOWN

here having been no positive sightings of the two Whirlwinds within the Chemical Defence Establishment ince 3/82, it is best that they be left as a 'casual' mention to see if confirmation of their xistence comes rolling in. (HAS.3 XG573, HAR.5 XJ445). Or have the *things* eaten them?

SALISBURY

uring late 1987 Hampshire Light Plane Services, Cliff Lovell's restoration company, moved into a new orkshop here from their previous location at Kingsclere. As is usual with the aircraft Cliff works n, many are of a short term nature and not within the scope of W&R. Accordingly, it is quite ifficult, at this early stage, to work out which airframes are long termers at the new premises.

G-ADMT+	Hornet Moth	ex Kingsclere, Perth, Strathallan, Southampton. CoA expired 27/3/60. Arrived by 9/87.
G-ADPR+	Gull Six	ex Old Warden, Ampthill, AX866, G-ADPR. Arrived by 10/87 for restoration to flying condition. CoA expired 31/12/69.
G-AEZJ+	Vega Gull	ex Sweden, SE-ALA, PH-ATH, G-AEZJ. Arrived by 9/87.
G-AHUN+	GC-1B Swift	ex Kingsclere, EC-AJK, OO-KAY, NC77764. Arrived by 9/87.
EC-ADE+	Moth Major	fuselage, noted 1/88.
51-15431+	PA-18-95	frame, first noted 1/88. Ex Kingsclere?

SWINDON

Written out of W&R9, Auster AOP.9 XN412 'surfaced' here and moved to Innsworth 1/6/86.

UPAVON

The Auster is still stored in the locality.

G-AIGF	J/1N Alpha	CoA expired 19/5/85. Stored dismantled.

WINTERBOURNE GUNNER

(On the A338 north of Salisbury) At the playfully named Nuclear, Bacteriological and Chemical Defenc Centre the airframes held in a compound have not changed.

XK531	Buccaneer S.1	8403M, ex Boscombe Down, Honington, 736, 809, 700S.
XR478	Whirlwind HAR.10	ex Wroughton. Service use?
XR482	Whirlwind HAR.10	ex Wroughton, 28, 110, 103, 110, 103.
XT430	Wasp HAS.1	ex Wroughton, 829, '444'.

WROUGHTON

Science Museum Air Transport Collection and Storage Facility This out-station of the South Kensington based Science Museum continues to grow in stature. The facility is not yet open to the public on regular basis, but special events are frequently held during the year when the hangars are open t inspection. The emphasis is very much on transport aircraft here, but all forms of flight are embrace as witness the arrival of the only airship to be preserved in the UK and the Short SC.1 making a ver welcome 'escape' from storage. The L.37 G-AVZB is due here from Southend during 1988. North Eas Aircraft Museum hope to be able to move Trident 1E G-AVYE up to Sunderland. Details of events planne at Wroughton can be had from : The Science Museum, South Kensington, London SW7 2DD. 01 938 8000.

G-AACN	HP Gugnunc	ex Hayes and K1908.
G-ACIT	DH.84 Dragon	ex Southend, Beagle, ANT Blackpool, BEA, Scottish Airways, Highland Airways. wfu 19/8/81.
G-AEHM	HM.14 Pou du Ciel	ex Hayes, Whitchurch, Bristol.
G-ALXT	Dragon Rapide	ex Strathallan, Staverton, 4R-AAI, CY-AAI, G-ALXT, NF865, 5 MU, 18 MU, MCS.
G-APWY	Piaggio P.166	ex Southend, Marconi. CoA expired 14/3/81.
G-APYD	Comet 4B	ex Dan-Air, Olympic SX-DAL, G-APYD, BEA. CoA expired 3/8/79.
G-AVYE	Trident 1E	ex BA, Northeast, BEA, Channel. wfu 24/4/81. See notes above.
G-AWZM	Trident 3B-101	ex Heathrow, BA, BEA. Flew in 28/2/86.
G-MMCB	Huntair Pathfinder	microlight.
G-RBOS+	Colt AS-105	hot air airship. Donated by Royal Bank of Scotland 9/87.
BAPC162	Newbury Manflier	MPA - major parts.
BAPC172	Chargus Midas	hang glider.
BAPC173	Birdman Grasshopper	powered hang glider.
BAPC174	Bensen B.7	gyroglider.
BAPC188	McBroom Cobra 88	hang glider.
EI-AYO	DC-3A-197	ex Shannon, N655GP, N225J, N8695E, N333H, NC16071.
NC5171N	Lockheed 10A	G-LIOA, ex Wings and Wheels, Orlando, N5171N, NC243 Boston-Maine A/W, NC14959 Eastern..
N18E	Boeing 247	ex Wings and Wheels, Orlando, Sky Tours, NC18E, NC18, NC13340 CAA, United/National Air Transport.
N7777G	L-749A-79	G-CONI, ex Dublin, Lanzair, KLM PH-LDT, PH-TET.
VP975+	Devon C.2/2	ex RAE Farnborough, A&AEE, CCCF, 19 GCF, CPE. Flew in 2/86.
XG900+	Short SC.1	ex Hayes, South Kensington, RAE Bedford. Arrived by 8/87.
XW276	Gazelle 03	ex Southampton, Middle Wallop, Farnborough, Leatherhead, F-ZWRI.

Fleet Air Arm Museum Storage Facility The FAAM store is not open to the public, and indeed neither is the rest of the entry for Wroughton. There have been two depatures and three arrivals. Going : Sea Fury VR930 to Lee-on-Solent 1/5/86 and Scimitar XD220 exported to the USA in exchange for the incoming F-4S Phantom at Yeovilton. It left for Portsmouth 7/6/86 and thence on the RFA *Olna* to New York where it is now displayed on board the USS *Intrepid*.

WP313+	Sea Prince T.1	ex Kemble, 750, Sydenham SF, 750, Lossiemouth SF, 750. Arrived 1/87.
WS103	Meteor T.7	ex Lee-on-Solent, FRU, Kemble, Yeovilton Standards Squadron, Anthorn.
XA129	Sea Vampire T.22	ex Yeovilton, CIFE, 736.
XA466+	Gannet COD.4	ex Yeovilton, Lee-on-Solent, Lossiemouth, 849. Arrived 25/3/87.
XG574	Whirlwind HAR.3	A2575, ex Lee-on-Solent, 771.
XN332+	SARO P.531	A2579, ex Yeovilton, Manadon, G-APNV. Arrived 8/4/87.
XN385	Whirlwind HAS.7	ex Culdrose, Wroughton, HS, A&AEE, 771, 824, 825, 824.

Royal Naval Aircraft Yard All three services store their helicopters here, but the vast majority of the storage that goes on here is too transitory for coverage within W&R. There are some long-termers however, and recently a whole batch of Wasp HAS.1s have come in that may well merit a mention in W&R12. Two items listed in W&R10 have moved on : Whirlwind HAR.9 XN386 was acquired by Jim Wilkie and moved to Heysham 26/2/87; Magister 'L6906' was donated to the Berkshire Aviation Group and moved to Woodley during 6/87. The following Scouts were reduced to just forward fuselages by late 1987 : XP190 (arrived from Arborfield 8/12/86), XP846, XP850, XP852, XP890, XP897, XP898, XP900, XP903, XR600, XR603, XR629, XR637, XR639, XT616, XT620, XT637, XT639, XT642, XT645, XW284, XW615. Of these, the following have more precise fates : XP852 left 1/9/87 for Hildesheim; XP897 left for Soest 1/9/87; XP898 left for Minden 1/9/87; XR600 left for 'Northern Ireland' 18/9/87; XR603 left 5/10/87 reportedly for Australia; XT620 left 18/9/87 for 'Northern Ireland'. Current inmates on long-term storage are :-

XD163	Whirlwind HAR.10	8645M, ex CFS, Akrotiri SAR Flt, MoA, 228, 275, 155, MoA. For British Rotorcraft Museum, Weston-super-Mare.
XK911	Whirlwind HAS.7	A2603, ex Lee-on-Solent, Arbroath, 771, 829, *Ark Royal* Flt, 824, 820, 845.
XM916	Wessex HAS.3	ex RNAY. Fire dump, poor state.
XS120+	Wessex HAS.1	8653M, ex Abingdon, Wroughton. On the dump by 1/87.
AE-520+	CH-47C Chinook	ex Fleetlands, Brize Norton, Fleetlands, Portsmouth, St Athan, Stanley, Argentine Army. Arrived 8/9/86.

Princess Alexandra Royal Air Force Hospital Near the airfield, the inmates are guarded by :-

WJ676	Canberra B.2	7796M, ex Colerne, Melksham, 245, 35, 50.

North Yorkshire

BRIDGE HEWICK

Westland-Bell 47G-3B1 G-BGOZ moved to Chilbolton.

CATTERICK

Royal Air Force Fire Fighting and Safety School The trend in numbers of airframes here is certainly downwards, with four aircraft expiring and one getting up and leaving, but only two coming in as replacements. With changes coming in for Catterick in 1988/89 and a new air mobile special response Army unit with Lynxs, perhaps the wind-down of the fire school is to be a reality during late 1988 when the school will move to Manston to amalgamate the service and RAF fire service training. Those airframes that expired and went to meet their maker by 1987 were : Vulcan K.2 XH561, Sea Vixen FAW.2s XJ572 and XN652; and Vulcan B.2A XL321. Hunter F.6A XG226 moved to Faygate by 12/87. Current situation :-

G-ASGE	Super VC-10 1151	ZD233, ex Brize Norton, Prestwick, BA, BOAC. Fuselage only. Up for tender 4/88 and likely to go to Manston.
TG536	Hastings C.1A	8405M, ex Colerne, SCBS, BCBS, 242 OCU, 35, 511, 24, Lyneham Wing, Topcliffe Wing, Dishforth Wing. Reduced to cockpit section only. See also Elvington.
VP971	Devon C.2/2	8824M, ex Northolt, 207, 60, 207, SCCS, SCS, AAFCE, SCS, HS, MoA, SCS, MCS, MCCS, MCCF, BCCF.

WH794	Canberra PR.7	8652M, ex Abingdon, 13, 58, 82, 540.
WH925	Canberra B.2	ex BCDU, 231 OCU, 35, 207. Nose section only.
WJ825+	Canberra PR.7	8697M, ex Honington, Abingdon, 13, Wyton SF, 58, 100, 58, 82. Arr by 12/85.
WT362	Canberra B(I).8	ex 3, 14, 88. Nose section only.
XA939	Victor B(K).1A	ex 214, 15, 10. Nose section only.
XD182+	Whirlwind HAR.10	8612M, ex Odiham, Wroughton, 202, 22, 202, 228, 155, FAA. Arr 28/1/86.
XM997	Lightning T.4	ex Leconfield, 226 OCU, 92, 226 OCU, LCS. Poor shape.
XN925	Buccaneer S.1	8087M/A2602, in Nuclear Weapons Compound.

CHOP GATE

(On the B1257 north of Helmsley) The base of the North Yorkshire Aircraft Recovery Centre. Please note visits can only be made by prior arrangement. Aircraft held have not changed.

WM145	Meteor NF.11	ex Rotherham, Finningley, 5, 29, 151, 219. Cockpit section only.
WZ557	Vampire T.11	ex Huntingdon, Acaster Malbis, Woodford, Chester, St Athan, 5 FTS, 16. All black colour scheme.

CHURCH FENTON

On the dump, the hulk of Jet Provost T.5A XW329 had expired by mid 1986. The nose section of XN473 is used for crash rescue training. The precious Mk Vb Spitfire still guards the gate.

BM597	Spitfire Vb	5718M, ex Linton-on-Ouse, Church Fenton, St Athan, 58 OTU, 317. 609 Squadron colours as 'PR-O'.
XN473	Jet Provost T.3A	8862M, ex 7 FTS, RAFC. Crashed 15/8/84. Nose section only.

DISHFORTH

Held here since at least 1982 were the following Grasshopper TX.1s ; WZ754, WZ778, WZ781, WZ784, WZ787, WZ792, WZ817, WZ824, XA237. All were put up for tender during 12/87.

ELVINGTON

(Off the A1079 south east of York) Yorkshire Air Museum and Allied Air Forces Memorial have unveiled the first part of their impressive Halifax project which should have scotched critics good and proper. Using the Halifax sections salvaged from Mk II Series 1A HR792 (ex Isle of Lewis), the wings and main spars from Hastings T.5 TG536 from Catterick and many other Halifax items scoured from all over the UK and beyond, the aim is to create a fully fledged Halifax on a restored World War Two airfield. The control tower has been lovingly restored and is open to inspection. The Museum is open weekends and Bank Holidays only between May and September, Saturdays 1400 to 1700, Sundays and Bank Holidays 1100 to 1700. Weekdays and evenings can be arranged by prior appointment. Terrier 2 G-ASCD arrived here from Hole-on-Spalding Moore by 10/86, but moved during 1987 to 'Southampton'. Contact : Yorkshire Air Museum, Elvington, York, YO4 5AT. Telephone : 0904 85 595. The Vampire is on loan from 58 Squadron ATC in Harrogate and is parented by Linton-on-Ouse.

F943+"	SE.5A replica	G-BKDT, ex Sherburn. Full size replica.
HR792+	Halifax II	ex Isle of Lewis. Complex composite - see notes above.
XD453+	Vampire T.11	7890M, ex Old Sarum, Salisbury, St Athan, 1 FTS, CNCS, Oldenburg SF, 26. First noted 5/87.
+	Auster	fuselage frame, first noted 10/86. Not G-ASCD as noted above.

HUNTINGTON

(Between the B1363 and the A164 north of York) Tony Agar's beautiful composite Mosquito is kept here.

HJ711	Mosquito NF.II	composite, nose NF.II HJ711 ex Blackpool, rear fuselage TT.35 RS715 ex Elstree, centre section B.XVI PF498 ex Leyland, outer wings T.III VA878. 169 Sqn colours as 'VI-C'.

KIRBYMOORSIDE

At the Slingsby plant two T-67s have joined the gondola from the AD-500 Skyship in store.

G-BECE	AD-500 Skyship	destroyed 9/3/79. Gondola only, stored.
G-BIUZ+	T-67B	static test airframe. First allocation of registration, c/n 1998.
+	T-67	static test airframe, c/n 2006.

LEEMING

Now a base for Panavia *electric flick knives*, the building work has taken out the dump and Hastings C.2 WJ329 has perished. The gate remains guarded by no less than three aircraft. The Chipmunk PAX Trainer moved to Stowmarket.

TE356	Spitfire XVI	7001M, ex Cranwell, Little Rissington, 2 CAACU, 34, 695. On parade ground.
WG471	Chipmunk T.10 PAX	8210M, ex Abn UAS, 1 FTS, 6 FTS, 229 OCU, MCCS, Not UAS, Lee UAS, 19 RFS, 24 RFS, 3 BFTS, 16 RFS, 4 BFTS.
WS844"	Meteor NF.14	WS788/7967M, ex Patrington, 1 ANS, 2 ANS, 152. 'JCF'. Gate guardian.
XA634	Javelin FAW.4	7641M, ex Shawbury, Colerne, Melksham, makers. Gate guardian.

LINTON-ON-OUSE

By 10/86 another forlorn Jet Provost had joined the dump. The Provost is still on the gate.

XF545	Provost T.1	7957M, ex Swinderby, Finningley, Shawbury, 6 FTS, 2 FTS. 'O-K'.
XM372+	Jet Provost T.3A	8917M, ex 1 FTS, 2 FTS. Crashed 6/12/85. On dump by 120/86.
XN585	Jet Provost T.3A	ex 1 FTS, RAFC. Crashed 28/3/79. Forward fuselage, on dump.

MARKINGTON

(West of the A61 south of Ripon) A Jodel has been in store at a farm here, possibly since 1979.

G-AZII+	SAN D.117A	ex F-BNDO, F-OBFO. CoA expired 28/6/79. Stored.

SHERBURN-IN-ELMET

Locally The former Newark Magister joined the Aeronca being rebuilt in this area during 2/87.

G-AEVS	Aeronca 100	ex Breighton, Selby, Berkswell. Crashed 19/8/66. Under restoration.
T9738+	Magister I	G-AKAT, ex Winthorpe, Leicester East, 24 EFTS, 15 EFTS. Arrived 2/87.

Airfield After being somewhat depleted, the W&R population here has taken a slight upswing.

G-AVDC"	Cessna F.172H	G-AVKG, ex Breighton. Crashed 11/8/75. See Breighton.
G-WYMP+	Cessna F.150J	ex G-BAGW, SE-FKM. Crashed 8/11/85. Wreck, first noted 8/86.
F-BHDT	TriPacer 150	G-BHCW, ex Shobdon. Stored.

SUTTON BANK

Home of the Yorkshire Gliding Club, the hangar is still home to the Pawnee wreck.

G-BENL	Pawnee 235D	ex N54893. Crashed 10/7/85. Wreck, spares use.

TOPCLIFFE

There have been no reports relating to the continued existence of the Bulldog T.1 fuselage XX557 here.

South Yorkshire

ARMTHORPE

(On the A630 north of Doncaster) 1053 Squadron ATC base their Chipmunk T.10 PAX here.

WG419	Chipmunk T.10 PAX	8206M, ex Finningley, MoA, Laarbruch SF, Gutersloh SF, Ahlhorn SF, Oldenburg SF, CFS, Abn UAS, Bir UAS, 15 RFS, 4 BFTS, 6 RFS.

ECCLESFIELD

(North of Sheffield) Paul Flynn has an ex Bingley Vampire pod here under restoration. He has another Vampire pod at Firbeck - which see. The aircraft here has now been identified.

WP255	Vampire NF.10	ex Bingley, Church Fenton, 27 MU hack, CNCS, 1 ANS, CNCS, 23.

FINNINGLEY

Sadly, another 'preserved' Vulcan has slipped the net. XJ782 was put up for tender here 3/88 and will almost certainly be scrapped. The Vulcan was planned as a gate guard, but a more modest one, the Meteor from St Athan in 616 Squadron colours, will be unveiled near the guardroom on 10/6/88. Argosy C.1 XN819 gave up the ghost on the dump during 1986, otherwise the other airframes listed in W&R10 are undisturbed. The arrival of Nimrod AEW.3 XV263 in 7/87 caused many rumours and just what it is here for will have to unfurl in W&R12. A former Red Arrows Hawk, suitably modified, has joined the dump.

G-ATXH Jetstream 1 ex Filton. Cockpit only, procedure trainer.

WL168+ Meteor F.8 7750M, ex 'WH456', St Athan, Swinderby, Finningley, APS Sylt, 604, 111. For the gate - see notes above.

XJ380 Sycamore HR.14 8628M, ex Catterick, CFS, MoA, HS, 275. Displayed outside SAREW, but put up for tender 4/88.

XJ729+ Whirlwind HAR.10 8732M, ex 22, 202, 228, MoA, 22. With SAREW by 1986.

XJ782 Vulcan B.2A 8766M, ex 101, Wadd Wing, Akrotiri Wing, Cott Wing, Wadd Wing, 230 OCU, 12, 83. See notes above.

XP404 Whirlwind HAR.10 8682M, ex Benson, 22, SAR Wing, 202, 228. With SAREW.

XS216 Jet Provost T.4 ex 6 FTS, CAW. Fuselage only.

XV263+ Nimrod AEW.3 ex Waddington, JTU, Woodford, St Mawgan Wing, 203. Flew in 14/7/87.

XX297+ Hawk T.1A 8933M, ex Red Arrows. Crashed 30/11/86. On dump by 5/87.

XX477 Jetstream T.1 8462M, ex Little Rissington, CFS, G-AXXS. Crashed 1/11/74. Dominie escape trainer, fuselage only.

ROTHERHAM

Coopers Metals here scrapped Vulcan B.2A XH563 at Scampton and brought it all here 11/86. The nose was offered for sale and may well still be here, if the money they wanted was anything to go by!

XH563+ Vulcan B.2MRR 8744M, ex Scampton, 27, 230 OCU, MinTech, 230 OCU, Wadd Wing, 230 OCU, 12, 83. Nose section. See notes above.

SHEFFIELD

Brimpex Metal Treatments are working on their HM.14 Pou du Ciel here, for eventual display.

BAPC.13+ HM.14 Pou du Ciel ex Derby, Wigan, Peel Green, Styal. Under restoration.

West Yorkshire

BATLEY

Staravia have a yard here, in the High Street. Inside it could be found the Hunter that was presumed to have come across with the famous NLS example PH-NLH, to be found at Exeter. It is dismantled and would appear to have been here some time.

N-315+ Hunter T.7 ex Amsterdam, NLS spares, Dutch AF, XM121 ntu. See notes above.

BINGLEY

Alan Allen picked up the pod of Vampire NF.10 WM729 5/9/86 and took it to <u>Ruislip</u>. Paul Flynn's example at Ecclesfield is now known to be WP255. That should leave the following pods lying in the yard of Auto Spares (Bingley) Ltd in Walsh Lane ;-

WM705 Vampire NF.10 ex Bradford, Church Fenton, CNCS, 1 ANS, CNCS, 25, 23, 151. Pod only.

WM711 Vampire NF.10 ex Bradford, Church Fenton, CNCS, 2 ANS, A&AEE. Pod only.

WM712 Vampire NF.10 ex Bradford, Church Fenton, CNCS, 2 ANS, 'Q'. Pod only.

WM713 Vampire NF.10 ex Bradford, Church Fenton, CNCS, 1 ANS, CNCS. Pod only.

WM714 Vampire NF.10 ex Bradford, Chruch Fenton, CNCS, 1 ANS, CNCS. 'T'. Pod only.

WM727 Vampire NF.10 ex Bradford, Church Fenton, CNCS, 2 ANS, CNCS. Pod only.

WM730 Vampire NF.10 ex Bradford, Church Fenton, CNCS, 1 ANS, CNCS, 23. 'W'. Pod only.

WP232 Vampire NF.10 ex Bradford, Church Fenton, CNCS, 1 ANS, CNCS, A&AEE. 'L'. Pod only.

WP239 Vampire NF.10 ex Bradford, Church Fenton, CNCS, 2 ANS, CNCS, 25, CFE. Pod only.

WP242 Vampire NF.10 ex Bradford, Church Fenton, CNCS, 2 ANS, CNCS, 25. Pod only.

DEWSBURY

<u>Northern Aeroplane Workshops</u> Work on the Sopwith Triplane for the Shuttleworth Trust is making great progress with the aircraft now in the fitting out stage. Work is also well in hand on the replica Bristol Monoplane for the Bristol Industrial Museum. Visits to the workshop are possible, but by prior arrangement.

Contact : Northern Aeroplane Workshops, F W Found, 7 Scoton Drive, Knaresborough, North Yorks.
G-BOCK Sopwith Triplane c/n NAW.1. Under construction - see notes above.
Bristol M.1D Mono c/n NAW.2/PFA 112-10678. Under construction - see notes above.

ELLAND

(On the A6026 between Halifax and Huddersfield) Michael Runciman is thought still to have the Comet nose section at his home. It is used for a 'home' for his avionics collection.
XK659 Comet C.2R ex Northenden, Pomona Dock, Manchester Airport, 51, 192, G-AMXC. Nose.

LEEDS

Anne Lindsay and Nigel Ponsford Collection There are quite a few changes to record with the famous 'Ponsford Air Force'. Chipmunk T.10 fuselage WB685 moved to Sunderland on loan to NEAM by 8/86. Guy Black's Bristol F.2b restoration project was given a boost when F.2b frame BAPC.19 moved to St Leonards-on-Sea during 1987, coming the other way was a 'basket case' of F.2b bits. Additionally, a series of gliders have been taken on, including the Addyman Zephyr which was once thought burnt. We will take this opportunity to delete the Agricola rear fuselage VP-GAZ, as it should not enter the W&R terms of reference.
G-AEFG HM.14 Pou du Ciel BAPC.75, ex Harrogate, Kirkby Overblow, Wigan.
BGA.491+ Dagling ex Great Hucklow. Arrived 6/86. Stored.
BAPC.14 Addyman STG ex Harrogate, Wigan.
BAPC.16 Addyman Ultra-Light ex Harrogate, Wigan.
BAPC.18 Killick Gyroplane ex Harrogate, Irlam.
BAPC.39+ Addyman Zephyr ex Harrogate. Substantial parts, acquired 12/87.
+ Hutter H.17a ex Accrington. Arrived 11/86. Stored.
+ Dickson Primary ex Harrogate. Arrived 2/87. Under restoration.
+ Bristol F.2b ex St Leonards-on-Sea. See notes above.
RA848 Cadet TX.1 ex Harrogate, Wigan, Handforth. Cockpit section.
168 Squadron ATC Located in Middleton Grove, the unit and its Jet Provost nose section have evaded W&R to date. Their 'JP' was put up for tender in 3/88 and so they 'surfaced'. Pity, it's probably moved on again by now....
XN600+ Jet Provost T.3 ex 3 FTS. SOC 28/5/76. Nose section - see notes above.

LEEDS-BRADFORD AIRPORT

(Or Yeadon) The Cessna cache at Yorkshire Light has gone down somewhat, with two machines taking to the air again - F.150M G-BFIY in 1987 and F.150H G-OJVH in 1986. The hulk of Cessna 340 G-BAWO was sold as spares for G-MLBY and left by road 1/86 and is now thought sold in the USA. That leaves ;-
G-ATND Cessna F.150F crashed 9/12/72. Forward fuselage, engine test-rig with YLA.
G-AVGG Cherokee 140 wfu 16/3/73. Used for spares.
G-AWES Cessna 150H ex Blackpool, Glenrothes, N22933. Crashed 2/10/81.
G-AXZJ Cessna F.172H crashed 12/12/76. Under rebuild, using parts of T-41 N5162F.
Locally The restoration of Avian III G-ACGT continues in a workshop near the Airport.
G-ACGT Avian IIIA ex Linthwaite, EI-AAB. Under restoration.

LIVERSEDGE

2490 Squadron ATC in Bradford Road took on the former Wallsend Jet Provost nose section, only to have it put up for tender 3/88!
XM426+ Jet Provost T.3 ex Wallsend, Abingdon, Kemble, 6 FTS, 2 FTS, 6 FTS, CFS. See notes above.

SIDDAL

(On the A646 south of Halifax) The J S Shackleton Ltd yard is still to be found here and the airframes listed in W&R10 (other than the Lightning F.3 nose) all live on.
XG597 Whirlwind HAS.7 ex Warton SAR Flt, CA, makers.
XH587 Victor K.1A ex St Athan, 57, 15, A&AEE, makers. Nose section.
XL868 Whirlwind HAS.7 A2595, ex Arbroath, 705, HS, 771, 815.
XM663 Whirlwind HAS.7 ex Arbroath, 824.
XT774 Wessex HU.5 ex 845. Crashed 17/5/69.

WHINMOOR

(On the A64 north east of Leeds) There have been few reports from the Heli-Leeds base here, other than two 'in-comings'. The following are thought still to be present.

G-AVSN	AB.206A JetRanger	crashed 15/5/77. Wreck.
G-AVTE	B.206A JetRanger	crashed 25/9/83. Wreck.
G-BBIT+	Hughes 269B	ex N9546F. CoA expired 1/12/81. Stored.
G-BBIV	Hughes 269	ex N9690F. CoA expired 23/3/78.
G-BFCY+	AB.206B JetRanger	ex Westbury-sub-Mendip, OE-DXA. Crashed 3/4/84.
G-BGEB	AB.206A JetRanger	ex D-HAVE. Crashed 29/3/81. Wreck.
EI-BMP	AB.206B JetRanger	ex G-JUMP. Crashed 29/7/82. Wreck.
VR-BEV	AB.206A JetRanger	ex Thruxton, G-AYMH, N7052J. Crashed 22/2/76. Wreck.

Part 2

SCOTLAND

Central

CAUSEWAYHEAD

(North of Stirling) The Sycamore is still to be found in William Kerr's scrapyard.

XG504	Sycamore HR.14	ex Dunblane, Nostell Priory, Rotherham, 32, MCS, CFS, Khormaksar SF, Aden SF. Poor state.

Dumfries & Galloway

FALGUNZEON

No news to hand of W&R fodder at the Dumfries and Galloway Gliding Club. The T.21B is thought still extant up in the rafters.

	T.21B	possibly BGA.1315. Stored.

TINWALD DOWNS

Dumfries & Galloway Aviation Group (Off the A701 north west of Dumfries on the former airfield) Space restrictions forced the scrapping of Varsity T.1 WJ903 during 1987 - the nose section has been retained. On the positive side, D&G acquired a Sycamore during 1987 and wings for its complete Gannet fuselage - a composite is underway. The Museum is open to the public every Sunday April to September from 1000 to 1700. Other times by appointment. Contact : Dumfries & Galloway Aviation Group, 11 Ninian Court, Lochside, Dumfries.

P7540	Spitfire IIA	ex Loch Doon, 312, 266, 609, 66. Substantial sections.
WA576+	Sycamore 3	7900M, ex East Fortune, Strathallan, Halton, RAE, A&AEE, G-ALSS ntu. Arrived 7/6/87.
WJ903	Varsity T.1	ex Glasgow Airport, 6 FTS, AE&AEOS, 1 ANS, 2 ANS, 3 ANS. Nose section only - see notes above.
WL375	Meteor T.7(mod)	ex West Freugh, RAE.
XD425	Vampire T.11	ex Stranraer, Woodford, Chester, St Athan, 8 FTS, 5 FTS, 7 FTS, 202 AFS.
	Vampire	pod only, single seater.
	Venom	ex Silloth. Pod only, single seater. Possibly WK394.
	Gannet	ex Carlisle. Fuselage, anti-submarine version. Wings from XL471.
42163	F-100D-11-NA	ex Sculthorpe, French Air Force. '11-YG'.
FT-36	T-33A-1-LO	ex Sculthorpe, Belgian Air Force, USAF 55-3047.
318	Mystere IVA	ex Sculthorpe, French Air Force.

WEST FREUGH

The contents of the dump at this RAE airfield are unchanged. By 11/87 a 'Mil 24 *Hind*' appeared on the dump - not a run of the mill (sorry!) occurance, even in the Eastern *Bloc*. The clever money is on it being the converted Whirlwind that used to be as Thruxton (XN382), doubtless W&R12 will reveal all.

VP977	Devon C.2/2	ex Northolt, 207, Baghdad Attache, Rangoon Attache, Bangkok Attache, Djakarta Attache, Saigon Attache, Bangkok Attache, 31, G-ALTS.
XN817	Argosy C.1	ex A&AEE, MinTech, 115, MoA.
	'Mil Mi 24'	see notes above.

Fife

CUPAR

A case of all change at the strip here. Super Cub G-BIYJ was flying by 3/87. Contrary to W&R10 Cessna F.152 G-BGOC did not come here, but went to Glenrothes. A Cadet is stored here.

XE802+	Cadet TX.3	stored here since 1985.

GLENROTHES

(Or Fife Airport) Is still clear of W&R fodder, but the entry will serve to clear up a few points. As noted above under Cupar, the hulk of Cessna F.152 G-BGOC (crashed 26/1/83) came here and was acquired quickly by an American spares salvage organisation - along with Aztec G-AZZA. Of the two Aztec hulks mentioned in W&R10 (G-AZZL and G-BAVO) one left in 1984 for training purposes at the local fire station. The firemen got bored with it by 11/84 and it almost certainly went to the Kirkcaldy yard - see below.

KIRKCALDY

A visit here in late 1985 found no aircraft content of any worthy size. Accordingly, the hulk of Aztec G-AYEM had been processed, along with the Aztec from the fire station at Glenrothes - see above.

LEUCHARS

As promised in W&R10, a gate guardian shuffle took place here during 1986, Spitfire XVI TB252 going to Bentley Priory in 3/86 and Spitfire F.21 LA198 arriving from Locking 2/4/86. Neil Moffatt acquired Gannet AEW.3 XL502 when it was put up for tender in 1985. After a lot of work it was ferried to Carlisle on 19/5/87 and is now well known on the show circuit as G-BMYP. Other airframes as listed in W&R10 are unchanged, but there have been several additions :-

LA198+	Spitfire F.21	7118M, ex Locking, Worcester, 3 CAACU, 602, 1. Arr 2/4/86. Gate guardian. 602 Squadron colours as 'RAI-G'.
WF320	Sea Prince T.1	ex Kemble, 750, Lossiemouth SF, 750, Lee-on-Solent SF, 781, 744. BDR.
XM144	Lightning F.1A	8417M, ex Leuchars TFF, 23, Leuchars TFF, Wattisham TFF, 226 OCU, 74. 74 Squadron colours, 'J'. Gate guardian.
XM169	Lightning F.1A	8422M, ex Leuchars TFF, 23, Binbrook TFF, 111, A&AEE, MoA, EE. Decoy.
XM178	Lightning F.1A	8418M, ex Leuchars TFF, 226 OCU, 56. Decoy.
XN781	Lightning F.2A	8538M, ex 92, 19. Decoy.
XR713+	Lightning F.3	8935M, ex LTF, 5, 11, 5, LTF, 11, LTF, 5, 111, Wattisham TFF, 111. Flew in 11/3/87. BDR.
XR749+	Ligntning F.3	8934M, ex 11, LTF, 11, LTF, Binbrook pool, 29, 226 OCU, 56, EE. Overstressed on landing 17/2/87. BDR.
XT857+	Phantom FG.1	8913M, ex 111, PTF, 767, A&AEE, RAE. Damaged 7/85. ASF airframe.
XV588	Phantom FG.1	ex Lee-on-Solent, 892. Wreck, crashed 17/5/77. Poor state, minus forward fuselage.

Grampian

ABERDEEN

In Anderson Drive the Grampian Fire Service Headquarters still holds its instructional Whirlwind.

VR-BBN	Whirlwind Srs 3	ex Redhill, Bristows, G-AOYB.

ABERDEEN AIRPORT

(Or Dyce) The assorted helicopter store has had a sort out, with three leaving and another arriving. Going have been S-61N G-AYOY flying again, from Beccles, by 1987; S-61N-II G-BDKI moving to Sumburgh 10/2/86; and S-76A G-BITR to Redhill ready to fly again, by 10/87. Aztec 250C G-ASTD was stored here from at least 1985 when it was cancelled as sold in the USA. It parted with its wings in 10/87, going 'south' to help with a rebuild. The fuselage had joined the dump by 1/88.

G-ARPN	Trident 1	ex Heathrow, BA, BEA. With fire service.
G-AWFX+	Sikorsky S-61N	ex Gatwick, BIH, BAH, BEAH, AP-AOB, N653X. Arrived 27/11/85 for spares.
G-BJGX	Sikorsky S-76A	ex Bristow, N103BH, N4251S. CoA expired 8/10/85. Stored.
N64P+	Aztec 250C	ex G-ASTD. Fuselage on the dump. See notes above.
N150JC	Bonanza A35	ex Wick. Crashed 18/6/83. Under rebuild.

ABOYNE

By 5/87 the rebuild of a Stampe had begun near here.

G-BALK+	SNCAN SV-4C	ex 'Cheshire', Liverpool, Littleborough, F-BBAN, French military.

FORRES

By 3/87 D&S Metals was cleared in every sense of the word - the site will next be a *FineFare*!

KINLOSS

Building work on the airfield meant the clearance of the dump during late 1987 and with this Shackleton T.4 WB847 gave up the ghost. Also on the dump at that point was the bulk of Nimrod MR.1 XV256 (crashed here 17/11/80). The Anson frame lives on and the centre section of a Comet 4C has arrived for BDR.

G-BDIU+	Comet 4C	8882M, ex Woodford, Bitteswell, Dan-Air, XR396, 214. Centre section etc, BDR. Arrived by 2/86.
VV950	Anson T.21	ex 1 BANS, 14 RFS. Wreck.
XW549	Buccaneer S.2B	8860M, ex St Athan, 12, 16. BDR. Sectioned by 11/87.

LOSSIEMOUTH

Another place where building work has put paid to the former fire dump. Here the dreaded hardened shelters for the *Bricks* of 12 Squadron were responsible. Perishing in this building work, late 1986/ early 1987 were ; Hunter FGA.9 XG151, Argosy E.1 XP439 and Buccaneer S.2 XW538. Buccaneer XW545, allocated here for BDRT, did not arrive and is still to be found at St Athan. A Shackleton arrived by road from Cosford 1/87 for spares for 8 Squadron, but otherwise things have been rather quiet.

WL738	Shackleton MR.2C	8567M, ex 8, 204, 210, A&AEE, 210, 37, 204, 240. Gate guardian.
WL798+	Shackleton MR.2C	8114M, ex Cosford, 204, 205, 38. Arrived 1/87, 8 Squadron spares.
WR967	Shackleton MR.2C	8398M, ex 8, 210, MOTU, 210, 38, 224, 38, 205, 38, 42, JASS. Fuselage only, AEW.2 procedure trainer. *Dodo*.
XG882	Gannet T.5	8754M, ex dump, 845. Gate guardian, composite including XA463, XG889.
XK532	Buccaneer S.1	8867M/A2581, ex Manadon, Lossiemouth, 736. Gate guardian.
XL609+	Hunter T.7	8866M, ex 12, 216, 237 OCU, 4 FTS, 56. Damaged here 10/85, for BDR.
XN929	Buccaneer S.1	8051M, ex Honington. Procedure trainer, nose only.
XT281	Buccaneer S.2B	8705M, ex 12. Weapons loading trainer.

NETHERLEY

(On the B979 north of Stonehaven) Terrier G-ASBU had gone from here by 5/87 - status?

QUARRYWOOD

(On the B9012 north west of Elgin) The famous George F Williamson yard contained only the following of aeronautical interest 12/87 ; tail section of Firefly AS.7 WJ192, smashed pieces from Sea Hawk FGA.6 XE459 and chunks of Gannet.

Highlands

EDDERTON

(On the A9 north west of Tain) The Condor rebuild continues here. Written out of W&R sometime ago, a Beagle Pup fuselage was still to be found in a private house here during 1985 at least. This was c/n 180 and has travelled a fair bit.

G-ASEU D.62A Condor CoA expired 29/3/74. Under restoration.
G-AVKM D.62B Condor CoA expired 30/6/82. Spares for G-ASEU.
+ Pup c/n 180, ex Kindeace, Delny, Prestwick, Rearsby. Fuselage only.

TAIN
Out on the range the remains of the Sea Venom hang on to this mortal coil.
XG731 Sea Venom FAW.22 ex Lossiemouth. Pod and inner wings. Poor state.

The Islands

ORPHIR
(near Kirkwall, Orkney) At a farm strip here a Jodel DR.1050 is stored following a ditching.
G-ASRP+ SAN DR.1050 ex F-BITI. Ditched in Scapa Flow 17/3/86. Stored.

STORNOWAY AIRPORT
(Isle of Lewis) During 1985 a wrecked Cessna was donated to the fire dump.
G-GUNN+ Cessna F.172H ex G-AWGC. Damaged 10/11/82.

SUMBURGH AIRPORT
(Shetland) The Potez 840 continues to serve the local firemen and is now engineless.
F-BMCY Potez 840 wheels-up landing 29/3/81. Fire dump.
From 1984 a store of Sikorsky S-61Ns was accumulated here, all having been taken in part exchange by Aerospatiale for new AS.332L Pumas. During late 1987 and early 1988, all were being moved out, sold in the USA. As they have been here for at least four years, and some stored at Dyce before that, further details are given below, in a more condensed format than usual. First to leave was N9119Z on 4/11/87.
G-AZDC CoA exp 19/ 3/85, ex Aberdeen, Bristows, C-GSPI, G-AZDC, I-EVMA, N6956R. Sold as N9115B.
G-AZRF CoA exp 12/ 8/85, ex Aberdeen, Bristows, PK-HBT. Sold as N9115Z.
G-BAKA CoA exp 29/ 4/86, ex Bristows. Sold as N9119Z.
G-BAKB CoA exp 8/ 2/85, ex Bristows. Sold as N9118M.
G-BAKC CoA exp 1/ 4/86, ex Bristows. Sold as N9119S.
G-BBGS CoA exp 4/ 8/85, ex Aberdeen, Bristows, VR-BDO, N6970R. Sold as N9116R.
G-BDDA CoA exp 4/ 8/85, ex Aberdeen, BAH. Sold as N91201.
G-BDKI CoA exp 3/ 3/85, ex Aberdeen, BAH. Sold as N9118Y.
G-BDRH CoA exp 14/ 5/85, ex Aberdeen, Bristows, VH-BHY, G-BDRH, 9M-ARV, VR-BDN, N6969R. Sold as N9116Y.
G-BEDI CoA exp 17/11/84, ex Aberdeen, BAH, N4043S. Sold as N4043S.

Lothian

EAST FORTUNE
Royal Museum of Scotland - Museum of Flight During 1988-1989 Hangar 1 here will have its roof, walls and doors replaced and Hangar 4 will get a new roof. Several of the old wartime buildings will be renovated and turned into workshops or specialised displays. Please note that not all aircraft here are on public view, but it is hoped eventually to set up tours of the storage area. Three hang gliders and a glider have been acquired since W&R10 and the MoF is to be congratulated on its aim of illustrating the whole range of methods of flight. To further extend this a collection of airship models is also being established. There have been no subtractions from the exhibits, although readers should note that the Weir W-2 is due to be away at the Glasgow Garden Festival during 1988.

The Museum is open 1000 to 1600 all week during July and August. Beyond this period prior application should be made. contact ; Museum of Flight, East Fortune Airfield, North Berwick, East Lothian, EH39 5LF. Telelphone 062 088 308.

G-ACYK	Spartan Cruiser	ex Hill of Stake, Largs. Crashed 14/1/38. Fuselage section.
G-ADAH	Dragon Rapide	ex Peel Green, Booker, Allied Airways. On loan from TAC.
G-AGBN	Cygnet II	ex Strathallan, Biggin Hill, ES915, G-AGBN. CoA expired 28/11/80.
G-ANOV	Dove 6	ex CAFU Stansted, G-5-16. CoA expired 31/5/75.
G-ARCX	Meteor 14	ex Ferranti Flying Unit, Edinburgh, WM261.
G-ASUG	Beech D.18S	ex Loganair, N575C, N555CB, N24R. wfu 12/3/75.
G-ATOY	Comanche 260B	ex Elstree, N8893P. Crashed 6/3/79. Sheila Scott's *Myth Too.*
G-AXEH	Bulldog 1	ex Prestwick, Shoreham. Prototype. CoA expired 15/1/77.
G-BBVF	Twin Pioneer 2	ex Shobdon, XM961/7978M, SRCU, Odiham SF, 230, 21. dbr 11/3/82.
G-BDFU	Dragonfly II MPA	ex Blackpool Airport, Warton, Prestwick.
G-BDIX	Comet 4C	ex Lasham, Dan-Air, XR399, 216. wfu 29/10/80.
G-BIRW	MS.505 Criquet	ex Duxford, OO-FIS, F-BDQS. CoA expired 3/6/83. Luftwaffe c/s 'FI+S'.
VH-SNB	Dragon I	ex Strathallan, VH-ASK, RAAF A34-13.
VH-UQB	Puss Moth	ex Strathallan, G-ABDW.
BGA. 852	T.8 Tutor	ex Portmoak, TS291.
BGA. 902	Gull I	ex Newbattle, 'G-ALPHA'. Possibly ex VW912.
BGA.1014	T.21A	ex Feshie Bridge.
W-2	Weir W-2	BAPC.85, ex Hayes, Cathcart. See notes above.
BAPC 12	HM.14 Pou du Ciel	ex Chester-le-Street, Newcastle, Wigan. TAC loan.
BAPC160	Chargus 18/50	hang glider.
BAPC195+	Moonraker 77	hang glider.
BAPC196+	Sigma IIM	hang glider.
BAPC197+	Cirrus 3	hang glider.
N9510	Tiger Moth	G-AOEL, ex Strathallan, Dunstable, N9510, 7 FTS, 2 GU, 11 RFS, 1 RFS, 7 RFS, 7 EFTS.
TE462	Spitfire XVI	7243M, ex Ouston, 101 FRS, Finningley SF.
VM360	Anson C.19	G-APHV, ex Strathallan, Kemps Aerial Surveys, TRE, A&AEE.
WF259	Sea Hawk F.2	A2483, ex Lossiemouth SF, 736. '171/A'.
WV493	Provost T.1	G-BDYG/7696M, ex Strathallan, Halton, 6 FTS.
WW145	Sea Venom FAW.22	ex Lossiemouth, 750,891. '690/LM'.
XA109	Sea Vampire T.22	ex Lossiemouth, 831, JOAC.
XJ314+	Rolls-Royce TMR	ex Strathallan, Hayes, South Kensington, RAE. Arrived 3/6/87. Science Museum loan.
XL762	Skeeter AOP.12	8017M, ex Middle Wallop, 2 RTR, 9 Flt, 651.
XM597	Vulcan B.2A	ex Waddington, 50, 35, 101, 9, 50, 35, Wadd Wing, 12.
XN776	Lightning F.2A	ex Leuchars, 92. 'B'.
591+	Rhonlerche II	ex D-0359. Acquired 1987.
9940	Bolingbroke IVT	ex Strathallan, RCAF 5 B&GS. Under restoration.
	WACO CG-4A	ex Aberlady. Nose section only.
191659	Me 163B-1a	ex Cambridge, Cranfield, Brize Norton, II/JG.400.

Aircraft Preservation Society of Scotland APSS work in support of MoF and maintain their own workshop here. Their Auster is now complete and on show with the other Museum aircraft, but is best listed here. During 1987 a replacement Brantly arrived from Newport Pagnell. Main work is centred upon the Miles Monarch. APSS aircraft are open to inspection by prior permission only (SAE please), contact ; Aircraft Preservation Society of Scotland, c/o Museum of Flight, East Fortune Airfield, North Berwick, East Lothian, EH39 5LF.

G-AFJU	Miles Monarch	ex York, Strathallan, Lasham, Staverton, X9306, G-AFJU. wfu 1965.
G-ARTJ	Bensen B.8M	ex Currie, Cupar. wfu 12/73.
G-ATFG+	Brantly B.2B	ex Newport Pagnell. Arrived 1987.
TJ398"	Auster AOP.6	BAPC.70, ex Inverkeithing, Perth. See notes above.

Others D&GAG acquired Sycamore WA576 and it moved to Tinwald Downs 7/6/87.

EDINBURGH

Royal Museum of Scotland, Chambers Street. The original Pilcher Hawk is still displayed here. The Museum is open Monday to Saturday 1000 to 1700 and Sunday 1400 to 1700. Contact ; Royal Museum of Scotland, Chambers Street, Edinburgh, EH1 1JF. Tel 031 225 7534.

BAPC49	Pilcher Hawk	first flown at Eynsham 1896, crashed at Stanford Hall 30/9/99.

Locality There has been no news of the continued existence of Cessna F.172P-II G-PPHJ used as a spares source, or of the reported Tiger Moth (G-ANPC?) rebuild. If news is forthcoming, this will save them from the realms of *LOST!* in W&R12!

EDINBURGH AIRPORT

(Or Turnhouse) Delving back into previous editions, the Chipmunk WB584 written off here by the compiler in fact turned up at Kilmarnock - which see. The Trident and Spitfire are still to be found.

G-ARPL Trident 1C ex Heathrow, BA, BEA. Fire service.
RW393 Spitfire XVI 7293M, ex 602, 3 CAACU, 31, FCCS, 203 AFS. 'XT-A' 602 c/s. Gate.

KIRKNEWTON

On 8/3/86 the fuselage of Cessna G-AXBU was removed by road to Bearsden. By 6/87 the hulk of Aztec 250C G-ASYB had gone, presumed broken up.

Strathclyde

BEARSDEN

(North of Glasgow) The fuselage of a wrecked Cessna arrived here during 1986.

G-AXBU+ Cessna FR.172F ex Kirknewton, Inverkeithing. CoA expired 23/8/75. Arr 8/3/86.

CARLUKE

Chipmunk WZ866 did not venture to Greenock, although the direction was reasonable. It went to Dunoon.

DUNOON

2296 Squadron ATC here are the new owners of Chipmunk T.10 PAX WZ866. They are making a flight simulator out of it, using compressed air jacks to thrash it about.

WZ866+ Chipmunk T.10 PAX 8217M, ex Carluke, Wishaw, Cumbernauld, CoAT G-ATEB, Lee UAS, Abn UAS, Bir UAS, Abn UAS, Oxf UAS, Detling SF, Colerne SF.

GLASGOW

The Museum of Transport closed during 1987 and will be relocated in another development in the city. By 6/86 the Kay Gyroplane G-ACVA had moved for temporary exhibition at Perth and then moved to Strathallan. It is assumed the Pilcher replica is stored.

BAPC 48 Pilcher Hawk rep see notes above.

GLASGOW AIRPORT

(Or Abbotsinch) Continues to be a hive of W&R activity. First off, ignore the reference to Trident 3B G-AWZS made in W&R10, the Compiler has never cared for *aluminium toobing* and is easily confused by references to them! There has been a clear-out of some of the inmates. During 2/87 three hulks were carted off to the yard at Paisley - Aztec G-ASNA, Aztec G-BAHC and Cessna 172 G-OPEL. The hulk of Cessna F.337F G-BACF was sold along with the airworthy G-BJIY and moved 'south' by 5/86. Current state is as follows :-

G-ARFD+ Tri-Pacer 160 ex Kilkerran, N3667Z. CoA expired 20/4/78. Arrived by 10/85 for storage.
G-ARPP Trident 1C ex Heathrow, BA, BEA. Fire service.
G-ATJC Airtourer 100 moved off site 10/87 for storage pending rebuild.
G-BKMK+ Tomahawk 112 ex OO-GME, OO-HKD ntu. Damaged 9/4/87. Stored dismantled.
G-BMDZ+ Cessna 310Q ex OY-BJU, SE-FRB, N7621Q. Arrived 2/86, for spares.
J-1614 Venom FB.50 G-BLIE, ex Dubendorf, Swiss Air Force. Unflown since arrival 27/2/85.

GREENOCK

See both Carluke and Dunoon for an interesting plot!

HOLLYBUSH

(On the A713 south east of Ayr) The Tiger Moth is still stored in Skeldon Mill.

G-ANNN Tiger Moth ex Kilkerran, T5968, Wattisham SF, 61 GCF, 3 FTS, 28 EFTS, 57 OTU.

KILKERRAN

Tri-Pacer G-ARFD escaped being listed here, but has made the realms of W&R under Glasgow Airport to where it moved during 1985. Tiger Moth G-ANMO is but a rear fuselage and should no longer be listed. G-AREH is unchanged.

G-AIGU	J/1N Alpha	CoA expired 5/9/74. Under restoration.
G-AREH	Tiger Moth	ex G-APYV ntu, 6746M, DE241. CoA expired 19/4/66.

KILMARNOCK

The Canberra nose situation here could well rival *Dynasty* as a soap. It *is* here and 'parented' by RAF Turnhouse (aka Edinburgh Airport). Inspection of the fuselage line number confirms the identity. Also here is the former Turnhouse Chipmunk PAX and an anonymous Hunter nose.

WB584+	Chipmunk T.10 PAX	7706M, ex Edinburgh Airport, Bri UAS, 12 RFS, 22 RFS.
WJ872	Canberra T.4	8492M, ex Halton, Wyton SF, 360, 13, Akrotiri SF, 231 OCU. Nose.
	Hunter	single seat nose section.

MACHRIHANISH

The Vulcan received some pretty severe undercarriage modifications during 1986 - the legs were blown off to render it safer for the fire crews! The Varsity continues to serve with the RAF Police Provost Training School. The hulk of Boeing 707 N90651 (see W&R10) was removed to a scrapyard in Glasgow - ideas?

WL635	Varsity T.1	ex RAE Farnborough, Kemble, 5 FTS, 4 FTS, 1439 Flt, Weston Zoyland SF.
XL427	Vulcan B.2A	8756M, ex 44, Wadd Wing, Scampton Wing, 83. Dump - see above.

PAISLEY

Scrapyard Alex D Stewart Ltd of Hamilton Street here took three airframes from Glasgow Airport during 2/87. It is not known if they still survive.

G-ASNA+	Aztec 250B	ex Glasgow Airport, '5N-ATA'.
G-BAHC+	Aztec 250C	ex Glasgow Airport, 5Y-ADX. CoA expired 11/3/82.
G-OPEL+	Cessna F.172G	ex Glasgow Airport, G-BGLV ntu, D-EDHB.

PRESTWICK AIRPORT

Sure enough, Prestwick received its Trident 3B in the form of G-AWZJ on 24/2/86. With BAe, Bulldog XX662 was scrapped during 1987. Jetstream 31 travelling demonstrator G-ATXJ was brought 'home' during 1987 and is now sectioned being turned into the Series 41 mock-up. It has been decided to delete reference to test airframe specimens here as several Jetstream and Bulldog rigs and test fuselages are present and is consequently difficult to tell which is which. During September and October 1986 the former Kuwait Air Force Strikemasters were airfreighted into Prestwick for storage. They stayed until April 1987 when they were roaded to Samlesbury. For the record they arrived here as follows ; 24/9/86 111 & 112; 7/10/86 115, 119, 120 & 121; 14/10/86 110, 113 & 114. Current here are :-

G-ATDB	Noralpha	ex F-OTAN-6, French military. CoA expired 22/11/78. Open store.
G-ATXJ	Jetstream	Series 41 mock-up.
G-AWZJ+	Trident 3B-101	ex Heathrow, BA, BEA. Flew in 24/2/86.
XL497	Gannet AEW.3	ex Lossiemouth, 849. '041/R'. Gate guardian.
XX660	Bulldog T.1	crashed 25/3/85. Sectioned.

Tayside

ARBROATH

The restoration of Anson C.19 TX183 continues in the area.

TX183	Anson C.19	ex Duxford, Old Warden, A&AEE, HS, CNCS, 1 ANS, Abingdon SF.

DUNDEE AIRPORT

(Or Riverside) Makes an entry into W&R with :-

G-ASAI+	Airedale	ex Islay. CoA expired 20/5/77. First noted 6/87. For rebuild.
G-BDOW+	FRA.150M Aerobat	battered fuselage. dbr 15/8/87. First noted 10/87.

MONTROSE

The Whirlwind is still to be found at the Offshore Petroleum Industry Training Board.

XJ723 Whirlwind HAR.10 ex Wroughton, 202, 228, 155.

PERTH AIRPORT

(Or Scone) Scottish Aircraft Collection Trust Work continues on the three aircraft held by the SACT. Beech 18 G-BKRN did not go to the operation described in W&R10, but moved to Cranfield by 3/87. The aircraft are not open to the public, but enquiries can be made to : SACT, Tillywhally, Milnathort, Tayside. Tel 0577 63326.

G-AHKY	Miles M.18 Srs 2	ex Strathallan, Blackbushe, HM545, U-0224, U-8. CoA expired 18/9/87.
VS356	Prentice T.1	G-AOLU, ex Strathallan, Biggin Hill, EI-ASP, G-AOLU, VS356, CFS, 2 FTS.
VZ728	Desford Trainer	G-AGOS, ex Strathallan, Thruxton, Kemps Aerial Surveys.

Air Service Training The fleet of instructional airframes has changed little, save for the scrapping of very tired Cessna 310 G-ARCH and Cessna 150 G-ARTW by 1987.

G-ALWS	Tiger Moth	ex N9328, Upwood SF, 6 FTS, 15 EFTS, 17 EFTS, 15 EFTS, 19 EFTS, Duxford SF, Farnborough SF.
G-ARBC	Cessna 310D	ex N6934T. Withdrawn 24/ 8/76.
G-ARPX	Trident 1C	ex Heathrow, BA, BEA.
G-ARTX	Cessna 150B	ex N7377X. Crashed 14/9/72. Fuselage.
G-ARTY	Cessna 150B	ex N7382X. Withdrawn 4/12/68.
G-ATNJ	Cessna F.150F	Crashed 24/ 9/74.
G-ATOF	Cessna F.150F	Crashed 25/11/71.
G-ATOG	Cessna F.150F	Crashed 27/ 1/81.
G-AVDB	Cessna 310L	ex N2279F. Withdrawn 8/ 7/79.
G-AYBW	Cessna FA.150K	Crashed 8/10/72.
G-AYGB+	Cessna 310Q	ex N7611Q. Arrived 17/9/86.
G-BBCF+	Cessna FRA.150L	ex Leeds-Bradford. Crashed 8/ 9/84. Fuselage. First noted 5/85.
G-BEWP	Cessna F.150M	Crashed 4/10/83.
F-BGNR	Viscount 708	ex Air Inter.
WW453	Provost T.1	ex Huntings, 1 FTS, 2 FTS.
XL875	Whirlwind HAR.9	ex Wroughton, Lee-on-Solent SAR Flt, Culdrose SAR Flt, 847, 848, 815.
XT140	Sioux AH.1	ex Middle Wallop.
XX467	Hunter T.73	ex 1 TWU, Jordan AF 836, Saudi AF 70-617, G-9-214, XL605, 66, 92.
	Chipmunk T.10	ex 'G-ASTD', G-AOJZ, WB732, Not UAS, 16 RFS, 11 RFS, Abn UAS, 11 RFS.

Others Omitted from W&R10, an Auster 5 is under rebuild here for a private owner.

G-AOFJ Auster 5 CoA expired 20/9/79. Under rebuild. See notes above.

STRATHALLAN

Strathallan Aircraft Collection Further disposals from the collection continue to indicate the problems of maintaining such a collection in a somewhat 'thin' tourist area. Work on the Swordfish continues and with the help of the Strathallan Aircraft Society two Fokker replicas are underway. Disposals have been as follows ; Lancaster X KB976 was acquired by Charles Church and left by road for Woodford 9/4/87 - and disaster; Rolls-Royce TMR XJ314 to East Fortune 3/6/87; Battle I 1899 also went to Charles Church, this time to Sandown 12/86; Bolingbroke IVT 10201 made the road journey to Duxford 28/1/88.

The Museum is open April to October daily 1000 to 1700. Contact : Strathallan Aircraft Collection, Strathallan Airfield, Auchterarder, Tayside, PH3 1LA. Tel 07646 2545. The Strathallan Aircraft Society supports the Collection and can be contacted at the above address. Also based on the airfield, with their Vampire T.11 pod, is the Scotland West Aircraft Investigation Group. They can be contacted at ; SWAIG, 9 Frankfurt Street, Shawlands, Glasgow G41 3XG.

G-ACVA+	Kay Gyroplane	ex Perth, Glasgow, Perth. Arrived early 1987.
G-ANOK	SAAB Safir	ex East Fortune, SE-CAH ntu. CoA expired 5/2/73.
G-AYWA	Avro XIX Srs 2	ex Thruxton, OO-VIT, OO-DFA, OO-CFA. Under restoration.
G-BEPV	Fokker S.11-1	ex PH-ANK, Dutch AF E-31. CoA expired 3/12/84.
BAPC170	Pilcher Hawk rep	ex BBC Glasgow.
F5447+"	Scale SE.5A	G-BKER. Airworthy, on loan. Arrived during 1987.
R1914	Magister I	G-AHUJ, ex Aboyne, Balado, Kemble, 137, 604, Middle Wallop SF, 604.
V9441"	Lysander III	G-AZWT, ex RCAF 2355. 309 Sqn c/s 'AR-A'. Airworthy.
W5856	Swordfish II	G-BMGC, ex Alabama, RCAF, Wroughton, Manston. Under restoration.

VP293	Shackleton T.4	ex RAE, MOTU, 206, 46, 224. *Zebedee*.
XD547	Vampire T.11	ex Milngavie, Glasgow, CATCS, 8 FTS, 1 RS, 263. Pod only, with SWAIG.
XE340	Sea Hawk FGA.6	ex Wroughton, Gloucester-Cheltenham, Brawdy. '131/Z'.
XE897"	Vampire T.11	XD403, ex Woodford, Chester, 4 FTS, 1 FTS, 7 FTS, 8 FTS, 5 FTS, 4 FTS.
XG594	Whirlwind HAS.7	ex Wroughton, 771, A&AEE, 705, 846, 737, 701, RAE Bedford, 700.
XK655	Comet C.2R	ex 51, BOAC, G-AMXA.
+	Fokker D.VI	replica, under construction.
+	Fokker D.VII	replica, under construction.

Part 3 # WALES

Clwyd
Gwynedd
England
Powys
Dyfed
Gwent
W
Glam
Mid
Glam
S
Glam

Clwyd

CHESTER AIRPORT

(Or Hawarden or Broughton) With three to delete from the listing in W&R10 and four to add, it is virtually all change here. There is now considerable doubt that the nose section of HS.125-3B/RA G-AZCH was *ever* here and accordingly it should be deleted. Vampire T.11 XE852 moved across the road to Hawarden 3/11/87. Former IAAC HS.125-600A 236 fuselage was restyled as the -800 *Roadshow* and is now based at Hatfield. The Apprentice School replaced their Vampire with a Sea Vixen and have also taken on the nose section of the prototype HS.125 from Connah's Quay. During 1985 a BAe 146 no less entered the realms of W&R - surely a long time before it really should have made a debut. The HS.125 that arrived during 1/88 is reported to be under preparation for a UK museum.

G-ARYA+	HS.125-1	ex Connah's Quay, Chester, Hatfield. Nose section, arrived mid 1986 for the Apprentice School. See also Connah's Quay.
TZ-ADT+	BAe 146-100	flew in 28/10/85, stored. Mali Government.
5N-AMK+	HS.125	ex Southampton. Arrived by road 14/1/88 - see notes above.
9J-SAS	HS.125-1	ex Coventry, ZS-MAN, 9J-RAN, G-ASSM. Arrived by road 31/1/85 - current status?
XN685+	Sea Vixen FAW.2	8173M, ex Cosford, Cranwell, 890, 766, 893, HSA Hatfield. Arr 19/8/87.

CHIRK

At John Pierce's former strip the situation is very much static, save for the addition of a SIPA that has been dormant for some time. Two airframes can be deleted from the listing in W&R10 after prooving too small for consideration ; Dragon Rapides G-AEMH and G-AKRN were both reduced to usuable spares. DH.88 Comet G-ACSP moved on to Bodmin. That leaves :-

G-AIUL	Dragon Rapide	ex Southend, British Westpoint, NR749, Kemble, 2 RS. wfu 6/4/73. Stored.
G-AJBJ	Dragon Rapide	ex Coventry, Blackpool, NF894, 18 MU, HQ TCCF. CoA exp 14/9/61. Stored
G-AKOE	Dragon Rapide	ex British Airways, Booker, X7484, PTS. CoA expired 25/2/82. Stored.
G-BDAO+	SIPA 91	ex Winsford, F-BEPT. Crashed 20/6/76. First noted 11/87.
G-BEDB+	Norecrin	ex Liverpool, Chirk, F-BEOB. CoA expired 11/6/80. Stored.

CONNAH'S QUAY

(On the A548 west of Chester) North East Wales Institute of Higher Education The nose of prototype HS.125 G-ARYA moved to Chester Airport during mid 1986. Its 'guts' are still here as a systems rig, but hardly look like, let alone constitute an aircraft! Otherwise, all is calm.

G-APMY	Apache 160	ex Halfpenny Green, EI-AJT. CoA expired 1/11/81.
G-AZMX	Cherokee 140	ex Chester Airport, Halfpenny Green, SE-FLL, LN-LMK. CoA expired 9/1/82.
XA460	Gannet AS.4	ex Brawdy, 849. '768/BY'.
XF114	Swift F.7	ex Aston Down, CS(A), Cranfield.

HAWARDEN

(On the A55 south west of Chester) In Manor Lane, 2247 Squadron ATC took delivery of the former BAe Apprentices' Vampire T.11 XE852 on 3/11/87.

XE852+	Vampire T.11	ex Chester Airport, Woodford, Chester, Shawbury, 1 FTS, 4 FTS. See above.

LLANDEGLA

Skeeter 8 G-APOI left here by road 14/8/86 for Old Buckenham.

SEALAND

The Spitfire still perches on its plinth, distracting drivers on the A550.

TD248	Spitfire XVI	7246M, ex Hooton Park, 610, 2 CAACU, 695. 'DW-A'.

Dyfed

ABERPORTH

On the dump, the Varsity still soldiers on - just. The Hunter is kept on the airfield by 1429 Squadron ATC. Interesting sighting out on the ranges during 5/86 was a Scimitar hulk.

WJ893	Varsity T.1	ex RAE, SCBS, BCBS, 1 ANS, RAFC. Dump, poor state.
WT680	Hunter F.1	7533M, ex Weeton, DFLS, West Raynham SF.
+	Scimitar F.1	see notes above.

BRAWDY

A much reduced entry here with a large emigration of Hunter airframes. On the dump Canberra B.2(T) WJ681 had perished by 1987, leaving the situation vacant. BDR Hunter FGA.9 XG264 left for a more tenuous existence at Otterburn. Gate guardian Hunter F.51 E-408 moved by 3/86 to Cranwell, being replaced by an FGA.9 from the store. Of the stored Hunters, only two are thought to remain, the others leaving as follows : XE597 to Bentley Priory 1/86; XE624 to the gate by 6/86; XE627 to Duxford 14/11/86; XF382 to Coventry 1/12/86. Current situation is therefore as follows :

XE624	Hunter FGA.9	8875M, ex store, 1 TWU, 2 TWU, TWU, 229 OCU, West Raynham SF, 1. Gate.
XF419	Hunter FGA.9	ex 1 TWU, 2 TWU, TWU, 58, 45, 229 OCU, 1, 74. Stored.
XJ683	Hunter FGA.9	ex 1 TWU, 2 TWU, 1 TWU, TWU, 20, 43, 93. Stored.

HAVERFORDWEST

(Or Withybush) The dismantled French Cessna has not been noted here since 8/85. Il est mort?

F-BUBA	Cessna F.150L	ex Tredegar.

LLANELLI

Jeremy Hassel continues with the restoration of his Proctor.

G-AHTE	Proctor V	ex Cardiff-Wales, Swansea, Llanelli. CoA expired 10/8/61.

LLANGENNECH

The axe will swing on this Navy stores depot during 1988 and the Sea Hawk was put up for tender 3/88.

XE327	Sea Hawk FGA.6	A2556, ex Sydenham, 738. '644/LH'. Gate guardian.

PENDINE RANGES

(On the A4066 east of Tenby) Only confirmed sightings here **are** the arrival of a Buccaneer and a Canberra from Farnborough. Previous inmates are listed although their continued existence is unproven.

WH844+	Canberra T.4	ex Farnbrough, RAE, 231 OCU.
XA938	Victor K.1	ex Foulness Island, St Athan, RAE, 214, 15, 10. Fuselage only.
XN965+	Buccaneer S.1	ex Farnborough, RAE, Lossiemouth, 736. '636'. Arrived 17/1/86.
XP708	Lightning F.3	ex Foulness Island, Wattisham, 29, 23.
XV340	Buccaneer S.2	8659M, ex Foulness Island, Honington, Brough, 15.

Mid Glamorgan

BRIDGEND

(On the A473 west of Cardiff) Long since thought dead and gone, the Viscount nose is *still* with 192 Squadron ATC at the TAVR centre.

G-AOHR	Viscount 802	ex Cardiff-Wales, BA, BEA. Nose section only.

KENFIG HILL

(North of the B4281 east of Pyle) 2117 Squadron ATC still have their Hunter. 'Parented' by St Athan it is to be found in the school grounds on Main Street.

WT569	Hunter F.1	7491M, ex St Athan, A&AEE, Hawkers trials.

NELSON

(On the A472 north of Cardiff) There having been no reports on the continued existence of Cricket G-AXRD here with Mr G Rees, this entry will mutate into *LOST!* come W&R12.

South Glamorgan

CARDIFF WALES AIRPORT

(Or Rhoose) Wales Aircraft Museum Since the publication of W&R10 there have only been two additions to the WAM 'fleet', both of these being noses. The Canberra nose will hopefully form the basis of a 'PR.9' composite using existing spares. On the site itself an extensive restoration and repainting scheme has been underway, with several exhibits taking on new colours. Canberra T.17 WJ581, noted in W&R10, is best deleted as this does not constitute sufficient aircraft at present, although it does 'appear' in two other aircraft at WAM!

WAM is open daily June to September from 1000 to 1800. October to May it is open Saturdays 1100 to dusk and Sundays 1400 to dusk. Contact : Gwyn Roberts, 19 Clos Glyndwr, Hendy, Dyfed, SA4 1FW. Tel 0792 883451.

G-AOJC	Viscount 802	ex British Airways, BEA. Cambrian colours. wfu 9/10/75.
G-ARBY"	Viscount 732	ex 'G-WHIZ', G-ANRS, British Eagle, Misrair SU-AKY, Hunting G-ANRS, MEA OD-ACH, Hunting Clan G-ANRS. Fuselage only. Dan-Air colours.
WB491	Ashton	ex Dunsfold, Farnborough, RAE. Nose section only.
WE925	Meteor F.8	ex Tarrant Rushton, FRL, 229 OCU, 34, 43, 92, 64, 63, 64. Composite, including parts from VZ530.
WG718	Dragonfly HR.3	A2531, ex Yeovilton, SAH Culdrose, Fleetlands.
WH798	Canberra PR.7	8130M, ex St Athan, 31, 17, 13, 80, 17, 100, 542. Fuselage, rear end of WJ581 fitted.
WJ576	Canberra T.17	ex St Athan, 360, MoA, Swifter Flight, 231 OCU.
WJ944	Varsity T.1	ex 6 FTS, 1 ANS, 5 FTS, 1 ANS, 2 ANS, CNCS.
WL332	Meteor T.7	ex Croston, Moston, FRU, Lossiemouth SF, Ford SF.
WM292	Meteor TT.20	ex Yeovilton, FRU, Kemble, 527.
WR539	Venom FB.4	8399M, ex 'Midlands', Cosford, Kai Tak, 28, 60.
WT518	Canberra PR.7	8133M/8691M, ex CTTS St Athan, 31, 80, 31. Wings of WJ581.
WV753	Pembroke C.1	8113M, ex St Athan, 207, SCS, FCCS, BCCS, MoA, FECS, 81. Omitted from both W&R9 and W&R10!
WV826	Sea Hawk FGA.6	A2532, ex Swansea, Culdrose SAH-2, Lossiemouth, 738. '147/CU'.
WW388	Provost T.1	7616M, ex Llanelli, Chinnor, Chertsey, Cuxwold, Chessington, Halton, 2 FTS.
WX788	Venom NF.3	ex Bledow Ridge, Connah's Quay, Makers trials.
WZ425	Vampire T.11	ex Woodford, Chester, St Athan, 5 FTS, MoA, RAFC, 229 OCU, CGS.
WZ826+"	Valiant BK.1	XD826/7872M, ex Abingdon, Stratford, Cosford, 543, 232 OCU, 138, 90, 7. Nose section only, arrived by 6/86.
XA459	Gannet AS.4	A2608, ex Culdrose SAH-7, Lee-on-Solent, 831.
XA903	Vulcan B.1	ex Farnborough, RB.199 test-bed, Olympus test-bed, Blue Steel trials, Avro. Nose section only.
XF383"	Hunter F.51	E-409, ex Dunsfold, G-9-437, Aalborg store, Danish AF, ESK-724. 4 FTS c/s.
XG592	Whirlwind HAS.7	ex Wroughton, 705, 846, 705, 700, C(A), HS, Westlands.
XG737	Sea Venom FAW.22	ex Yeovilton, FRU, Sydenham, 894, 893, 891. '438/BY'.
XG883	Gannet T.5	ex Yeovilton, 849. '773/BY'.
XH177+	Canberra PR.9	ex Boscombe Down, 13, 58. Nose section only, arrived 3/2/88.
XJ409	Whirlwind HAR.10	ex Wroughton, Warton SAR Flight, 1310 Flt, 228, 275, 155, XD779 ntu.
XL449	Gannet AEW.3	ex Lossiemouth, 849.
XM300	Wessex HAS.1	ex Farnborough, RAE, Westlands.
XM569	Vulcan B.2A	ex 44, Waddington Wing, 27, Cottesmore Wing, 27.
XN650	Sea Vixen FAW.2	A2639/A2620/A2612, ex Culdrose SAH-12, RAE Bedford, 892.
XN928	Buccaneer S.1	8179M, ex St Athan.
29963	T-33A-1-LO	ex Sculthorpe, French Air Force. '5-MB'.
42160	F-100D-16-NA	ex Sculthorpe, French Air Force. USAF colours.
59	Mystere IVA	ex Sculthorpe, French Air Force. '314-TH'.

Airport The Viscount continues to inhabit the fire dump. A Yankee is now in store. The current status of the Cambrian Flying Club Tomahawk cockpit section is unconfirmed.

G-AOJE	Viscount 802	ex BA, BEA, G-AOHE ntu. wfu 31/3/81. Fire dump.
G-SEXY+	AA-1 Yankee	ex G-AYLM. CoA expired 6/6/85. Stored.
	Tomahawk 112	cabin section with Cambrian F/C. Almost certainly from G-BGSS.

ST ATHAN

Historic Aircraft Collection A brave move early in 1988 to establish regular viewing weekends here was stifled shortly afterwards by the impending uncertainties of a Ministerial review of what-happens-next at St Athan. The workmanship of restorations here is of the highest quality - and the policy of ground running types such as the Focke Wulf is a major innovation. Another Colerne *cannot* be allowed to happen. In view of the changes that may or may not take place here, opening times cannot be given and enquiries should be made to ; Officer in Charge, RAF St Athan Historic Aircraft Collection, RAF St Athan, Barry, South Glamorgan, CF6 9WA. Tel 04465 3131.

There have been few changes in the fleet in terms of movements, but great strides in terms of restoration. There have been five departures ; Bleriot XI G-AVXV to Duxford and Bristol BAPC.38 and Sopwith Camel BAPC.59 to St Mawgan; Meteor 'WH456'/WL168 going back to Finningley for the gate; Me 163B-1a 191904 was handed over to West Germany 4/88 for a new national museum. The Swinderby Mosquito TT.35 arrived by road during 11/86, but sadly suffered an unloading accident, damaging the fuselage. This has since been remedied. Restoration of the Battle is now so far advanced that the aircraft is back on its undercarriage. The aircraft that came from Canada, P2183, should now be deleted as it has been 'consumed' in the rebuild.

G-AEEH	HM.14 Pou du Ciel	ex Colerne.
BAPC.47	Watkins CHW	ex Cardiff. *Robin Goch*.
BAPC.83	Ki 100-1b	8476M, ex Cosford, Henlow, Biggin Hill, Fulbeck, Wroughton, Stanmore.
BAPC.92	Fi 103 (V1)	ex Henlow.
6232"	BE.2c replica	BAPC.41, ex Halton. Travelling exhibit.
H1968"	Avro 504K replica	BAPC.42, ex Halton. Travelling exhibit.
L5343	Battle I	ex Cardington, Leeming, Iceland, 98, 266. Crashed 13/9/40. Under restoration - see notes above.
Z7197	Proctor III	8380M, ex Swinderby, Finningley, G-AKZN, AST, 18 EFTS, 1 RS, 2 SS.
EE549	Meteor IV Special	7008M, ex Abingdon, Hendon, St Athan, Cranwell, CFE, FCCS, RAFHSF.
MK356	Spitfire IX	5690M, ex Henlow, Bicester, Hawkinge, Halton, 84 GSU, 443. '2I-V'. Omitted from W&R10.
TJ138+	Mosquito TT.35	7607M, ex Swinderby, Finningley, Colerne, Bicester, Shawbury, 5 CAACU, 98. 'VO'. Arrived 11/86 - see notes above.
WD935	Canberra B.2	8440M, ex 360, 97, 151, CSE, EE, BCDU, RAAF A84-1 ntu.
WE600	Auster C4	7602M, ex Swinderby, Finningley, Trans-Antarctic Expedition, 663.
WK281	Swift FR.5	7712M, ex Swinderby, Finningley, Colerne, Northolt, 79. 'S'.
WL505	Vampire FB.9	7705M, ex Ely Barracks, 19, RAFC, 73.
WS843	Meteor NF.14	7937M, ex Henlow, St Athan, Kemble, 1 ANS, MoA, 228 OCU.
WV499	Provost T.1	7698M, ex Weeton, 6 FTS. 'P-3'.
XM602	Vulcan B.2A	8771M, ex 101, Wadd Wing, 35, 230 OCU, Wadd Wing, Cott Wing, 12.
XN341	Skeeter AOP.12	8022M, ex 4 SoTT, 3 RTR, 651.
XR243	Auster AOP.9	8057M, ex Quedgely. St Athan. Middle Wallop.
XR486	Whirlwind HCC.12	8727M, ex 32, Queen's Flight.
XS650	Swallow TX.1	8801M, ex CGS.
112372	Me 262A-2a	8482M, ex Cosford, Finningley, Gaydon, Cranwell, Farnborough, VK893/AM.51, I/KG.51. Fitted with the wings of 500200.
120227	He 162A-2	8472M, ex Colerne, Leconfield, VH513, AM.65, Farnborough, Leck, JG.1.
420430	Me 410A-1/U2	8483M, ex Cosford, Fulbeck, Wroughton, Stanmore Park, Brize Norton, Farnborough, AM.72, Vaerlose. 'PD+VO'.
475081	Fi 156C-7	7362M, ex Coltishall, Bircham Newton, Finningley, Fulbeck, VP546, AM.101, Farnborough, 'RR+KE', 'GM+AK'. Under restoration.
584219	Fw 190F-8/U1	8470M, ex Gaydon, Henlow, Fulbeck, Wroughton, Stanmore Park, Wroughton, Brize Norton, AM.29, Farnborough, Grove/Karup.
5439	Mitsubishi Ki 46	8484M/BAPC.84, ex Stanmore Park, ATAIU-SEA.

Civilian Technical Training School There has been some movement with the small fleet of instructional airframes. The opportunity has been taken to slot in the two glider airframes used for teaching the skills of how to deal with a 'wood' under this title, although they are technically not with CTTS, but are kept in Building 341. Gnat T.1 XM705/8574M was lodged here briefly after arrival from Bruggen and put up for tender 8/86. It was snapped up and moved to the USA, flying before too long as N705XM. Some of the airframes below have not been reported for some time, but are thought to be on charge.

VP958	Devon C.2/2	8795M, ex Northolt, 207, 26, WCS, MCS, 31, Air Attache Paris.
WH984	Canberra B.15	8101M, ex Cosford, HS, 9, Binbrook SF, 9. Nose section.
XA243+	Grasshopper TX.1	8886M, ex Bournemouth School, Glider Ground School. Allocated 5/87. See notes above.
XE793	Cadet TX.3	8666M, Glider Ground School - see notes above.
XN458+	Jet Provost T.3	8334M, ex Halton, Shawbury, 1 FTS. Arrived by 11/85.
XN632	Jet Provost T.3	8352M, ex Kemble, Shawbury, 3 FTS.
XP502	Gnat T.1	8576M, ex 4 FTS.
XP542	Gnat T.1	8575M, ex 4 FTS.
XP558	Jet Provost T.4	8627M/A2628, ex SAH Culdrose, CAW, 3 CAACU, RAFC.
XP680	Jet Provost T.4	8460M, ex CAW, 6 FTS.
XR541	Gnat T.1	8602M, ex CFS, 4 FTS.
XX635	Bulldog T.1	8767M, ex EMS UAS.

St Athan Maintenance Unit As with previous editions, the longer term residents of the storage side of St Athan's busy schedule are best dealt with type-by-type. New type being handled, albeit for scrap and therefore listed under 'Others' is the Victor K.2.

Buccaneer S.2 The up-date programme which has given the odd aspect of *Bricks* on a 'production line' at Woodford has helped to thin the Buccaneer store here. Listed in W&R10 as allocated for BDR at Lossiemouth, XW545 did not in fact go and instead is here for BDR - see under 'Others'. Also noted in the last edition was XT274 this did indeed go to Abingdon - which see. Disposals have been ; XT271 flew away to Lossiemouth 5/87; XT273 flew to Lossiemouth for 208 Squadron 8/87; and the following flew out to Woodford for up-dating - XT279 9/86, XT286 3/11/86, XV342 22/10/86, XW543 27/1/87. That leaves :-

XV163	Buccaneer S.2A	ex 208, 237 OCU, 208, 237 OCU, 809.
XW550	Buccaneer S.2B	ex 16, 15.

Canberras As with the Buccaneers, a lot to talk of when it comes to Canberras. Of the machines mentioned in W&R10, a couple require further comment. E.15 WH964 did not go to Macclesfield, but went instead to Cosford. Omitted from W&R10, T.17 WJ565 moved from store to Cosford by 6/87. The following have departed ; E.15 WH957 moved to Cosford by 6/87; TT.18 WK126 rejoined FRADU at Yeovilton 21/4/86; PR.9s XH131 and XH135 moved initially to Sydenham for rework before joining 1 PRU at Wyton. There have been no additions to the store.

WH775	Canberra PR.7	8868M/8128M, ex 13, 100, 13, 31, 17 ,31, 13, 82, EE. Allocated to Cosford.
WH780	Canberra T.22	ex FRADU, 81, 82, 527, 58, 542.
WH797	Canberra T.22	ex FRADU, 81, 58, 542.
WH801	Canberra T.22	ex FRADU, 17, 31, 13, 58, 540.
WH803	Canberra T.22	ex FRADU, 7, 17, 540.
WJ574	Canberra TT.18	ex FRADU, 57, 540.
WT510	Canberra T.22	ex FRADU, 31, 80, 31.
WT525	Canberra T.22	ex FRADU, 17, 80.
WT535	Canberra T.22	ex FRADU, 17.
XH168	Canberra PR.9	ex 39, MoD, 39, MoD, 39, 58.

Hunter FGA.9 XG254 moved by road to Coltishall 10/3/86. On 30/9/87 Heavylift Belfast G-HLFT touched down here and swallowed Hunter FGA.9s XF431 and XG228, taking them for a new life with the Air Force of Zimbabwe. It came back on 5/10/87 for another two and a similar destination. Cargo this time is presumed to have been FGA.9s XF435 and XG154. As this cannot be confirmed as W&R11 hurtles towards press, they are listed below.

XF435	Hunter FGA.9	8880M, ex 1 TWU, TWU, 229 OCU, 208, 8, 43, 247. Allocated for BDR at Brawdy, but see notes above.
XG154	Hunter FGA.9	8863M, ex 1 TWU, 229 OCU, 54. 43, 54. Allocated to the RAF Museum, but see notes above.
XL578	Hunter T.7	ex 1 TWU, TWU, 229 OCU.
XL595	Hunter T.7	ex 1 TWU, TWU, 229 OCU, DFLS, AFDS.

Others As with the last edition, this is a listing of the occupants of the dump, or that general area. Hunter F.1 WT648 briefly left for use in a play (!) 5/86, but was back by 7/86. Hunter F.6 XF526 is held in external store for an officer on the base and will move at some stage. The nose section of Phantom FG.1 XT595 moved to Wattisham by 12/85. The forward fuselage of Hunter T.8C WT745/8893M arrived from Shawbury in early 1987 for paint training, but was put up for tender 7/87. It was successfully bid for by Ed Stead of Manchester, New Hampshire, and exported in late 1987. However, this does not explain the aircraft's allocation, with the rear end of XL565 to Coltishall - it is therefore noseless? Two Victors from 57 Squadron arrived during 1986, and both joined the dump. XL233 was offered for tender 1/88 and was chopped into small bits for Calverts of Thirsk on 10/5/88.

WT648	Hunter F.1	7530M, ex 4 SoTT, DFLS. See notes above. Dump.
XF526	Hunter F.6	8679M, ex Halton, Laarbruch SF, 4 FTS, 229 OCU, 56, 43, 56, 63, 66. See notes above. External store.
XL163+	Victor K.2	8916M, ex 57, 55, 57, 55, 232 OCU, Witt Wing, 100, 139. Flew in 8/7/86, allocated for BDR.
XV156	Buccaneer S.2A	8773M, ex store, Honington, 237 OCU, 208. Fuselage on dump.
XW545	Buccaneer S.2B	8859M, ex store, BAe, 15. BDR.

West Glamorgan

SWANSEA AIRPORT

(Or Fairwood Common) West Glamorgan makes a re-entry into W&R courtesy of a stored Pup.

G-AWKM+	Pup 100	CoA expired 29/6/84. Stored.

Gwent

CWMBRAN

(South of Newport) 2308 Squadron ATC, located in Greenhill Road, still have their Chipmunk.

WD293	Chipmunk T.10 PAX	7645M, ex QUB UAS, STA UAS, G&S UAS, STA UAS, Chatham Flt, SMR, 1 BFTS.

TREDEGAR

With the information in W&R10 not having been added to since, it is felt wrong to give out now very dated information. Derelict here were Tri-Pacer G-APXM, Cherokee 140B G-AXTM and Commodore 150 F-BNBM. An up-to-date report from here would be much appreciated.

Gwynedd

CAERNARFON AIRPORT

(Or Llandwrog) Snowdon Mountain Aviation & Museum Planned opening date for the Museum is now 1989 and three more airframes have been added to the 'fleet' ready for that date. Under the command of Ray Mackenzie-Blyth pleasure flying is now available from here in SMA's lovely Rapide G-AIDL. Airframes for the Museum are not available for public inspection at present. Enquiries should be made to :- Snowdon Mountain Aviation, Caernarfon Airport, Llandwrog, Caernarfon, Gwynedd, LL54 5TP. Tel 0286 830800. Cherokee 140 G-AVWF moved to Liverpool Airport by 7/86.

G-AIDL+	Dragon Rapide 6	ex Biggin Hill, Allied Airways, TX310. Flew 10/86 - see above.
WV781	Sycamore HR.12	7839M, ex Finningley, Odiham, Digby, HDU, CFS, ASWDU, G-ALTD ntu.
XA282+	Cadet TX.3	ex Syerston. Arrived 1986.
XD599	Vampire T.11	ex Bournemouth, Blackbushe, Staverton, Stroud, CATCS, RAFC, 1.

XH837+	Javelin FAW.7	8032M, ex Northolt, Ruislip, 33. Nose section. Arrived 1987.
XJ726+	Whirlwind HAR.10	ex Sibson, Wroughton, 2 FTS, CFS, ME SAR Flt, 22. Arrived 1986.
XK623	Vampire T.11	ex 'G-VAMP', Bournemouth, Moston, Woodford, Chester, St Athan, 5 FTS.

LLANBEDR

The fire dump at the RAE airfield here continues to hold the Canberra. The Sea Vixen D.3 is next to the dump, but not yet torched.

WK145	Canberra B.2	ex RAE, 7, 98, 245, 527. Dump, poor state.
XN657	Sea Vixen D.3	ex RAE, FRL, RAE, ADS, 899, 893. See above.

VALLEY

On 6/7/87 the remains of Shackleton AEW.2 WL754 and Hawk T.1 XX300/8827M (ex Abingdon and unidentified in W&R10) were cleared from the dump, leaving just the Vulcan. The other airframes here are unchanged.

XE874	Vampire T.11	8582M, ex Woodford, Chester, Shawbury, 1 FTS, 4 FTS, 8 FTS, 4 FTS, 1 FTS, 4 FTS, 7 FTS. Gate guardian.
XL392	Vulcan B.2A	8745M, ex 35, 617, Scampton Wing. Dump.
XP361	Whirlwind HAR.10	8731M, ex Boulmer, Chivenor, 202, 22, 103, 110, 225. Gate guardian.
XR534	Gnat T.1	8578M, ex 4 FTS, CFS. '65'. Gate guardian.
XT772	Wessex HU.5	8805M, ex Wroughton. BDR.

Powys

WELSHPOOL

The Tiger Moth is still stored at the Montgomeryshire Ultra-Light Flying Group's strip.

G-ANJK	Tiger Moth	ex T6066, 1 GU, 2 GS, 2 RFS, 25 RFS, 28 EFTS, 24 EFTS. CoA exp 12/5/85.

Part 4

CHANNEL ISLES

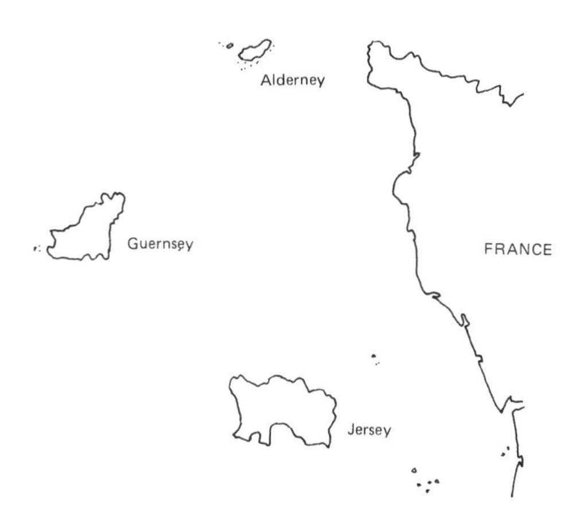

GUERNSEY

Airport *Ailes Anciennes* have failed to pick up the battered Anson C.19 here and it still resides with the fire crews. The other fire aircraft remain unchanged. Trislander G-BCYC is unlikely to be rebuilt as its wings have gone through to PBN at Bembridge for use in the AEW Defender project. Long since thought gone, the local Air Scouts still have their Meteor F.8 nose section, kept on the airfield.

G-BAZJ	Herald 209	ex Air UK, Alia 4X-AHR, G-8-1. Fire section - non destructive.
G-BCYC	Trislander	ex Glasgow, Loganair, EL-AIB, G-BCYC. Fuselage. Crashed 15/5/79. See notes above.
TX192	Anson C.19	ex WCS, NCS, 23 GCF, Tech Trng Command CF, Benson Ferry Wing, MCS, 23 GCF, 2 ANS, CFS, Wyton CF. Poor state, see notes above.
WJ350	Sea Prince C.2	ex FAAM, Yeovilton, Yeovilton SF, A&AEE, Yeovilton SF, Lossiemouth SF, Yeovilton SF, 781, Yeovilton SF, 781, FOFT, 781, Yeovilton SF. Fire dump.
WL131	Meteor F.8	7751M, ex APS Sylt, 601, 111. Nose section, with Air Scouts.

Elsewhere Lewis Martin's three aircraft, the EAA Biplane, Mooney and Noralpha continue to be stored in various locations. Status of the rebuild of Tiger Moth G-AOAC is unconfirmed.

G-AOAC	Tiger Moth	ex N6978, Upwood CF, 16 EFTS, 22 EFTS. Crashed 22/6/74. Under rebuild.
G-ASTH	Mooney M.20	ex France, N6906U. Crashed 16/11/66. Stored Sausmarez Park.
G-ATEP	EAA Biplane	CoA expired 18/6/73. Stored at Sausmarez Park.
G-ATHN	Noralpha	ex F-BFUZ, French military. CoA expired 27/6/75. Stored St Peter Port.

JERSEY

Airport The two aircraft used by the fire crews soldier on, the Herald being only a fuselage used for smoke training. Baron G-ASDO was donated to the local 2498 Squadron ATC during 1987.

G-AOJD	Viscount 802	ex British Airways, BEA. Fire service.
G-ASDO+	Baron A55	CoA expired 16/4/83. 2498 Sqn ATC - see notes above.
G-BBXJ	Herald 203	ex BIA, I-TIVI. Crashed 24/12/74. Fire service.

Others By 1987 the dismantled GY-80 Horizon G-AYOL held at St Lawrence had moved to Stonnall by 1986. It is thought that the Herald nose continues to serve as a plaything in a garden in Longueville.

G-APWG	Herald 201	ex Jersey Airport, Air UK, BIA, BUA. Nose section, see above.

IRELAND

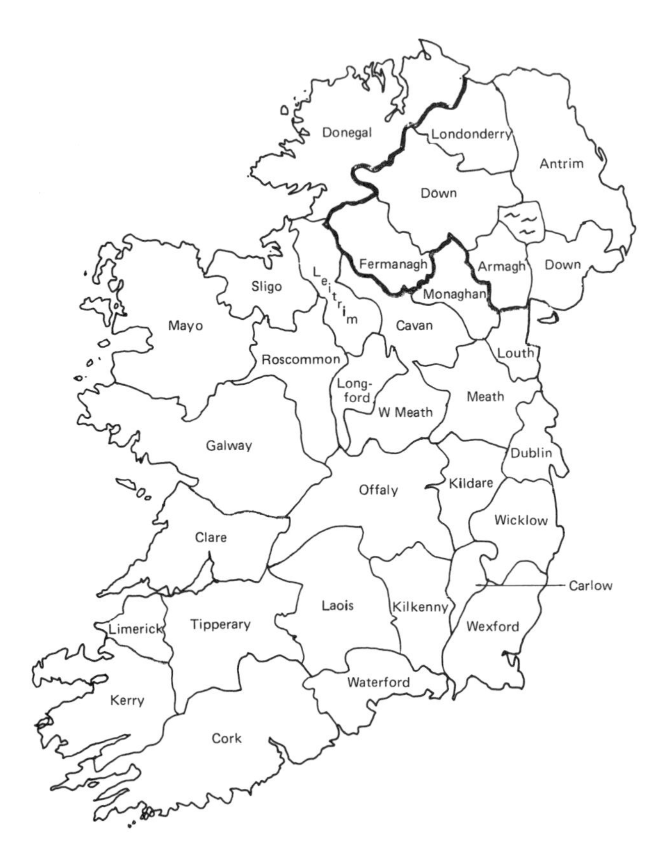

Northern Ireland

Antrim
Armagh
Down
Fermanagh
Londonderry

Eire

Carlow
Cavan
Clare
Cork
Donegal
Dublin
Galway
Kerry
Kildare
Kilkenny
Laois
Leitrim
Limerick
Longford
Louth
Mayo
Meath
West Meath
Offaly
Roscommon
Sligo
Tipperary
Waterford
Wexford
Wicklow

Northern Ireland

BELFAST

(County Antrim) The CCF at Campbell College have a Vampire pod on charge for instruction. It is 'parented' by RAF Aldergrove and has been here for a considerable period of time.

XD525+	Vampire T.11	7882M, ex Aldergrove, 1 FTS, 4 FTS, 5 FTS, 7 FTS. Fuselage pod only.

BELFAST AIRPORT

(Or Aldergrove, County Antrim) There has been little change here, although the passenger/reader will immediately notice that the Ferguson replica IAHC.9 has gone from the terminal, going back to Holywood during 1987. Restoration work has started on the Meteor NF.14, with a view to putting it on the gate of RAF Aldergrove. A damaged Wessex HC.2 has become an instructional airframe and an HU.5 has arrived for BDRT work.

G-AVFE	Trident 2E	ex Heathrow, BA, BEA. Flew in 12/2/85. Fire service.
WS840	Meteor NF.14	7969M, ex Bishop's Court, 1 ANS, 64, 264. See notes above.
WT486	Canberra T.4	8102M, ex Wildenrath, 14, 17, 88, Wildenrath SF. Fire dump.
XR700	Jet Provost T.4	8589M, ex Abingdon, Shawbury, CATCS, 3 FTS, 1 FTS. Nose section with RAFEF Northern Ireland detachment.
XT456+	Wessex HU.5	ex Wroughton. Arrived 9/11/87. BDRT.
XT669+	Wessex HC.2	8894M, ex 72. Damaged 25/10/85.

BELFAST HARBOUR AIRPORT

(Or Sydenham, County Down) With the Shorts Apprentice School, the Sea Hawk is thought to live on. The Tucano engine test bed has been identified. During 1987 Shorts donated the prototype SD.330 to the Ulster Aviation Society (see under Newtownards) and it is held in store here for them.

G-BSBH+	Short SD.330	CoA expired 13/4/81. See notes above.
WN108	Sea Hawk FB.3	ex Bournemouth, FRU, 806, 895, 897, 800. Apprentice School.
1317	T-27 Tucano	ex San Jose dos Campos, Brazil AF. Fuselage, engine test bed.

BISHOP'S COURT

(County Down) At the home of Ulster Radar, a former 207 Squadron Devon is used for instruction.

VP957	Devon C.2/2	8822M, ex Belfast Airport, Northolt, 207, 21, WCS, SCS, NCS, SCS, WCS, SCS, Andover SF, 38 GCF, AAFCE, 2 TAF CS, BAFO CS.

CASTLEREAGH

(County Down) To clear up the reference for the College of Further Education in W&R10, the Sea Venom that moved to Wellesbourne Mountford was XG692. XG734 was used as spares for both this aircraft, and the UAS aircraft - see under Newtownards - and should be deleted.

HOLYWOOD

Ulster Folk and Transport Museum. Located at Cultra Manor, the Museum has made great strides in its aim to portray the history of aviation and that of Northern Ireland in particular; Policy leans heavily towards civil aviation and, with this in mind, Spitfire XVI TE184 was exchanged through Nick Grace for the Short Sealand from the USA. TE184 moved to Sandown. The Ferguson replica that was displayed at Belfast Airport returned during 1987 and late in the year two McCandless gyroplanes arrived from Killough. Space restrictions mean that not all of the aircraft can be displayed at any one time.

The Museum is open October to April, Monday to Saturday 1100 to 1700, Sunday 1400 to 1700 and May to September, Monday to Saturday 1100 to 1800, Sunday 1400 to 1800. Contact : Ulster Folk and Transport Museum, Cultra Manor, Holywood, Northern Ireland BT18 0EU. Tel 02317 5411.

G-AJOC	Messenger 2A	ex East Fortune, Strathallan, Dunottar. CoA exp 18/5/72. Stored.
G-AKEL	Gemini 1A	ex Kilbrittain Castle. wfu 30/5/84.) For rebuild
G-AKGE	Gemini 3C	ex Kilbrittain Castle, EI-ALM, G-AKGE. wfu 30/5/84.) into one.
G-AKLW+	Sealand	ex Bradley Air Museum, Windsor Locks, Connecticut, Jeddah, RSaudiAF, SU-AHY, G-AKLW. Arrived 4/8/86. See notes above.
G-AOUR	Tiger Moth	ex Belfast, NL898. Crashed 6/6/65. Stored.
G-ARTZ+	McCandless M-2	ex Killough. G-ARTZ the first. Arrived late 1987.

G-ATXX+	McCandless M-4	ex Killough, wfu 9/9/70. Arrived late 1987.
BGA.470	Nimbus I	ex Bishop's Stortford, Duxford. Stored.
IAHC6	Ferguson Monoplane	ex Dublin.
IAHC9+	Ferguson Monoplane	ex Belfast Airport, Holywood. Returned 1987, stored.
VH-UUP	Scion I	ex East Fortune, Strathallan, G-ACUX, VH-UUP, G-ACUX.
XG905	Short SC.1	ex Shorts, Sydenham, Thurleigh, RAE.

KILLOUGH

(County Down) The McCandless store here was emptied in late 1987 when G-ARTZ and G-ATXX were donated to the Ulster Folk and Transport Museum at Holywood. The M-4 marked 'QUB' noted in W&R10 is unaccounted for.

LOUGH FOYLE

(County Londonderry) Just off shore can be seen the hulk of Corsair II JT693:R, ex 1837 Squadron.

MOVENIS

(Near Garvagh, County Londonderry) It is thought that the fuselage of the Cessna 182 can still be found at the strip here.

G-AWJA	Cessna 182L	ex N1658C. CoA expired 21/4/85. Fuselage only.

MULLAGHMORE

(County Londonderry) The wreck situation here is unchanged.

G-AYTB	Rallye Club	CoA expired 17/10/82. Wreck.
G-BFPC	AA-5B Tiger	ex Breighton. Crashed 8/5/82. Wreck.

NEWTOWNARDS

(County Down) Ulster Aviation Society Restoration work is coming along on both the Wildcat and the Sea Venom. During 1987 UAS were presented with the prototype Shorts SD.330 and this is stored on their behalf at Belfast Harbour Airport, which see. The UAS aircraft are not available for public inspection, but general enquiries can be made to ; Raymond Burrows, 20 Carrowreagh Gardens, Dundonald Belfast BT16 0TW. At the Airfield Auster J/1 G-AHHK moved out to Shobdon, leaving two Cessna hulks.

G-ARFM	Cessna 175B	ex N8176T. CoA expired 23/10/79. Stored.
G-BBTT	Cessna F.150L	CoA expired 12/3/76. Fuselage only.
JV482	Wildcat V	ex Castlereagh, Lough Beg. Under restoration.
XG736	Sea Venom FAW.22	ex Castlereagh, Sydenham, Yeovilton, ADS. Under restoration.

UPPER BALLINDERRY

(Near Crumlin, County Antrim) The Whitney Straight is kept warm and dry and some work has been carried out on it.

G-AERV	Whitney Straight	ex Newtownards, EM999, Kemble, Abingdon SF, Halton SF, G-AERV.

Eire

ABBEYSHRULE

(West of Mullingar, off the L18, Westmeagh) During 1985 Bruton Aircraft Engineering folded, but Sam Bruton is now trading again and continues to specialise in keeping Ireland's Rallyes going. There has been a clear-out, but the general view is one of expansion here - at least in terms of W&R material! Rallye Commodore 150 EI-BKU was flying again by 1987. The hulks of Cessna EI-ATH, Rallyes EI-AUD and G-AZGH went to the scrapyard at Kildimo by 10/87. Aztec EI-BML was here briefly before it, too, went to Kildimo. Champion EI-ATL noted as off site in W&R10, was back within the confines of the airfield by 4/86. Current here are the following :-

EI-ABU	Spartan II	ex Cloughjordan, G-ABYN. Stored.
EI-ANN+	Tiger Moth	ex Dublin, Kilcock, G-ANEE, T5418, 63 GCF, 24 EFTS, 19 EFTS, 12 EFTS. First noted 7/86.
EI-AOP+	Tiger Moth	ex Dublin, G-AIBN, T7967, 18 EFTS, 1667 CU, 1 GCF, 16 PFTS. Arrived by late 1976, for rebuild.

EI-ATL+	Champion 7AC	ex 'local', Abbeyshrule, Clondalkin, N1119E. Damaged 26/11/75. Spares for EI-AVB.
EI-AUP+	Rallye Club	ex Coonagh, G-AVVK. Crashed 1/9/83. Arrived by 4/86.
EI-AVB+	Champion 7AC	ex Shannon, 7P-AXK, ZS-AXK. Under rebuild.
EI-BAG	Cessna 172A	ex G-ARAV, N9771T. Stored.
EI-BDB	Rallye Club	ex Weston. Crashed 28/7/78. Fuselage only.
EI-BDH	Rallye Club	ex G-AWOB. Stored.
EI-BGN	Rallye Club	ex TU-TJC. Cancelled 10/8/83. Fuselage only.
EI-BKE+	Super Rallye	ex F-BKUN. Crashed 5/4/81. Wreck.

CARBURY

(Kildare) Dick Robinson's 1937 vintage HM.14 is still stored in the town.

IAHC.3	HM.14 Pou du Ciel	stored, engineless. Never flew.

CASEMENT

(Or Baldonnel, west of Dublin, County Dublin) Instructional airframes at this the Headquarters of the Irish Army Air Corps, remain unchanged, but the famous dump has lost two of its very long-standing Vampire T.55s. 187 and 192 had both perished by 4/87. Otherwise, things are much as before :-

164	Chipmunk T.20	stored, reported to be for preservation.
171	Chipmunk T.20	fuselage only, dump.
172	Chipmunk T.20	stored, poor state.
193	Vampire T.55	fuselage pod only, poor state, on the dump.
198	Vampire T.11	ex XE977, 8 FTS, never flew with IAAC. On display outside Officers' Mess.
221	CM-170 Magister	ex French Air Force No 79 '3-KE', instructional airframe.
233	SF-260MC Warrior	ex I-SYAS, fuselage only. Instructional airframe.
	Alouette III	instructional, non-flying, rig. In Technical Block.
	Cessna 172B	ex Southend, G-ARLU, N8002X. Damaged 30/10/77. *AVIONICS 2*, rig in Technical Block.

CASTLEBRIDGE

(North of Wexford, County Wexford) John O'Loughlin's Avro 643 Cadet continues to be stored here, with a seized engine. Stored at the airstrip for a long time has been a Cadet TX.2, for Cork Gliding Club.

EI-ALP	Cadet	ex G-ADIE. Stored following engine seizure 6/77.
VM659	Cadet TX.2	stored. See notes above.

CHARLEVILLE

(Cork) There having been no reports for a very long time, Chipmunk EI-AHR is now LOST! fodder.

COONAGH

(West of Limerick, off the N18, Limerick) The French Auster continues its hibernation, but Rallye EI-AUP moved to Abbeyshrule by 4/86.

F-BGOO	J/1 Autocrat	stored.

CORK AIRPORT

(South of the City, County Cork) There have been two departures, but otherwise no change. Cessna 310B EI-AOS had gone to Kildimo by 4/87. Dove 6 VP-YKF had gone by mid 1987 - fate unknown.

EI-AUT	F.1A Aircoupe	ex G-ARXS, D-EBSA, N3037G. Under rebuild.
G-ACMA	Leopard Moth	ex BD148, DH, HQ Army Co-Op CCF, 7 AACU, G-ACMA. CoA expired 10/7/85.
G-ASNG	Dove 6	EI-BJW ntu, ex Coventry, HB-LFF, G-ASNG, HB-LFF, G-ASNG, PH-IOM. Stored.
N4422P	Geronimo	Stored.

DUBLIN

Irish Aviation Museum IAM have a store of aircraft at Castlemoate House, near to Dublin Airport. Plans for a permanent exhibition are still no nearer to fruition and the store is not open to public inspection. A Tiger Moth, previously in use for spares with the Strathallan collection and long since thought consumed, appeared here as long ago as 1980 - W&R gets there in the end!

EI-AOH	Viscount 808	ex Dublin Airport, Aer Lingus. Nose section.
IAHC1	HM.14 Pou du Ciel	ex Coonagh. Owned by the Aviation Society of Ireland.
G-AOGA	Aries 1	ex Kilbrittain Castle, EI-ANB, G-AOGA.

G-ANPC+	Tiger Moth	ex Edinburgh (?), Strathallan, Portmoak, R4950, 2 GS, Kirton in Lindsey SF, Hemswell SF, Oakington SF, 28 EFTS, 25 PEFTS, 17 EFTS, Benson SF. Crashed 2/1/67. Arrived by 7/86. Dismantled, stripped airframe.
34	Magister	ex Casement, N5392.
141	Anson XIX	ex Casement. Dismantled.
183	Provost T.51	ex Casement. Dismantled.
191	Vampire T.55	ex Casement. Dismantled.

Institute of Technology Tiger Moth EI-AOP moved out to Abbeyshrule during 1976, hopefully for rebuild to flying condition. Previously disappeared EI-ANN went by the same route. The Cherokee and Aztec serve on as instructional airframes at Bolton Street.

G-ATHI	Cherokee 180	ex Shannon Airport. Crashed 9/5/74. Fuselage only.
G-AYWY	Aztec 250D	ex EI-ATI, N6735Y. Crashed 15/10/75. Battered hulk.

Others Dove 4 176 which was held at Phoenix Park moved to Waterford in 1987.

DUBLIN AIRPORT

(Or Collinstown, north of the city on the N1, County Dublin) Aer Lingus reflew their lovely DH.84 Dragon EI-ABI on 10/4/86 and it has been a regular attender at aviation events since. As such, it should be deleted from the realms of W&R. CASA 352L N9012N holds on to a tenuous existence here, having been dismantled for removal to Sweden, but is still to be found on the north ramp in poor state. Other wrecks here are very long term now, the bulk being located in the Iona National Airways hangar. Aer Turas donated CL-44 EI-BGO to the fire service in 1985.

EI-ALU	Cadet	ex G-ACIH. Dismantled.
EI-AMK	J/1 Autocrat	ex G-AGTV. wfu 5/79.
EI-ARY	Cessna F.150H	crashed 14/6/70. Wreck.
EI-AUH	Cessna F.172H	crashed 25/2/72. Fuselage, wings on EI-AVA.
EI-AYJ	Cessna 182P	ex N52229. Crashed 19/9/76. Wreck.
EI-BEO	Cessna 310Q II	ex D-ICEG, N7733Q. Crashed 27/8/85. Stored.
EI-BGO+	Canadair CL-44J	ex Aer Turas, TF-LLH, CF-MKP-X. Last flight 3/1/86. Fire service.
EI-BIA	Cessna FA.152	Crashed 28/9/80. Wreck.
G-BHIA	Cessna F.152-II	CoA expired 4/5/86. Stored, poor shape.
N9012N	CASA 352L	ex Casement, Biggin Hill, Cuatro Vientos, Spanish AF T2B-142. See notes.

GALWAY AIRPORT

(County Galway) The Islander hulk still resides out on the airfield.

EI-BBR	BN-2A-26 Islander	ex Aer Arran, F-BVOE ntu, G-BDJS. Crashed 7/8/80.

GORMANSTON

(County Dublin) The other IAAC base holds two withdrawn Chipmunks in store.

168+	Chipmunk T.20	stored, first noted 4/87.
199+	Chipmunk T.20	stored, first noted 4/87.

KILBRITTAIN CASTLE

It is very likely that the "Morane-like" fuselage frame at Kildimo is the MS.230 IAHC.5 from here.

KILDIMO

(County Limerick) Dennehy Commercials Ltd on the N69 to the north of the town have established an aircraft breaking business. All of the aircraft listed below are by definition new to this location, the bulk being first noted 10/87. A frame here, reported as "Morane-like", is most likely IAHC.5 from Kilbrittain Castle.

EI-AOS+	Cessna 310B	ex Cork, G-ARIG, EI-AOS, G-ARIG, N5378A. Fuselage and wings.
EI-ATH+	Cessna F.150J	ex Abbeyshrule. Damaged 10/3/82. Fuselage only.
EI-AUD+	Rallye Club	ex Abbeyshrule. Crashed mid 1983. Fuselage only.
EI-AUV+	Aztec 250C	ex Shannon, N80WT. Fuselage and wings.
EI-BDM+	Aztec 250D	ex Shannon, Dublin, G-AXIV, N6826Y. Fuselage and wings.
EI-BFE+	Cessna F.150G	ex G-AVGM. Fuselage and wings.
EI-BJA+	Cessna FRA.150L	ex G-AZTE. Fuselage and wings.
EI-BML+	Aztec 250C	ex Abbeyshrule, G-ATSB, G-ATZJ, N6179Y. Fuselage only.
G-AZGH+	Rallye Club	ex Abbeyshrule. Crashed 20/4/83. Fuselage only.
HB-CFI+	Cessna F.172P	fuselage only.
	MS.230 (?)	see notes above.

KILMOON

(County Meath) The two Cubs remain in store at the strip here.

EI-AKM J-3C-65 Cub ex Weston, N88194, NC88194. Stored.
EI-BCO J-3C-65 Cub ex F-BBIV, composite. Stored.

PORTLAOISE

(County Laoise) The Aldritt Monoplane is still stored in a garage in the town.

IAHC2 Aldritt Monoplane engineless, stored.

POWERSCOURT

(South of Dublin, County Wicklow) Auster EI-AMY is here acting as a source of spares for EI-AUS.

EI-AMY J/1N Alpha ex Kells, G-AJUW. Spares use.

RATHCOOLE

(County Cork) Condition normal at this farm strip.

EI-AFF BA Swallow II ex Coonagh, G-ADMF. Damaged 16/5/66. Stored.
EI-AFN BA Swallow II ex Kilkenny, G-AFGV. Stored.
EI-ASU Terrier 2 ex G-ASRG, WE599, AAC, LAS, HCCS. wfu 15/6/77. Stored.

SHANNON AIRPORT

Once a very active W&R venue, Shannon has settled down somewhat. Both of the Boeing 707s intended for Omega Air, 60-SBM and 9Q-CKP, left for the USA during 1986. Champion EI-AVB moved to Abbeyshrule for rebuild. Otherwise the situation remains unchanged.

EI-AYW Aztec 250C ex N5801Y. Stored following accident 9/80.
G-AWUP Cessna F.150H ex Abbeyshrule. Damaged 1983, stored.
N3760D Caribou ex 5H-MRQ. External store.
4R-ALB Boeing 707-321B ex Air Lanka, 9V-BBA. Fire service.

Industrial Training School Located on the Industrial and Trading Estate at the edge of the airport, the small instructional airframe fleet lost Aztec EI-BDM to Kildimo. But otherwise is thought unchanged.

EI-BHU Skipper ex Waterford. Crashed 19/7/83.
HB-CCW Cessna F.172N wreck.
SP-AFX Wilga 35 crashed 12/8/85. Wreck.

SLIGO

(County Sligo) Gerry O'Hara's aircraft, designed and built by himself, are stored in the town.

IAHC7 Sligo Concept single seat low wing monoplane. Stored, not flown.
IAHC8 O'Hara Autogyro on Bensen lines. Unflown. Stored.

WATERFORD AIRPORT

(South east of the town, County Waterford) South East Aviation Enthusiasts SEAE have taken on the former IAAC Dove last used for instructional work in Dublin. The restoration of the DC-7C is coming on well and a compound is now in place around the collection.

G-AOIE Douglas DC-7C ex Shannon, Autair, Schreiner PH-SAX, G-AOIE Caledonian, BOAC.
VP-BDF Boeing 707-321 ex Dublin, Bahamasair. Nose section.
Gemini cockpit section. Almost certainly G-ALCS, ex Kilbrittain Castle.
173 Chipmunk T.20 ex Gormanston, IAAC.
176+ Dove 4 ex Dublin, Casement, IAAC.

WESTON

(West of Dublin on the L2, County Kildare) For the first time in many an edition, Weston is without a W&R candidate. The frame of Auster G-ASLS lingered for a little while longer than W&R10 would have you believe, but it and the hulk of Rallye Minerva 220 EI-BDS were cleared from the airfield during development work in 1987.

B O A C
BRITISH EUROPEAN AIRWAYS
G-AMOG

ERIAL RECONNAISSANCE - 1
View from a hot-air balloon propelled *Peter J. Bish* in May 1986 of part of the airliner collection at the Cosford Aerospace Museum: Comet XB G-APAS in BOAC livery alongside Viscount 701 G-AMOG in BEA colours, on opposite page.

ERIAL RECONNAISSANCE - 2
hots from gliders overhead Lasham uring August 1986. *Top:* view of he SWWAPS compound containing ea Hawk, Whirlwind 10, Drover II, ea Prince, Wessex, Meteor, Hunter, Whirlwind 9, Prentice and composite Meteor TT.20 *(Ken Ellis)*. *Bottom:* Airspeed Ambassador G-ALZO outde the Dan-Air facility. It moved y road to Duxford two months ater *(Alan Curry)*.

BDR PHANTOMS

Above: Former Texas ANG F-4C Phantom 63419 at Alconbury *(Alan Curry)*
Below: F-4C Phantom 40707 and *(right)* Molesworth-bound Mystere IV at Mildenhall *(Alan Curry)*
Bottom: USN F-4N 153008 of VF-154 USS *Coral Sea* at Alconbury 27 July 86 *(Ian Griffiths)*

AIRLINERS

Above: Trident 3B-101 G-AWZU used by the BAA fire crews at Stansted *(Simon Murdoch)*

Below: Former Aer Turas CL-44J EI-BGO being stripped of spares at Dublin, July 86 *(Peter J. Bish)*

Bottom: Comet 4 G-APDT at Heathrow, is expected to go to Hatfield as gate-guardian *(Peter J. Bish)*

FINNINGLEY

Nimrod AEW.3 XV263 arrived in June 1987, following the much publicised cancellation. *(Alan Curry)*

Vulcan B.2A XJ782, sadly put up for tender in March 1988. *(Alan Curry)*

Dumped Hawk hulk of T.1A XX29 which crashed in November 1986 *(Alan Curry)*

EMA VISIT (27 Feb 87)

Engineless Argosy 101 G-BEOZ in open store at East Midlands Airport prior to joining the Aeropark. *(Tim R. Badham)*

Former Cuckfield Whirlwind srs 3 at the Aeropark. *(Tim R. Badham)*

Viscount 813 G-AZLR employed at East Midlands as a cabin trainer. *(Tim R. Badham)*

ON GUARD

F-100D Super Sabre '63319' (42269) on its plinth at Lakenheath, 29 September 1987. *(Peter J. Cooper)*

Whirlwind HAS.7 XG577 watching over the Army at Waterbeach. *(Ken Ellis)*

Hunter F.1 WT651 in the grounds of 8 Group Royal Observer Corps Church Lawford. *(Tim R. Badham)*

ɔREIGN JETS

ɔrth East Aircraft Museum's Greek 84F Thunderstreak 541 at Sun-ɛrland. *(Alan Curry)*

arfighter Preservation Group's ɛrman F-104G 22+57 in store at nbrook *(Ken Ellis)*

idland Air Museum's ex-Danish -104G R-756 at Coventry Airport. *īim R. Badham)*

HALTON

Forlorn-looking Gnat T.1s XR53 and XR951 awaiting removal in th summer of 1986 *(J.A.Simpson)*

Shell of Vampire T.11 WZ559, lor time a puzzle to historians. *(J.A.Simpson)*

Jet Provost 8236M (XP573) wit 'Halton code' 19 on fin and nos *(Roger Richards)*

ELICOPTERS – 1

nonymous Wasp and Wessex HU.5 T450 side by side at Netheravon - x-BDR machines. *(Peter J. Cooper)*

'hirlwind HAR.10 8674M (XP395) ft Halton in June 1987 for Tatter- all Thorpe. *(Lloyd P. Robinson)*

azelle G-SFTA (G-BAGJ on fin) ill present a challenge to restorers NEAM, Sunderland. *(Alan Curry)*

HELICOPTERS – 2

Sheep in Hind's clothing, Whirlwi
HAS.7 XN382 with cosmetic surge
at Thruxton. *(Alan Curry)*

Gutted and battered – Wasp HAS
XT469 at Stafford, with the Tactic
Supply Wing. *(Alan Curry)*

'Full Metal Jacket' extras – Wess
60s stored at Bournemouth Airpo
(Alan Curry)

SELAGES

stream N14234 at East Midlands
or to becoming a travelling dem-
strator. *(Alan Curry)*

ostantial — yet anonymous Jet-
eam at Hatfield Polytechnic.
n Oliver)

rmer resident of Malta, Widgeon
50M adjusting to the Ipswich Air-
t climate. *(Lloyd P. Robinson)*

MILITARY HULKS

Long serving Varsity T.1 WJ902
the dump at RAF Wittering.
(Alan Curry)

Mortal remains of the Sea Ven
FAW.22 on the Tain ranges.
(John G. Chree)

Beaver AL.1 XP827 in a somewh
sorry state at Netheravon.
(Peter J. Cooper)

VIL HULKS

zza Express' Sir? Failed STOL ssna Skyhawk in Golders Green. *en Ellis)*

ndowner G-BARI amongst the rtinas at Bushey. *eil Reynolds)*

rmer SABENA Cessna 310B 20GS in the long grass at Sibson. *lf Jenks)*

TWO-SEAT HUNTERS

Hunter pair at Macclesfield, FGA XJ690 and T.7 ET-273 *(Alan Curr*

Dutch Flying Laboratory PH-NL continues to be stored at Exet Airport. *(Peter J. Cooper)*

Former RAE T.8 XF321 at RNE Manadon, in the systems buildin 1987. *(Peter Castle)*

GHTNINGS

ɜvelopmental line-up at Cosford, 3-5 WG768, P.1A WG760 and F.1 G337 *(Alan Curry)*

ghtning F.1A XM192 on the gate RAF Wattisham *(Alan Curry)*

.d end to T.5 8532M (XS423) at AF Binbrook, September 1987. *laurice Baalham)*

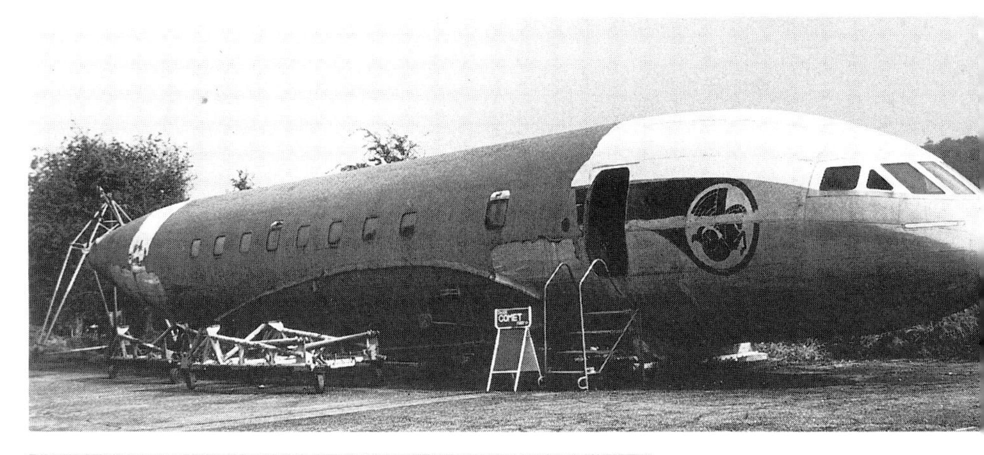

'MAM' UPDATE

Mosquito Aircraft Museum's Com
fuselage shows its French connectio
(Ian Oliver)

Remember to look up at the fram
of Tiger Moth G-ANFP in the rafte
at London Colney. *(Ian Oliver)*

Under restoration in the main ha
gar, DH.87B Hornet Moth G-ADO
(Ian Oliver)

›G ALLEY

›assed invasion as containerised ›agots' and 'Midgets' sit it out at ›iddlesbrough. *(Alan Curry)*

›iddlesbrough defector - 1120 in›alled in the RAF Museum, Hendon *›im R. Badham)*

›20 at Gamston after its debut at RAF ›nningley (now at Yeovilton) *›im R. Badham)*

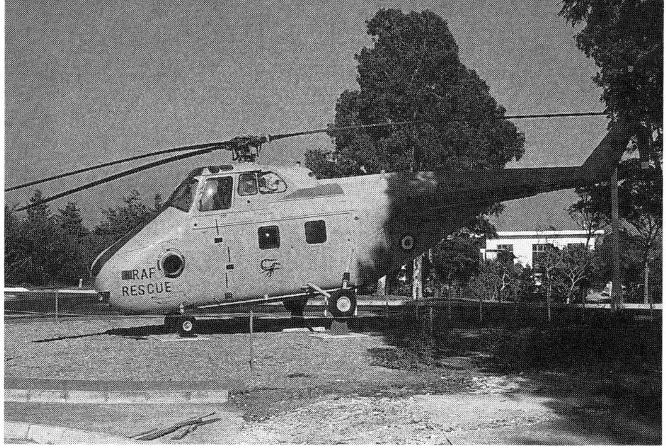

RAF OVERSEAS

Alas no more. 'Zap-board' Vulca
B.2A XL317 at RAF Akrotiri.
(J.A.Simpson)

Whirlwind HAR.10 XD184 with 8
Sqdn badge, also at RAF Akroti
(J.A.Simpson)

Whirlwind HAR.9 XM666 at Salv
dor Settlement, Falkland Islands.
(Douglas A. Rough)

TRAINERS

Berkshire Aviation Group's Magister on show at Wroughton, before going to Woodley. *(Alf Jenks)*

Provost T.1 WW442 from Cranfield at its new home at Leverstock Green. *(Alan Allan)*

Brooklands Museum Avro 504K replica 'G1381' (BAPC.177) ex-Henlow. *(Lloyd P. Robinson)*

ST. ATHAN

BMW 801D engine in action on the Fw 190F-8/U1. (RAF St Athan)

Ground-running magic as Kawasak Ki 100 fires up. *(Alan Curry)*

End of the line for these Victor K.2s (XL163 and XL233). *(Alan Curry)*

RAF MUSEUM

Bristol 173 XF785 (was G-ALBN) in store at Henlow. *(Mike Packham)*

Former Yugoslavian P-47D Thunderbolt 13064 stripped at Cardington. *(Tim R. Badham)*

Miles Hawk Major DG590 (G-ADMW) under wraps at Henlow, Sept 1987. *(Mike Packham)*

VC-10 s

Frustrated tanker ZD232 in use a RAF Brize Norton with JATE. *(J.A. Simpson)*

Unflown nose section at Brookland for the museum. *(Lloyd Robinson,*

Former Gulf Air G-ARVJ in guttec and supported state at RAF Briz Norton. *(J.A. Simpson)*

ʼEOVILTON

ʌV-8A 159233, ex US Marine Corps, ɔined the FAAM in June 1987. *Alan Curry)*

ˡarvard IIA EX976 with 'ground-ʳrew'. *(Tim R. Badham)*

ˈ-4S 155848, also ex Marine Corps VMFA-232) one of two Phantoms ow with FAAM. *(Tim R. Badham)*

Part 6

RAF OVERSEAS

'RAF Overseas' was well greeted upon its first appearance in W&R10 and it appears again, this time following exactly the same format as the main text. There are examples of former RAF (etc) airframes all over the world, and it is not the intention of this book to start sneaking these aircraft in. The aircraft listed here are essentially still on charge with the British forces and held on British governed soil. One small exception to this is the inclusion in this issue of the Falkland Islands. Defining which aircraft to include on the Falklands was difficult and in the end the Compiler made the cop out of going for relatively whole preserved airframes and avoiding the many high ground wrecks and range targets. Details of aircraft in the Falklands can be found in the British Aviation Research Group's huge work *Falklands - The Air War* and an up-dated view of the wreck situation was published in the November 1987 issue of *FlyPast*.

This section is not in the index and was assembled from material supplied by ; Alan Allen, Dave Pope, Mark Harris, Doug Rough and the Compiler.

West Germany

BRUGGEN

The situation here remains much as before, with the Lightning F.2A and T.4s still serving as 'Special Display' airframes (RAF Germany parlance for surface decoy). Of the aircraft noted as current in W&R10, two have moved on :- Lightning F.2A XN788/8543M departed for *Laarbruch* during 2/87, courtesy of an 18 Squadron Chinook HC.1; Gnat T.1 XM705/8574M left by road and ferry for *St Athan*, arriving there by 8/86. Current are the following, with one new inmate :-

XE608	Hunter F.6A	8717M, ex 1 TWU, TWU, 229 OCU, CFCS, AFDS, CFE. BDRT, 20 Sqn c/s.
XL566+	Hunter T.7	8891M, ex Shawbury, Kemble, Laarbruch SF, 4 FTS, 208, 1417F, 43, A&AEE. Arrived 10/86, for BDRT.
XM970	Lightning T.4	8529M, ex 19, 92, 60 MU 'hack', 226 OCU, 92, LCS. 'Special display'.
XM973	Lightning T.4	8528M, ex 19, 226 OCU, 23, 111, 226 OCU, 74, AFDS. 'Special display'.
XN783	Lightning F.2A	8526M, ex 92, 19, 92. 'Special display'.
XN789	Lightning F.2A	8527M, ex 19, Handling Squadron, 92. 'Special Display'.
XN792	Lightning F.2A	8525M, ex 92. BDRT.
XP403	Whirlwind HAR.10	8690M, ex 22, SAR Wing, 202, 228. 431 MU for BDRT.
XV358	Buccaneer S.2C	8658M, ex 809. BDRT, minus wings and tail section.
XX822"	Jaguar GR.1	8563M, complex composite based upon nose and forward fuselage of S.07 XW563. On plinth outside 14 Sqn HQ, in their colours, coded 'AA'.

DETMOLD

At the Headquarters of 4 Regiment, Army Air Corps, a Scout has arrived.

XL739	Skeeter AOP.12	ex 15/19 Hussars, 1 Wing, 651, A&AEE, BATUS, A&AEE, C(A). Displayed outside of 4 Regiment AAC Headquarters.
XS571	Wasp HAS.1	ex Wroughton. Fitted with boom of XT436. BDRT airframe with 71 (Aircraft) Workshops. '614'.
XV627	Wasp HAS.1	ex Wroughton. BDRT airframe for 4 Regiment AAC. '321'.
XW615+	Scout AH.1	ex Wroughton. Arrived 1/9/87. Pod only. BDRT.

GATOW

(West Berlin) Far from being nearly wiped out on the fire dump, as W&R10 would have readers believe, Varsity T.1 WF382 has been upgraded and is now considered a display airframe along with the Dakota and Hastings. The Valetta still hangs on to this mortal coil by a thread.

TG503	Hastings T.5	8555M, ex SCBS, A&AEE, BCBS, MoA, BCBS, C.1 RRE, RRF, A&AEE, AFEE, A&AEE. Preserved as monument to the Berlin Air Lift.
WF382	Varsity T.1	8872M, ex 6 FTS, 1 ANS, 2 ANS, 5 FTS, 1 ANS, 2 ANS, 1 ANS, 3 ANS, CNCS. Preserved on base.
WJ491	Valetta C.1	ex RREF, TRE. Remains on the fire dump.
ZD215	Dakota III	ex RAAF A65-69/VHCUZ, USAAF 43-49866. Monument to Berlin Air Lift.

GUTERSLOH

Airframes here have been swollen by the addition of a Wessex HU.5. The 1987 open day resulted in two aircraft being repainted to portray based units. Current situation is :-

XF949"	Hunter F.6A	8843M/XG152, ex 1 TWU, 237 OCU, 1 TWU, TWU, 229 OCU, 19, FCS, FWS, DFLS. Painted as 'XF949:L' of 4 Sqn for 9/87 open day. Usually for BDRT.
XM244	Canberra B(I).8	8202M, ex 16, 3, 16, 3, 16. Fire dump.
XP358	Whirlwind HAR.10	ex Farnborough, RAE, Wroughton, 28, 103, 110, 103, 225. BDRT.
XR504+"	Wessex HU.5	8922M/XT467, ex Wroughton. Arrived 1/87 for BDRT. Painted as 18 Sqn HC.2 'BF' for 9/87 open day.
XV278	Harrier GR.1	ex Filton, Farnborough, Filton, Holme-on-Spalding Moor, Bitteswell, HSA. Weapons loading trainer, 4 Squadron colours.
XZ989	Harrier GR.3	8849M, ex 1. BDRT, fuselage minus cockpit plus wings. Hit by ground fire over Falklands 9/6/82 and written off in crash-landing.

HILDESHEIM

Home of 1 Regiment AAC, the Wasp was joined by a Scout for BDR during 1987.

XP852+	Scout AH.1	ex Wroughton. Arrived 1/9/87. Fuselage pod. BDRT.
XT438	Wasp HAS.1	A2704, ex Detmold, Wroughton. Fuselage pod. BDRT. '465'.

LAARBRUCH

Of the airframes listed as current in W&R10, all survive. A Lightning F.2A flew in under a Chinook in 2/87 and an F.6 under its own power 5/88 to add to the fleet.

XJ673"	Hunter F.6A	8841M/XE606, ex 1 TWU, TWU, 229 OCU, 92, 74, 65, 54, CFE. 8737M ntu. Preserved on base in 20 Sqn colours as 'XJ673:XX'.
XM264	Canberra B(I).8	8227M, ex 16, 14, 3, 16. Displayed outside the 16 Sqn hangar.
XN732	Lightning F.2A	8519M, ex 92. 'Special display' with pieces added/removed to form a fairly convincing 'MiG 21'!
XN788+	Lightning F.2A	8543M, ex Bruggen, 92, 111, 92. Arrived mid 2/87 under a Chinook. BDRT.
XN956	Buccaneer S.1	8059M, ex Lossiemouth. BDRT, wears 15 Sqn colours as 'K'.
XR758+	Lightning F.6	ex Binbrook, 11, LTF, Binbrook Wing, 23, 74, 11, 23, Leuchars TFF, 5. Flew in 10/5/88.

MINDEN

Without information to the contrary, it is thought that the Gazelle continues to provide BDRT for 664 Squadron here. A Scout was delivered for similar purposes in 1987.

XP898+	Scout AH.1	ex Wroughton. Arrived 1/9/87. Fuselage pod.
XX376	Gazelle AH.1	forward fuselage, BDRT. Crashed 29/9/83.

SOEST

3 Regiment AAC still use their Wasp for BDRT work. It was joined by the compulsort Scout in 1987.

XP897+	Scout AH.1	ex Wroughton. Arrived 1/9/87. Fuselage pod.
XT436	Wasp HAS.1	ex Detmold, Wroughton. Fuselage pod, BDRT. '506'.

WILDENRATH

Lightning F.2As XN735/8552M, XN777/8536M, XN782/8539M and XN793/8544M were put up for tender during 7/86. A Dutch scrappy was successful and started to axe all but XN782 during 4/87 with the last remnants leaving by mid May. XN782 moved to Hermeskeil. The Buccaneer S.2C rear end XV358 listed in W&R10 is too small for inclusion and should be deleted. That leaves just three airframes :-

XF418	Hunter F.6A	8842M, ex 1 TWU, TWU, 229 OCU, FCS. Displayed in 92 Sqn 'Blue Diamonds' colours, although officially for BDRT.
XM995	Lightning T.4	8542M, ex 92. 'Special display'.
XN778	Lightning F.2A	8537M, ex 92, 19. 'Special display'.

Farewell Pembroke 1988 will see the last service use of the lovely, faithful Pembroke and by way of a little tribute to this workhorse below are the fates of the last seven. 'Last flight' signifies last sortie made with 60 Squadron.

WV701 last flight 3/ 3/87,	allotted 8936M.
WV740 last flight 22/ 3/87,	flown to Shawbury 23/ 3/87, became G-BNPH with John Allison.
WV746 last flight 31/ 3/87,	flown to Cosford 12/ 4/87, for the Aerospace Museum.
XF799	current 60 Squadron.
XK884 last flight 22/ 3/87,	flown to Shawbury 26/ 3/87, became G-BNPG with John Allison & Mike Searle.
XL929 last flight 16/ 3/87,	flown to Shawbury 18/ 3/87, became G-BNPU with Terry Warren.
XL944	current 60 Squadron.

Cyprus

AKROTIRI

Since W&R10 there has been a mass exodus of Whirlwind HAR.10s from the base, all back to the land of their construction. XP329/8791M, XP345/8792M, XP346/8793M and XP398/8794M arriving on the slipway at Lee-on-Solent on 2/10/86, 1/9/86, 1/9/86 and 1/10/86 respectively. They then moved on fairly swiftly to *Shawbury* where they were put up for tender. XK970/8789M and XK986/8790M appeared at *Odiham* by 3/87. XJ764 and XR454 have not been noted since 1985 and are thought to have been scrapped. Vulcan B.2A XL317/8725M was scrapped in late 1986. There being no new W&R residents, that leaves :-

WJ768	Canberra B.6(mod)	ex 51, BCDU, 139, Binbrook SF, 109. Remains on the fire dump.
XJ437	Whirlwind HAR.10	8788M, ex 84 'A' Flight *Club*, 22, 202, 22, SAR Flt, HAR.4 228, 225, 155. BDRT airframe.

LARNACA

Gate guardian at the barracks is unchanged.

XD184	Whirlwind HAR.10	8787M, ex Akrotiri, 84 'A' Flt *Spade*, 1563F, 228, 155. Gate guardian, opposite guard room.

Falkland Islands

MOUNT PLEASANT AIRPORT

While awaiting the establishment of the Falkland Island Museum at Britannia House in Port Stanley, the two restored former Argentine aircraft are held in store at Mount Pleasant Airport. Both were refurbished by a team headed by Mark Harrison.

A-529	FMA Pucara	ex Stanley, Pebble Island, FAA. Rebuilt to static condition using parts from A-509 and A-514. Stored.
AE-410	Bell UH-1H	ex Stanley, Stanley Racecourse. Stored.

SALVADOR SETTLEMENT

Ditched as long ago as 1969, amazing survival is the Whirlwind HAR.9 held by Robin Pitaluga at his home. Following salvage on the nearby beach it was sledged to the settlement and stripped of all useful spares. Since then Robin has looked after the airframe.

XM666	Whirlwind HAR.9	ex *Endurance* Flt, A&AEE, *Endurance* Flt, *Protector* Flt, 846, 737, 700H. Ditched 17/12/69. Stripped and rotorless.

Gibraltar

NORTH FRONT

The Vulcan is still kept on show at the airfield.

XM571	Vulcan K.2	8812M, ex 50, Wadd Wing, A&AEE, 44, A&AEE, 101, 617, Wadd Wing, 617, 35, Wadd Wing, 35, 27, Akrotiri Wing, Cott Wing, Wadd Wing, Cott Wing, 83. *City of Gibraltar*. On display at the airfield.

Hong Kong

SEK KONG

Of those aircraft listed in W&R10, Sioux AH.1 XT236 moved to <u>Middle Wallop</u>. The Wessex is thought still derelict. A Scout has joined the dump. For the record, the following former 660 Squadron Scouts were broken up for spares in late 1987 : XP887:C, XP894:D, XP901:E, XT627:H, XT618:K.

XP906+	Scout AH.1	ex 660. Dump.
XR500	Wessex HC.2	ex 28 Sqn, 78, 72, 1 FTU. Ditched off Hong Kong 19/4/79, derelict.

Appendix A LOST & FOUND!

Wrecks & Relics serves principally as a unique source of information on the fate of aircraft, rather than as a that's-another-number-in-me-notebook-guide. To act as a 'safety net' to the main text *LOST!* has been established to remind readers of long-lost 'chestnuts' that mostly are looking for the necessary 'paperwork' to clear them up as dead and gone, but there is also a slim chance that the machine in question still exists. Without this form of high-lighting a 'lost' aircraft, many readers would not be looking for them.

This being the second time the rejuvenated *LOST!* column has been published, it can now luxriate in some form of standard presentation. Space is limited, and some aircraft cannot be carried forever and this section is very blatant in going for the more 'classic' airframes and not worrying itself with the myriad bits of 'tin' that drop off the world of *W&R*. Numbers quoted in brackets give the edition number and the page reference when the aircraft mentioned was last listed. Military aircraft also fall into *LOST!* but will have to await W&R12 for their turn.

With the publication of W&R10, and follow-up research, fates or re-insertions to the main text, of any aircraft then listed can now be given and they appear in 'Found' below. Aircraft in the *LOST!* section are carried over from W&R10, or dropped off the plain of existence in that edition. Aircraft teetering on *LOST!* in this edition are listed as such in the main text and will appear as such in W&R12 - unless the compilers get information to keep them in the main section! Good hunting!

Compiled by Tom Poole with the assistance of Paul Crellin.

Lost

G-AACD DH.60M Moth Reported for a long time as extant in the Cambridge area. [8/20]

G-ABLE Cessna 170A Battered hulk las noted at Bournemouth Airport March 1974. [5/19]

G-AFEG De Bruyne Ladybird Now almost a legend as surviving in the Peterborough area. [9/28]

G-AGVF Auster J/1N Alpha Last noted as a wreck in a farm shed at Hook Norton, Oxfordshire, having previously been as Ardley and Enstone. [8/91]

G-AGVI Auster J/1 Autocrat Last noted wrecked at Newtownards, Northern Ireland, 1974. [5/81]

G-AHWO Percival Proctor 5 Removed from the roof of the *Crofton Airport Hotel* near Dublin Airport in 1982. Unconfirmed report that it went to the Derby area. [8/139]

G-AIDF Miles Hawk Trainer III Stored at Southend with the British Historic Aircraft Museum - fate unconfirmed. [3/31]

G-AIEW Percival Proctor 5 Converted to resemble a Junkers Ju 87 Stuka for the film *Battle of Britain*. W&R6 reported the airframe as leaving the Pinewood Studios and moving to 'Derbyshire'. Note that the real G-AIEW was sold as TJ-AAK in 1948. What of the fate of this *Proctuka*? [6/16]

G-AILL Miles Messenger Hulk in open store at Rush Green, Herts, last noted 10/84. [10/72]

G-AISL Miles Messenger Marked as 'G-AHBD', also stored in the open at Rush Green, Herts. Last noted 10/83. [10/72]

G-AIZF de Havilland Tiger Moth Coupe Thought to have been one of the three Tigers held by the famous A F Cheshire store at Minehead, Somerset. See also G-AMTO and G-ANNI. [6/60]

G-AJEM Auster J/1N Alpha Last noted at Timperley, Greater Manchester, before moving to 'Somerset'. [10/107]

G-AJHJ Auster 5 Last noted dismsantled at Cranwell North, Lincs, 1980. [9/81]

G-AJKK Miles Messenger 2A Last reported dumped at Trevenen Bal, Cornwall, 1979. [8/30]

G-ALCS Miles Gemini Forward fuselage last noted at Kilbrittain Castle 7/82. But see under Waterford, page 165. [10/182]

G-AMIV de Havilland Tiger Moth Last recorded as under rebuild near Exeter. [8/31]

G-AMJH Non-Rigid Airship *Bournemouth* Control car was stored at Booker, but is known to have left in the mid- to late-1970s. [9/19]

G-AMTB Auster J/5F Aiglet Trainer Converted into an instructional airframe for an overseas client by R F Saywell Ltd at Partridge Green, West Sussex. Where did it go? [7/71]

G-AMTO de Havilland Tiger Moth Last recorded at Rush Green, Hertfordshire, 1970 having previously been at Minehead, Somerset. Unconfirmed report that it was in Letchworth, Herts, 1984. See also G-AIZF and G-ANNI. [6/60]

G-ANEC de Havilland Tiger Moth Last noted at Letterkenny, Eire, dismantled. [8/137]

G-ANFS de Havilland Tiger Moth Was with P D Roberts of Swansea, West Glamorgan, then reported to have moved to 'East Anglia'.
G-ANLU Auster 5M Frame stored at Sherburn-in-Elmett, North Yorkshire. Last noted 8/81. [10/156]
G-ANNI de Havilland Tiger Moth Last of the Minehead trio - see G-AIZF (and G-AMTO). [6/60]
G-AOST de Havilland Canada Chipmunk Fictitious marks, real G-AOST went to the USA as N2790. Instructional airframe with AST at Perth, Tayside, last noted 1973. [5/76]
G-APRA de Havilland Tiger Moth Was in store at Kells, Eire. Last noted 1977. [8/140]
G-APSS de Havilland Tiger Moth Was stored at Ludham, Norfolk, as spares for G-APIG, then moved to Swanton Morley, Norfolk. [5/44]
G-APYZ Druine Turbulent Was on rebuild at Swanton Morley 1978. [7/58]
G-ARBO de Havilland Tiger Moth Fictitious identity, real G-ARBO was a Piper Comanche. Was part of the instructional AST fleet at Perth, Tayside. [3/27]
G-ARXL Beagle Terrier 1 Last noted at Northampton Airport, Northants, 1976. [5/45]
G-ARZI Brantly B-2 Last known stored at Old Colwyn, Clwyd. [8/128]
G-ASAH Beagle Airedale Fuselage with Chelsea College, Shoreham, West Sussex. Last noted 9/74. [7/71]
G-ASJN Bensen B.8 Last noted at Pocklington, Humberside, with G-ATIB. [9/99]
G-ASYG Beagle Terrier 2 Last noted at Banbury 1/84, then moved to 'Hertfordshire'. [10/121]
G-ATIB Bensen B.8 See G-ASJN above. [9/99]
G-AVBK Scheibe Motorfalke Cockpit section removed from Sunderland Airport for stroage 4/80. [9/131]
G-AVCR Beagle Terrier 1 Wreck 'disappeared' from Enstone, Oxfordshire, 1976. [6/57]
G-AWPI Percival Provost Last noted 1983 as spares ship for G-AWPH in Reading, Berkshire. [10/18]
G-AXTZ Beagle Pup 100 Last noted at Andrewsfield, Essex, 1/78. [6/25]
G-AYLK SNCAN SV-4C Stampe Was under rebuild at Southend, last noted 3/75. [6/26]
G-AYTE Fairchild-Hiller FH.1100 Was stored at the former Southampton Heliport. Last noted 1983. Thought exported. [4/24]
G-BDGX Scheibe Super Falke Stored at Husbands Bosworth, Leicestershire. Last noted 2/80.
EI-ACY Auster J/1 Autocrat Last thought stored at Oranmore, Eire. [3/27]
EI-AFI de Havilland Tiger Moth Was stored at Weston, Eire. [2/11]
EI-AFJ de Havilland Tiger Moth Also stored dismantled at Weston, Eire. [2/11]
EI-AHA de Havilland Tiger Moth Also stored dismantled at Weston, Eire. [3/22]
EI-AHC de Havilland Tiger Moth Another Weston Tiger in need of a fate. [2/11]
EI-AVW Auster J/1N Alpha Last reported in a shed at Naas, Eire. [8/139]

Found

G-ABBB Bristol Bulldog IIA Parts of the wrecks Shuttleworth Bulldog K2227 do still survive, but are now confirmed as too small for consideration by W&R.
G-AEUJ Miles Whitney Straight With Bob Mitchell at Sutton Coldfield - see page 97.
G-AGVG Auster J/1 Autocrat See Leicester Airport - page 78.
G-AJAP Piper J-3C-65 Cub Note, not an official and reference now deleted to it. Aircraft is a composite rebuild underway at Raveningham - see page 99.
G-AKNN de Havilland Dragon Rapide Moved from Dunkeswell, Devon, to East Midlands Airport 1971 and broken up for spares.
G-ALZK de Havilland Comet Confirmed now as a mis-identification in W&R4 - delete reference.
G-ANFL de Havilland Tiger Moth Last noted at Belchamp Walter, Essex, 1977. Moved to Fakenham Norfolk, by 1985 and restored to flying condition by 1987.
G-AODX de Havilland Tiger Moth Last reported in store at Bromley, Greater London. Reported sold in the USA 28/2/77, although yet to appear on their civil register.
G-AOJK de Havilland Tiger Moth Appeared at Kingsclere by 12/86 - see page 53.
G-AOVX Luton Major Moved to from Stoke-on-Trent to Lincolnshire to be used in G-ARAF, which itself was abandoned.
G-ARAD Luton Major Unfair to class this in W&R, this is an ultra-long term homebuild project!
G-ATLH Fewsdale Gyroglider At Thornaby-on-Tees - see page 32.
G-ATLO Brantly 305 Last noted at Fairoaks in 1975. Reflew in 1976 only to be destryoed 1/10/76.
G-AVLM Beagle Pup 150 Last noted at Newbury, moved to Chippenham, then to Nottingham Airport and now at Tatenhill - see page 118.
G-AVZA IMCO Callair A-9 Last noted at Shipdham, moved to Wickenby and became G-TDFS.
G-AWRA Beagle Pup 150 Frame still in a farm shed at Northampton Airport - see page 101.
G-BEUS AIA SV-4C Stampe From Gransden moved to Kings Cliffe - see page 101.

Appendix B

The BAPC

he British Aircraft Preservation Council (BAPC) is the representative body co-ordinating the efforts f a large number of organisations united in a desire to ensure the preservation, restoration and xhibition of tangible evidence of the United Kingdom's aviation heritage for the education and nterest of present and future generations.

ember organisations are drawn from the whole spectrum of National, Service, Local Authority, ommercial and Voluntary organisations and range in size from such bodies as the Science Museum to mall groups with a few dedicated members. Membership of the Council is by election and is available o any United Kingdom organisation or group with an active interest in aircraft preservation. ssociate Membership is available to organisations based in the United Kingdom or elsewhere who wish to upport the work of the Council.

ormed at a meeting in Derby called by the Northern Aircraft Preservation Society (now The Aeroplane ollection) on the initiative of their Chairman at that time, John Kenyon, the Council has grown teadily in both stature and membership. BAPC's origins lie with concern that the growth in numbers of ircraft preservation groups should not produce unfettered competition for exhibits or rivalries estructive to the general aims. At that meeting all the major participants of the day were brought ogether and the foundations laid for the Council.

uarterly conferences are staged by the Council, hosted by member organisations. This way the Council cts as a means of communication between aircraft preservation organisations, a channel of information o them, and as a representative body able to speak on their behalf. Close contacts established within he Council serve to reduce misunderstandings, and to prevent rivalries becoming jealousies. While not eeking to own exhibits, the Council is frequently able to place exhibits in the hands of member rganisations; and encourage the exchange of material. The Council also makes loans to member rganisations for the purchase of exhibits, erection of buildings or other large projects.

hrough membership of the Transport Trust and the Association of British Transport Museums, the Council s able to express the needs and interests of the aircraft preservation movement to similar, but roader-based, bodies. Three overseas associations, developed on similar lines to the BAPC - the anadian Aeronautical Preservation Association, the *Federation Francaise des Aeronefs de Collection* and he Irish Aviation Historical Council - have been granted Honorary Membership of the Council and, along ith Associate Members from overseas, help to spread the word of co-operation and information still urther.

nformation is one of the prime aims of the Council and to this end has developed several specialist ervices for member organisations. The Press Officer exists not only to promote the work of the ouncil in general in the eyes of the media, but to publicise achievements and acquisitions of member roups and to give advice on publicity. An innovation, launched in December 1987, was a quarterly nformation bulletin, provisionally named *Update*, supplying a variety of information to members and cting as a supplement to the quarterly Council Minutes.

echnical information and advice is available from the Technical Registrar, who also acts to funnel ueries to those who can answer them. The Project Co-ordinator is tasked with putting square pegs in quare holes - monitoring needs and where-ever possible finding items to meet them. An extensive ibrary has been established where member organisations can borrow technical publications and a full atalogue of material available is maintained.

987 saw the twentieth anniversary of the Council and this was celebrated with a prestigious two-day ymposium held at East Midlands Airport. A series of presentations were staged from various pecialists and there was some hard-hitting argument on the problems faced by the aircraft preservation ovement, both in terms of physical conservation and in the avoidance of duplicating effort. This was cclaimed as a very successful and professional convention and the Council has plans to stage such entures more regularly.

Individual membership of the Council is not possible, but any group working within the aircraf preservation movement is warmly invited to consider the benefits of membership. Enquiries about th Council should be addressed to the Secretary :- David Reader, 151 Marshalswick Lane, St Albans Hertfordshire AL1 4UX.

BAPC Executive Committee

Chairman	- Michael Hodgson (Lincolnshire Aviation Heritage Centre)
Vice Chairmen	- David Lee (Imperial War Museum, Duxford)
	David Ogilvy (Shuttleworth Collection)
	Commander Dennis White (Fleet Air Arm - retired)
Secretary	- David Reader (Shuttleworth Veteran Aeroplane Society)
Membership Secretary	- Peter Kirk (Derbyshire Historical Aviation Society)
Treasurer	- Alan Scholefield (Merseyside Aviation Society)
Press Officer	- Ross Sharp (Science Museum, Wroughton)
Committee Members	- John Bagley (Science Museum, South Kensington)
	Carl Speddings (South Yorkshire Aviation Society)
	Don Storer (Royal Museum of Scotland - retired)

Associated Members

Editor 'Update'	- Trevor Green (Merseyside Aviation Society)
Keeper of Aircraft Register	- Ken Ellis (*FlyPast* Magazine)
Librarian	- Peter Felix (Derbyshire Historical Aviation Society)
Project Co-Ordinator	- Tony Southern (Cotswold Aircraft Restoration Group)
Technical Registrar	- Ivor Jenkins (The Aeroplane Collection)

Member Organisations

Current members of the British Aircraft Preservation Council are given below. Full members mentione in the main body of the text do not have their contact address repeated here and a page referenc guides the reader to the appropriate entry in the book. Enquiries should be accompanied by a stampe addressed envelope to facilitate a reply. Associated Members are given a briefer mention, fo completeness, at the end.

A Aces High Ltd - see page 45
The Aeroplane Collection - see page 31
Airborne Forces Museum - see page 50
Aircraft Preservation Society of Scotland - see page 146
Aircraft Radio Museum and Percival Collection - see page 130
Avon Aviation Museum - see page 9
Air South Ltd, John Pothecary, Shed Eleven, Municipal Airport, Shoreham-by-Sea, Sussex BN4 5FF.

B B-17 Preservation Ltd - see page 24
Battle of Britain Memorial Flight - see page 80
Berkshire Aviation Group - see page 18
Biggin Hill Museum and Friends of Biggin Hill Museum - see page 72
Booker Aircraft Museum - see page 19
Brenzett Aeronautical Collection - see page 69
Brimpex Metal Treatments, Building 34/6, East Midlands Airport, Castle Donington, Derby DE7 2SA. See page 138 for their Flea.
British Aerial Museum of Flying Military Aircraft - see page 24
British Aerospace Avro Aircraft Restoration Society - see page 95
British Balloon Museum and Library - see page 17
British Rotorcraft Museum - see page 9
Brooklands Museum - see page 122

C City of Bristol Museum and Art Gallery - see page 8
City of Norwich Aviation Museum - see page 99
Cornwall Aircraft Park (Helston) Ltd - see page 34
Cotswold Aircraft Restoration Group - see page 49

D Derby Industrial Museum, The Old Silk Mill, off Full Street, Derby DE1 4AR.
Derbyshire Historical Aviation Society, Peter Kirk, 263 Birchover Way, Allestree, Derby DE3 2RS.

Douglas Boston-Havoc Preservation Trust, Richard Nutt, 17 Hinckley Road, Barwell, Leicester LE9 8DL.
Dumfries and Galloway Aviation Group - see page 142
Duxford Aviation Society - see page 24
East Anglian Aviation Society - see page 23
East Midlands Aeropark Volunteers Association - see page 77
Essex Aviation Group - see page 24
Fenland Aircraft Preservation Society, John Reid, 14 Millway, Fridaybridge, Wisbech, Cambs PE14 0HZ.
Fleet Air Arm Museum - see page 115
Friends of the DC-3, John and Maureen Woods, 3 Dalcross, Crown Wood, Bracknell, Berks RG12 3UJ.
Grantham Aviation Society, Peter Gibson, 12 Wardour Drive, Grantham, Lincs NG31 9TY.
Greater Manchester Museum of Science and Technology - see page 93
Humberside Aviation Preservation Society - see page 67
Imperial War Museum - see page 24 and 91
Ken Fern Collection - see page 118
Lashenden Air Warfare Museum - see page 70
Leicestershire Museum of Technology - see page 78
Lincolnshire Aviation Museum - see page 82
Merseyside Aviation Society, Trevor Green, 97 Barrington Road, Liverpool L15 3HR.
Midland Air Museum - see page 129
Military Aircraft Preservation Group - see page 37
Mosquito Aircraft Museum - see page 64
Museum of Army Flying - see page 56
Nene Valley Aviation Society, Ronald Houghton, 166 Sywell Road, Overstone, Northants.
Newark Air Museum - see page 103
Norfolk and Suffolk Aviation Museum - see page 119
North East Aircraft Museum - see page 128
Northern Aeroplane Workshops - see page 138
North Manchester College - Moston Centre, Alan Suffell, Ashley Lane, Moston, Manchester M9 1WU.
North Weald Aircraft Restoration Flight - see page 46
Pennine Aviation Museum - see page 73
Phoenix Aviation Museum - see page 79
Robertsbridge Aviation Society - see page 125
Rolls-Royce Heritage Trust (Bristol Branch), Doug Dyson, Technical Publications, Rolls-Royce plc, PO Box 3, Filton, Bristol BS12 7QE.
Rolls-Royce Heritage Trust (Derby Branch), L Fletcher, 40 Quarn Drive, Allestree, Derby.
Royal Aeronautical Society, Medway Branch - see page 72
Royal Museum of Scotland - see page 145 and 146
Russavia Collection - see page 62
The Science Museum - see page 91
Scotland West Aircraft Investigation Group - see page 149
Scottish Aircraft Collection Trust - see page 149
Second World War Aircraft Preservation Society - see page 54
The Shuttleworth Collection - see page 14
Snowdon Mountain Aviation Ltd - see page 157
Solway Aviation Society - see page 36
Southampton Hall of Aviation - see page 59
South Yorkshire Aviation Society - see page 102
Surrey and Sussex Aviation Society, R Hall, Atholl Cottage, Walpole Avenue, Chipstead, Surrey.
Tangmere Military Aviation Museum - see page 127
Torbay Aircraft Museum - see page 39
Ulster Aviation Society - see page 162
Ulster Folk and Transport Museum - see page 161
Viscount Preservation Trust, Paul St John Turner, *Cades Peak*, Old St John Road, St Helier, Jersey.
Wales Aircraft Museum - see page 154
Wartime Aircraft Recovery Group - see page 109
Wellesbourne Aviation Group - see page 132
Wessex Aviation Society - see page 42
The Winbolt Collection - see page 8
Yorkshire Air Museum - see page 136

Associate Members

Such members wish to support the work of the Council, but feel that they do not fill the criteria to b Full Members. As some of the Associate Members of the Council are preservation groups themselves, c support the work of other preservation bodies, and therefore may be of interest to readers, greate details are given here. Other Associate Members are given a brief mention at the end.

A Alpha Helicopters, Jeremy Parkin, 60-62 Broad Street, Teddington, Middx TW11 8QR.
B The Brooklands Society Ltd, Peter Dench, Reigate Lodge, Chart Way, Reigate, Surrey RH2 0NZ.
C Chiltern Aviation Society, Keith Hayward, 52 Pinn Way, Ruislip, Middx HA4 7QF.
F The Flying Boat Association, Brian Lewis, 17 Bramwell Close, Christchurch, Dorset BH23 2NP.
H Historic Aircraft Association, Tony Haig-Thomas, c/o City Deposit Brokers, Staple Hall, Stone House Court, 87-90 Houndsditch, London EC3A 7AR.
L Lincolnshire Aircraft Recovery Group, D. Stubley, 13 Granville Ave, Wyberton, Boston, Lincs PE21 7BY
Lincolnshire's Lancaster Association - see page 80
M Manchester Airport Archive, Brian Robinson, Manchester Airport, Manchester M22 5PA.
S Shuttleworth Veteran Aeroplane Society - see page 14

Also : Air Education and Recreation Organisation (AERO); *Aeroplane Monthly*; Air-Britain (Historians Ltd; *Aircraft Illustrated*; Air Data Publications; Airfield Research Group; Argus Specialis Publications Ltd; *Aviation News*; *FlyPast Magazine*; Girls Venture Corps Air Cadets; LAASI Internationa Macclesfield College of Further Education; Military Miniatures Museum; Southern Aircraft Researc Associates.

And overseas : *Aerospace Historian*, USA; Australian War Memorial; Fyfield Collection, USA; Gruppo Amic Velivoli Storici, Italy; Museum of Transport and Technology, New Zealand; National Museum and Ar Gallery of Papua New Guinea; National War Museum Association Malta; Naval Aviation Museum, Australi Norwegian Armed Forces Museum; Queensland Museum, Australia; Royal New Zealand Air Force Museum; Unite States Air Force Museum; Werftverein Oberschleissheim, West Germany; Western Canada Aviation Museu *World War One Aeroplanes*.

Appendix C BAPC REGISTER

Register presentation in this edition is briefer than in previous years and serves essentially as a index for aircraft that are registered within the BAPC system that appear within the main body of W&R where greater details of their pedigree will be found. The BAPC Register serves as a form of identi for airframes (generally those held by member groups) that otherwise would not aspire to another for of registration. (Note : SER = Static External Replica, outwardly accurate, but using materials ar internal structures not as the original.)

1 Roe Triplane Type IV replica - Shuttleworth Trust, Old Warden, see page 14
2 Bristol Boxkite replica - Shuttleworth Trust, Old Warden, see page 14
3 Bleriot Type XI - Shuttleworth Trust, Old Warden, see page 14
4 Deperdussin Monoplane - Shuttleworth Trust, Old Warden, see page 14
5 Blackburn Monoplane - Shuttleworth Trust, Old Warden, see page 14
6 Roe Triplane Type IV static replica - The Aeroplane Collection, Manchester, see page 93
7 Southampton University Man Powered Aircraft (SUMPAC) - Southampton Hall of Aviation, see page 59
8 Dixon Ornithopter static replica - Shuttleworth Trust, Old Warden, see page 14
9 Humber-Bleriot Type XI replica - Midland Air Museum, Birmingham Airport, see page 97
10 Hafner R-II Revoplane - British Rotorcraft Museum, Middle Wallop, see page 56
11 English Electric Wren - Shuttleworth Trust, Old Warden, see page 14
12 Mignet HM.14 Pou du Ciel - The Aeroplane Collection, East Fortune, see page 145
13 Mignet HM.14 Pou du Ciel - Brimpex Metal Treatments, Sheffield, see page 138
14 Addyman Standard Training Glider - Nigel Ponsford, Leeds, see page 139
15 Addyman Standard Training Glider - The Aeroplane Collection, Warmingham, see page 31
16 Addyman Ultra-Light - Nigel Ponsford, Leeds, see page 139

17 Woodhams Sprite - The Aeroplane Collection, Wigan, see page 94
18 Killick Man Powered Gyroplane - Nigel Ponsford, Leeds, see page 139
19 Bristol F.2b Fighter - Aero Vintage, St Leonards-on-Sea, see page 125
20 Lee-Richards Annular Biplane static replica - Newark Air Museum, Winthorpe, see page 103
21 Thruxton Jackaroo - status uncertain, last reported at Stevenage.
22 Mignet HM.14 Pou du Ciel - Aviodome, Amsterdam (on loan).
23 Allocated in error.
24 Allocated in error.
25 Nyborg TGN.III glider - Eric Rolfe & Paul Williams, Moreton-in-the-Marsh, see page 50
26 Auster AOP.9 fuselage frame - scrapped, no longer extant.
27 Mignet HM.14 Pou du Ciel - M J Abbey, Coventry, exact status unknown, see page 97
28 Wright Flyer replica - RAF Museum, Cardington, see page 10
29 Mignet HM.14 Pou du Ciel - Mike Beach, Brooklands, see page 122
30 DFS Grunau Baby - destroyed by fire at Swansea Airport, 1969.
31 Slingsby T.7 Tutor - not extant, believed scrapped.
32 Crossley Tom Thumb - Midland Air Museum, Coventry Airport, see page 129
33 DFS 108-49 Grunau Baby IIb - current status unknown.
34 DFS 108-49 Grunau Baby IIb - current status unknown, last reported at Hazlemere.
35 EoN Primary - current status unknown.
36 Fieseler Fi 103 (V-1) replica - Kent Battle of Britain Museum, Hawkinge, see page 70
37 Blake Bluetit - Shuttleworth Trust, Old Warden, see page 14
38 Bristol Scout static replica - RAF St Mawgan, see page 35
39 Addyman Zephyr - parts held with Nigel Ponsford Collection, Leeds, see page 139
40 Bristol Boxkite replica - Bristol City Museum & Art Gallery, see page 8
41 RAF BE.2c static replica - Historic Aircraft Collection, RAF St Athan, see page 155
42 Avro 504K static replica - Historic Aircraft Collection, RAF St Athan, see page 155
43 Mignet HM.14 Pou du Ciel - Lincolnshire Aviation Heritage Centre, East Kirkby, see page 82
44 Miles M.14A Magister - Berkshire Aviation Group, Woodley, see page 18
45 Pilcher Hawk replica - Percy Pilcher Museum, Stanford, see page 79
46 Mignet HM.14 Pou du Ciel - current status unknown, Coleford, see page 48
47 Watkins CHW Monoplane - Historic Aircraft Collection, RAF St Athan, see page 155
48 Pilcher Hawk replica - Glasgow Museum of Transport, Glasgow see page 147
49 Pilcher Hawk - Royal Museum of Scotland, Edinburgh, see page 146
50 Roe Triplane Type I - Science Museum, South Kensington, see page 91
51 Vickers FB.27 Vimy IV - Science Museum, South Kensington, see page 91
52 Lilienthal Glider Type XI - Science Museum, Hayes, see page 88
53 Wright Flyer replica - Science Museum, South Kensington, see page 91
54 JAP/Harding Monoplane - Science Museum, South Kensington, see page 91
55 Levasseur-Antoinette Developed Type VII Monoplane - Science Museum, South Kensington, see page 91
56 Fokker E.III - Science Museum, South Kensington, see page 91
57 Pilcher Hawk replica - Science Museum, South Kensington, see page 91
58 Yokosuka MXY-7 Ohka II - Science Museum, Yeovilton, see page 115
59 Sopwith Camel static replica - RAF St Mawgan, see page 35
60 Murray M.1 Helicopter - The Aeroplane Collection, Wigan, see page 94
61 Stewart Man Powered Ornithopter - Lincolnshire Aviation Heritage Centre, East Kirkby, see page 82
62 Cody Biplane - Science Museum, South Kensington, see page 91
63 Hawker Hurricane SER - Torbay Museum, Higher Blagdon, see page 39
64 Hawker Hurricane SER - Kent Battle of Britain Museum, Hawkinge, see page 70
65 Supermarine Spitfire SER - Kent Battle of Britain Museum, Hawkinge, see page 70
66 Messerschmitt 'Bf 109' SER - Kent Battle of Britain Museum, Hawkinge, see page 70
67 Messerschmitt 'Bf 109' SER - Midland Air Museum, Coventry Airport, see page 129
68 Hawker Hurricane SER - Midland Air Museum, Coventry Airport, see page 129
69 Supermarine Spitfire SER - Torbay Museum, Higher Blagdon, see page 39
70 Auster AOP.5 - Aircraft Preservation Society of Scotland, East Fortune, see page 146
71 Supermarine Spitfire SER - Norfolk & Suffolk Aviation Museum, Flixton, see page 119
72 Hawker Hurricane SER - North Weald Aircraft Restoration Flight, see page 46
73 Hawker Hurricane SER - current status unknown, last reported in Bishop's Stortford.
74 Messerschmitt 'Bf 109' - Torbay Museum, Higher Blagdon, see page 39
75 Mignet HM.14 Pou du Ciel - Nigel Ponsford, Leeds, see page 139 and BAPC.102.

76 Mignet HM.14 Pou du Ciel - Humberside Aircraft Preservation Society, Cleethorpes, see page 67
77 Mignet HM.14 Pou du Ciel - Cotswold Aircraft Restoration Group, Innsworth, see page 49
78 Hawker (Afghan) Hind - Shuttleworth Trust, Old Warden, see page 14
79 Fiat G.46-4b - current status uncertain, Lympne, see page 70
80 Airspeed Horsa II fuselage - Museum of Army Flying, Middle Wallop, see page 56
81 Hawkridge Nacelle Dagling - Russavia Collection, Eaton Bray, see page 13
82 Hawker (Afghan) Hind - RAF Museum, Hendon, see page 88
83 Kawasaki Type 5 Model 1b (Ki 100) - Historic Aircraft Collection, RAF St Athan, see page 155
84 Mitsubishi Ki 46 III Dinah - Historic Aircraft Collection, RAF St Athan, see page 155
85 Weir W-2, Museum of Flight, East Fortune, see page 145
86 de Havilland DH.82A Tiger Moth - rebuild of anonymous airframe, current status unknown.
87 Bristol Babe replica - Humberside Aircraft Preservation Society, Cleethorpes, see page 67
88 Fokker Dr I scale replica - Fleet Air Arm Museum, Yeovilton, see page 115
89 Cayley Glider replica - RAF Museum, Manchester, see page 93
90 Colditz Cock replica - Imperial War Museum, Duxford, see page 23
91 Fieseler Fi 103R-IV (V-1) - Lashenden Air Warfare Museum, Headcorn, see page 70
92 Fieseler Fi 103 (V-1) - Historic Aircraft Collection, RAF St Athan, see page 155
93 Fieseler Fi 103 (V-1) - Imperial War Museum, Duxford, see page 23
94 Fieseler Fi 103 (V-1) - Aerospace Museum, Cosford, see page 109
95 Gizmer Autogyro - current status unknown, last reported at Darlington.
96 Brown Helicopter - North East Aircraft Museum, Sunderland, see page 128
97 Luton LA-4 Minor - North East Aircraft Museum, Sunderland, see page 128
98 Yokosuka MXY-7 Ohka II - RAF Museum, Manchester, see page 88
99 Yokosuka MXY-7 Ohka II - Aerospace Museum, Cosford, see page 109
100 Clarke Chanute glider - Science Museum, Hendon, see page 88
101 Mignet HM.14 Pou du Ciel fuselage - Lincolnshire Aviation Heritage Centre, East Kirkby, see page 82
102 Mignet HM.14 Pou du Ciel (modified) - not completed; material incorporated in BAPC.75.
103 Pilcher Hawk replica - Personal Plane Services, Booker, see page 19
104 Bleriot Type XI - Imperial War Museum, Duxford, see page 23
105 Bleriot Type XI - Goldsmith Trust, Aviodome, Amsterdam.
106 Bleriot Type XI - RAF Museum, Hendon, see page 88
107 Bleriot Type XXVII - RAF Museum, Hendon, see page 88
108 Fairey Swordfish - RAF Museum, Henlow, see page 13
109 Slingsby Cadet TX.1 - RAF Museum, Henlow, see page 13
110 Fokker D.VIIF static replica - status unknown, Christie's sale 10/87, see page 123
111 Sopwith Triplane static replica - Fleet Air Arm Museum, Yeovilton, see page 115
112 de Havilland DH.2 static replica - Museum of Army Flying, Middle Wallop, see page 56
113 RAF SE.5A static replica - status unknown, Christie's sale 10/87, see page 123
114 Vickers 60 Viking IV taxiable replica - Brooklands Museum, Weybridge, see page 122
115 Mignet HM.14 Pou du Ciel - Rebel Air Museum, Earls Colne, see page 43
116 Santos-Dumont Demoiselle XX replica - Flambards Triple Theme Park, Helston, see page 34
117 RAF BE.2c taxiable replica - North Weald Aircraft Restoration Flight, see page 46
118 Albatros D.V static replica - North Weald Aircraft Restoration Flight, see page 46
119 Bensen B-7 Gyroglider - North East Aircraft Museum, Sunderland, see page 128
120 Mignet HM.14 Pou du Ciel - Humberside Aircraft Preservation Society, Cleethorpes, see page 67
121 Mignet HM.14 Pou du Ciel - South Yorkshire Aircraft Preservation Society, Firbeck, see page 102
122 Avro 504K taxiable replica - current status unknown, built for the TV series *Wings*.
123 Vickers FB.5 Gunbus replica - Vintage Aircraft Team, Cranfield, major components, see page 11
124 Lilienthal Glider Type XI replica - Science Museum, South Kensington, see page 91
125 Clay Cherub ground trainer - current status unknown, last reported at Coventry.
126 Rollason D.31 Turbulent non-flyer - Midland Air Museum, Coventry, see page 129
127 Halton Man Powered Aircraft Group *Jupiter* - current status unknown.
128 Watkinson CG-4 Cyclogyroplane Mk IV - British Rotorcraft Museum, Weston-super-Mare, see page 9
129 Blackburn 1911 Monoplane taxiable replica - Flambards Triple Theme Park, Helston, see page 34
130 Blackburn 1912 Monoplane taxiable replica - Flambards Triple Theme Park, Helston, see page 34
131 Pilcher Hawk replica - current status unknown, last reported stored in London.
132 Bleriot Type XI - current status unknown, possibly at *Musee de l'Automobile*, France.
133 Fokker Dr.I static replica - Torbay Museum, Higher Blagdon, see page 39
134 Aerotek Pitts S-2A non-flyer - current status unknown, was based at Higher Blagdon, see page 39

135 Bristol M.1C Monoplane static replica - status unknown, Christie's sale 10/87, see page 123
136 Deperdussin 1913 floatplane static replica - Robs Lamplough, North Weald, see page 146
137 Sopwith Baby floatplane static replica - status unknown, Christie's sale 10/87, see page 123
138 Hansa Brandenburg W.29 taxiable replica - status unknown, last at Thorpe Park, see page 123
139 Fokker Dr.I static replica - status unknown, Christie's sale 10/87, see page 123
140 Curtiss R3C-2 static replica - status unknown, Christie's sale 10/87, see page 123
141 Macchi M.39 taxiable replica - Robs Lamplough, North Weald, see page 146
142 RAF SE.5A static replica - status unknown, Christie's sale 10/87, see page 123
143 Paxton Man Powered Aircraft - current status unknown, last reported at Staverton.
144 Weybridge Man Powered A/C Group *Mercury* - current status unknown.
145 Oliver Man Powered Aircraft - current status unkown, last reported at Warton.
146 Pedal Aeronauts MPA *Toucan* - Mosquito Aircraft Museum, London Colney, see page 64
147 Bensen B-7 Gyroglider - Norfolk & Suffolk Aviation Museum, Flixton, see page 119
148 Hawker Fury II static replica - Aerospace Museum, Cosford, see page 109
149 Short S.27 Variant static replica - Fleet Air Arm Museum, Yeovilton, see page 115
150 SEPECAT Jaguar GR.1 SER - RAF Exhibition Flight, Abingdon, see page 105
151 SEPECAT Jaguar GR.1 SER - RAF Exhibition Flight, Abingdon, see page 105
152 British Aerospace Hawk T.1 SER - RAF Exhibition Flight, Abingdon, see page 105
153 Westland WG-33 mock-up - British Rotorcraft Museum, Weston-super-Mare, see page 9
154 Druine D.31 Turbulent - Lincolnshire Aviation Heritage Centre, East Kirkby, see page 82
155 Panavia Tornado GR.1 SER - RAF Exhibition Flight, Abingdon, see page 105
156 Supermarine S.6B static replica - Robs Lamplough, North Weald, see page 46
157 WACO CG-4A Hadrian fuselage - Pennine Aviation Museum, Bacup, see page 73
158 Fieseler Fi 103 (V-1) - Defence Explosive Ordnance School, Chattenden, see page 69
159 Yokosuka MXY-7 Ohka II - Defence Explosive Ordnance School, Chattenden, see page 69
160 Chargus 18/50 hang glider - Museum of Flight, East Fortune, see page 145
161 Stewart Man Powered Ornithopter - Humberside Aircraft Preservation Society, Cleethorpes, see 67
162 Goodhart MPA *Newbury Manflier* - Science Museum, Wroughton, see page 134
163 AFEE 10/42 Rotachute replica - Wessex Aviation Society, Middle Wallop, see page 56
164 Wight Quadruplane Type 1 static replica - Wessex Aviation Society, Wimborne, see page 42
165 Bristol F.2b Fighter - RAF Museum, Hendon, see page 88
166 Bristol F.2b Fighter - Aero Vintage, St Leonards-on-Sea, see page 125
167 RAF SE.5A static replica - Torbay Museum, Higher Blagdon, see page 39
168 de Havilland DH.60G Moth static replica - Gatwick Hilton Hotel, Gatwick, see page 126
169 SEPECAT Jaguar GR.1 engineering replica - 1 School of Technical Training, Halton, see page 20
170 Pilcher Hawk replica - Strathallan Aircraft Collection, see page 149
171 British Aerospace Hawk T.1 SER - RAF Exhibition Flight, Abingdon, see page 105
172 Chargus Midas Super E hang glider - Science Museum, Wroughton, see page 134
173 Birdman Promotions Grasshopper powered hang glider, Science Museum, Wroughton, see page 134
174 Bensen B-7 Gyroglider - Science Museum, Wroughton, see page 134
175 Volmer VJ-23 Swingwing powered hang glider - Gtr Manchester Museum, see page 93
176 RAF SE.5A scale static replica - South Yorkshire Aircraft Preservation Society, Firbeck, see 102
177 Avro 504K taxiable replica - Brooklands Museum, Weybridge, see page 122
178 Avro 504K taxiable replica - current status unknown, last at Henlow, see page 13
179 Sopwith Pup static replica - North Weald Aircraft Restoration Flight, see page 46
180 McCurdy Silver Dart static replica - RAF Museum, Cardington, see page 10
181 RAF BE.2b static replica - RAF Museum, Cardington, see page 10
182 Wood Ornithopter - Greater Manchester Museum of Science & Technology, see page 93
183 Zurowski ZP.1 helicopter - Newark Air Museum, Winthorpe, see page 103
184 Supermarine Spitfire IX SER - Aces High, North Weald, see page 45
185 WACO CG-4A Hadrian fuselage - Museum of Army Flying, Middle Wallop, see page 56
186 de Havilland DH.82B Queen Bee (Type D) - Mosquito Aircraft Museum, London Colney, see page 64
187 Roe Type I Biplane static replica - Brooklands Museum, Weybridge, see page 122
188 McBroom Cobra 88 hang glider - Science Museum, Wroughton, see page 134
189 Bleriot Type XI - current status unknown, Christie's sale 10/86, see appendix
190 Supermarine Spitfire prototype static replica - Biggin Hill Museum, Sevenoaks, see page 72
191 BAE/McDD Harrier GR.5 SER - RAF Exhibition Flight, Abingdon, see page 105
192 Weedhopper JC-24 microlight - The Aeroplane Collection, Warmingham, see page 31
193 Hovey Whing Ding microlight - The Aeroplane Collection, Warmingham, see page 31

194 Santos Dumont Demoiselle replica - Brooklands Museum, Weybridge, see page 122
195 Moonraker 77 hang glider - Museum of Flight, East Fortune, see page 145
196 Sigma 2m hang glider - Museum of Flight, East Fortune, see page 145
197 Cirrus III hang glider - Museum of Flight, East Fortune, see page 145
198 Fieseler Fi 103 (V-1) - Imperial War Museum, South Lambeth, see page 91
199 Fieseler Fi 103 (V-1) - Science Museum, South Kensington, see page 91
200 Bensen B-7 Gyroglider - Ken Fern Collection, Stoke-on-Trent, see page 118

Appendix D IAHC REGISTER

Run by the Irish Aviation Historical Council, the IAHC register operates on very similar lines to the BAPC Register. Enquiries about the IAHC should be addressed to ; Joe McDermott, Information Officer, IAHC, 151 Cloncliffe Avenue, Dublin 3, Eire.

1 Mignet HM.14 Pou du Ciel - Aviation Society of Ireland Preservation Group, Dublin - see page 163
2 Aldritt Monoplane - Aldritt family, Portlaoise, see page 165
3 Mignet HM.14 Pou du Ciel - R Robinson, Carbury, see page 163
4 Hawker Hector frame - thought to be under restoration in Florida, USA.
5 Morane-Saulnier MS.230, fuselage frame - status unknown, last at Kilbrittain, but see page 164
6 Ferguson Monoplane replica - Ulster Folk & Transport Museum, Holywood, Belfast, see page 161
7 Sligo Concept - Gerry O'Hara, Sligo, see page 165
8 O'Hara Autogyro - Gerry O'Hara, Sligo, see page 165
9 Ferguson Monoplane replica - Ulster Folk & Transport Museum, Holywood, see page 161.

Appendix E AUCTIONS

During 1987 a new name came into the aircraft auction world, Wilkins & Wilkins joining the well-established Christie's and Phillips. It is clear from readers' letters that there is great interest in aircraft auctions and this section serves as a 'safety net' for auctions not centred upon a museum or a collection and which would accordingly not be dealt with in the course of events in the main text. Please remember that the figures given below represent the 'high bid' and not necessarily a sale at that price. VAT and buyer's premiums are not included in these bid figures.

Enquiries relating to aircraft auctions can be made to :-

Christie's, 85 Old Brompton Road, London SW7 3LD. 01 581 7611.
Phillips, Blenstock House, 7 Blenheim Street, New Bond Street, London W1Y 0AS. 01 629 6602.
Wilkins & Wilkins, 31 High Street, Ashwell, Baldock, Herts. 046274 2718 or 2819.

Christie's, South Kensington, 31 October 1986

Held at Christie's Old Brompton Road premises, the majority of the auction dealt with aeronautica, but a handful of aircraft were also involved and on the premises. The Bleriot has been on temporary display at Middle Wallop (qv) and has not turned up since the auction. The Chanute went on to try again, this time care of Phillips at Old Warden - see below. The Spitfire is reasonably thought to have been acquired by Doug Arnold, but has not been sighted since that appearance in Christie's car park. For the record, this example's history is as follows ; ex Cape Town, Ysterplaat, SAAF 5631, 47 MU, 165, 316, 129, 453, 64.

Bleriot XI BAPC.189	£ 13,000	see above.
DH.94 Moth Minor G-AFPN	£ 17,000	
Octave Chanute c 1911 replica	£ 2,800	see above.
Supermarine Spitfire IX BR601	£ 70,000	sold to Warbirds of Great Britain.

Phillips, Old Warden, 13 May 1987

Using Old Warden as a central venue, this sale included several modern aircraft and W&R will quietly skirt around these. After a disappointing showing at the Christie's auction, the Chanute came here and also failed to sell - its current whereabouts are unknown.

Dart Kitten G-AEXT	£ 5,200	
DH.94 Moth Minor Coupe G-AFNG	£ 9,000	
Monocoupe 90A-782 G-AFEL	£ 17,000	
SNCAN SV-4A G-AZNK	£ 21,000	
Orlican L.40 Meta-Sokol G-ARSP	£ 7,000	Classic Aeroplane, Staverton, which see.
SAN D.150 Mascaret G-DISO	£ 15,000	
CEA DR.315 Petit Prince G-BGVB	£ 10,000	
Octave Chanute c 1911 replica	£ 1,400	see above.

Christie's, Bournemouth, 1 October 1987

In the former BAC production track at Hurn, Christie's auctioned the Hunter One Collection, following the tragic death of founder Mike Carlton. The aircraft involved and the bids they attracted are mentioned under the Bournemouth Airport heading, see page 40. Although largely auctioned *in absentia* also 'hammered' here was the remainder of the Leisure Sport Collection and they can be found under the Chertsey heading (page 123). Two other aircraft also 'guested', both of which are mentioned in the main text ; Roland Fraissinet's gorgeous Spitfire PR.XI was sold to Warbirds of Great Britain (see under Biggin Hill Airport, page 86) and Charles Church's Battle I R3950 (see under Sandown, page 68).

Wilkins & Wilkins, Luton, 3 October 1987

Using the London Aviation Centre hangar, and the grass landing area adjacent, Wilkins & Wilkins set off in a grand scale on their first aircraft auction. Several aircraft were not present. Reference to several of the aircraft listed below can also be found in the main text. During the day others were withdrawn for want of documentation. Accordingly, the notes given below are somewhat more involved than those for the above auctions. As with the Old Warden auction, there were several decidedly modern aircraft in the sale, all in the peak of health and not W&R territory, these are not listed.

Auster J/1 Autocrat G-AGXV	£ 6,250
Auster AOP.9 G-BWKK/XP279	£ 11,000
Avro Vulcan B.2A G-VULC/XM655	no bids, at Wellesbourne Mountford, see page 132
Beech D.18S N96240	withdrawn, at Rochester Airport, see page 72
CASA 352L G-BECL	withdrawn, at Coventry Airport, see page 130
CCF Harvard IV/'Zero' G-BJST	withdrawn, ex Kemble.
DH.104 Dove 8 G-ARBE	£ 58,000
Douglas C-47A N54607	£ 32,000, at Liverpool Airport, see page 95
Douglas DC-3-201A N4565L	withdrawn, at Ipswich Airport, see page 120
Fairey Gannet AEW.3 G-BMYP/XL502	£110,000
LET Super Aero 45-04 G-APRR	£ 13,000, *Luftwaffe* colours.
Lockheed C-130A-50-LM Hercules EL-AJM/A92-207	withdrawn, in Australia.
Lockheed T-33A-1-LO G-TJET	withdrawn, at Cranfield, see page 11
Max Holste Broussard G-BKPT	£ 11,000
Nord 3202 G-BIZK	£ 8,000, at Liverpool Airport, see page 95
Nord 3202 G-BIZM	withdrawn, at Liverpool Airport.
Nord 3400 No 37	withdrawn, on site, see Coventry Airport, see page 130
Nord 3400 No 124/N9048P	withdrawn, on site, see Coventry Airport, see page 130
North American TB-25N Mitchell NL9494Z	withdrawn at Coventry Airport, see page 130
Percival Pembroke C.1 N46EA	£ 2,000, at Staverton, see page 49
Percival Sea Prince T.1 G-DACA	withdrawn, at Staverton, see page 49
Percival Sea Prince T.1 G-GACA	withdrawn, at Staverton, see page 49
Percival Sea Prince T.1 G-RACA	£ 7,500, at Staverton, see page 49
Percival Sea Prince T.1 G-TACA	withdrawn, at Staverton, see page 49
Piaggio FWP.149D G-TOWN	withdrawn, on site.
Pilatus P.2-05 G-PTWO	£ 17,500
SARO Skeeter AOP.12 XL765	£ 1,800, see Leamington Spa, page 131
Slingsby Kirby Kite I BGA.285	£ 1,750
Stampe SV-4C G-BKSX	£ 16,000
Stinson L-5C-VW N8035H	withdrawn, at Liverpool Airport.
Vickers Viscount 813 G-BMAT	£ 90,000, at Coventry Airport, see page 130
Vickers Viscount 814 G-BAPF	£135,000, at Coventry Airport, see page 130

Wilkins & Wilkins, North Weald, 9 April 1988

Held in conjunction with Aces High, the second W&W auction was staged in and around the 'Aces hangar. There were no 'absentee' aircraft this time and again there was a large modern civil content which we will not list.

Auster AOP.9 WZ662/G-BKVK	£ 14,000
Beech C-45H Expediter G-BKRG	£ 15,000, Aces High, see page 45
CCF T-6G Texan G-BGPB	£ 37,500 Robs Lamplough, see page 45
DH Dove 8 G-ASMG	£ 40,000
DH Dove 8 G-AVVF	£ 40,000
DH Venom FB.54 N203DM	£ 7,500, Aces High, see page 45
Douglas AD-4W Skyraider G-BMFC	£ 67,000, Robs Lamplough, see page 45
Fairchild Argus III HB751/G-BCBL	£ 24,000
Fairchild C-119G Flying Boxcar N2700	£ 20,000, Aces High, see page 45
Gloster Meteor T.7 VZ638/G-JETM	£ 15,000, Aces High, see page 45
LET Super Aero 45-04 G-APRR	£ 12,000
LET Super Aero 45 dismantled for spares	£ 5,500
Morane-Saulnier MS.760 Paris IIB F-BNRG	£ 75,000
NAA TB-25J Mitchell N9089Z	£ 49,500, Aces High, see page 45
Supermarine Spitfire XIV G-FXIV/MV370	£150,000, Robs Lamplough, see page 45
Waco UPF-7 G-WACO	£ 56,000

Appendix F FURTHER READING

Space limitations have given rise to a reduced format for this section. Clearly, in putting together a book such as W&R, as well as the ever-so-vital human inputs, a lot of reference sources are dipped into and of these the enthusiast produced magazines are by far and away the most helpful. Addresses are given for readers to make enquiries of a group or society mentioned below. Following that comes a listing of professionally published magazines and journals and books, by way of a bibliography.

Enthusiast Magazines

Air-Britain News, Aeromilitaria, and Archive. monthly and quarterly magazines from Air-Britain (Historians) Ltd. Contact : B R Womersley, 19 The Pastures, Westwood, Bradford-on-Avon, Wiltshire.
Air-Strip monthly journal of the Midland Counties Aviation Society. Contact : R Queenborough, 17 Leylan Croft, Birmingham B13 0DB.
British Aviation Review and Roundel monthly and bi-monthly journal of the British Aviation Research Group. Contact : Paul Hewins, 8 Nightingale Road, Woodley, Berkshire RG5 3LP.
Humberside Air Review monthly journal of the Humberside Aviation Society. Contact : 4 Bleach Yard, New Walk, Beverley, Humberside HU17 7HG.
Irish Air Letter monthly journal published by Eamon Power, Karl Hayes and Paul Cunniffe. Contact : 25 Phoenix Avenue, Castleknock, Dublin 15, Eire.
NAG-MAG monthly journal of the Norfolk Aviation Group. Contact : Maurice Baalham, near Village Hall, Witton, North Walsham, Norfolk NR28 9TU.
Osprey monthly journal of the Solent Aviation Society. Contact : Doreen Eaves, 84 Carnation Road, Bassett, Southampton SO2 3JL.
South West Aviation News monthly magazine of the South West Aviation Society. Contact : Richard Hodgkinson, Marsh Farm, Salford Priors, near Evesham, Worcs WR11 5SG.
Stansted Aviation Society News monthly journal of the Stansted Aviation Society. Contact : D B Cullum, 1 Elmwood, Sawbridgeworth, Herts CM21 9NL.
Strobe monthly journal of the East of England Aviation Group. Contact : Alan Warnes, 7 Gayton Court, Westwood, Peterborough, Cambs PE3 7DB.
Winged Words monthly journal of The Aviation Society. Contact : Barrie Shore, 6 Martin Drive, Darwen, Lancs BB3 2HW.

Magazines and Periodicals

Aeroplane Monthly, monthly magazine published by Reed Business Publishing Ltd..
Aviation News, fortnightly magazine published by Alan W Hall (Publications) Ltd.
Control Column, eight-a-year magazine published by Neville Franklin.
FlyPast, monthly magazine published by Key Publishing Ltd.
Popular Flying, bi-monthly magazine published by the Popular Flying Association.
Propliner, quarterly magazine published by Tony Eastwood.
Update, quarterly bulletin published by the British Aircraft Preservation Council.
Warbirds Worldwide, quarterly published by Paul Coggan

Books

Air Min, P H Butler, Merseyside Aviation Society, 1977.
Avro Vulcan, R Jackson, Patrick Stephens, 1984.
British Gliders, P H Butler, Merseyside Aviation Society, 1980.
British Homebuilt Aircraft since 1920, K Ellis, Merseyside Aviation Society, 1979.
British Military Aircraft Serials 1878-1987, B Robertson, Midland Counties Publications, 1987.
British Military Aircraft Serials & Markings, M I Draper, M H Pettit, D A Rough, T E Stone, British Aviation Research Group, 1980.
Civil Aircraft Registers of Great Britain 1919-1985, J Appleton, The Aviation Hobby Shop, 1985.
DH Dove & Heron, C Barber, D Shaw & T Sykes, Air-Britain, 1973.
Douglas DC-3 Survivors, A Pearcy, Aston Publications, 1987.
English Electric/BAC Lightning, B Philpott, Patrick Stephens, 1984.
Falklands - The Air War, M I Draper, M H Pettit, D A Rough, T E Stone, D Wilton, British Aviation Research Group, 1986.

Harrier, F K Mason, Patrick Stephens, 1983.
Hawker Hunter : Biography of a Thoroughbred, F K Mason, Patrick Stephens, 1981.
Hawker Siddeley Gnat F.1 & T.1, P A Jackson, Alan W Hall Publications, 1982.
Hitch Hiker's Guide to the Galaxy, A Dent, F Prefect and others, Megadodo Publications, constantly updated.
In Uniform, K Ellis, Merseyside Aviation Society, 1983.
Irish Aircraft Register 1987, C F Corcoran, Irish Aviation Press, 1986.
Meteor : Britain's First Jet Fighter, S J Bond, Midland Counties Publications, 1985.
Mosquito Survivors, S Howe, Aston Publications, 1986.
Mustang Survivors, P A Coggan, Aston Publications, 1987.
Royal Air Force Aircraft WA100 to WZ999, J J Halley, Air-Britain, 1983 - and others in the series.
Royal Navy Instructional Airframes, BARG Naval Research Group, British Aviation Research Group, 1978.
Spitfire Survivors Around the World, G Riley & G Trant, Aston Publications, 1986.
Squadrons of the Fleet Air Arm, R Sturtivant, Air-Britain, 1984.
Squadrons of the Royal Air Force, J J Halley, Air-Britain, 1979.
Under B Conditions, D S Revell, Merseyside Aviation Society, 1978.
United Kingdom & Eire Civil Registers, M P Fillmore, Air-Britain, 1987
United States Military Designations & Serials since 1909, J M Andrade, Midland Counties Publications, 1979.
Vickers Viscount & Vanguard, P W Davis, Air-Britain, 1981.
Viking, Valetta & Varsity, B Martin, Air-Britain, 1975.

ABBREVIATIONS

Appendix G

Without the use of abbreviations for the 'potted' histories of the aircraft listed in *Wrecks & Relics* the book would be of unmanagable size. Greatest change with this edition is the removal of one abbreviation altogehter : 'Sqn' (Squadron), thus shortening the history entries for operational aircraft that saw a lot of units. Any one, two or three digit number presented in the history listings can be regarded as a squadron - other reference works follow such lines and it is believed readers will have no problems with this. Units etc currently in existence are denoted thus *.

A
A&AEE* — Aeroplane and Armament Experimental Establishment, *test and trials facility, based Boscombe Down.*
AAC* — Army Air Corps, *headquarters at Middle Wallop.*
AACU — Anti-Aircraft Co-operation Unit, *gunnery facilities unit.*
ACU — Andover Conversion Unit, *type conversion unit, based Abingdon.*
ADS — Air Director School, *FAA for aircrew training, now part of FRADU.*
AE&AEOS — Air Engineers and Air Electronic Operators School, *aircrew school.*
AEF* — Air Experience Flight, *Chipmunk units to give Cadets etc air experience.*
AES — Air Engineers School, *aircrew school, became part of AE&AEOS.*
AES* — Air Engineering School, *FAA ground school, based at Lee-on-Solent.*
AETW* — Air Engineering Training Wing, *AAC ground school, based at Middle Wallop.*
AFDS — Air Fighting Development Squadron, *tactics and trials unit.*
AFEE — Airborne Forces Experimental Establishment, *test and trials unit.*
AFNE* — Air Forces North East, *communications unit, based in Norway for NATO.*
AFS — Advanced Flying School, *replaced by the FTSs.*
AFWF* — Advanced Fixed Wing Flight, *AAC training unit, based at Middle Wallop.*
AIU* — Accident Investigation Unit, *ground based investigation unit, most well known example based at Farnborough, FAA also have an AIU based at Lee-on-Solent.*
ALAT* — Aviation Legere de l'Armee de Terre, *French army aviation.*
AMS* — Air Movements School, *loadmasters school, based at Brize Norton.*
ANS — Air Navigation School, *flying training unit.*
AOTS — Aircrew Officers Training School, *conitnuation training unit.*
APS* — Aircraft Preservation Society, *standard use suffix.*
APS — Armament Practice Station, *live firing and bombing facility.*
arr — arrived, *denotes airframe arrived at location by surface transport.*
ARWF* — Advanced Rotary Wing Flight, *AAC training unit, based at Middle Wallop.*
AS&RU* — Aircraft Salvage and Repair Unit, *recovery and transportation unit, based at Abingdon.*
ASS — Air Signals School, *radio and telegraphy flying training unit.*
AST* — Air Service Training, *civilian flying and ground school, based Perth.*
ASWDU — Anti-Submarine Warfare Development Unit, *based at St Mawgan.*
ATA — Air Transport Auxiliary, *ferry and communications unit.*
ATAIU-SEA — Allied Technical Air Intelligence Unit - South East Asia, *evaluation unit.*
ATC* — Air Training Corps, *RAF youth recruitment/training/educational body.*
ATDU — Air Torpedo Development Unit, *trials unit, based at Gosport.*
AuxAF — Auxiliary Air Force, *part time militia air arm.*
aw/cn — AWaiting CollectioN, *signal from manufacturer to a Service that an aircraft is ready to pick up, either new build, repaired or modified.*
AWFCS — All Weather Fighter Combat School, *operational training unit.*
AWOCU — All Weather Operational Conversion Unit, *operational training unit.*

B
BA — British Airways, *mega airline that swallowed BOAC, BEA, British Caledonian and a lot of taxpayers' money.*
BAAT — British Airways Airtours, *tour division of BA.*
BAC — British Aircraft Corporation, *now British Aerospace plc.*
BAe* — British Aerospace, *the United Kingdom's national aerospace industry.*
BAH — British Airways Helicopters.
BAOR* — British Army of the Rhine, *British Army forces in West Germany.*
BAPC* — British Aircraft Preservation Council, *national council to oversee and promote aircraft preservation.*

B	BATUS*	British Army Training Unit, Suffield, *British army cold weather training facility in Canada,*
	BBMF*	Battle of Britain Memorial Flight, *well known airshow attenders, based Coningsby,*
	BCBS	Bomber Command Bombing School, *became SCBS,*
	BCCF/S	Bomber Command Communications Flight/Squadron, *communications unit,*
	BCDU	Bomber Command Development Unit, *trials unit,*
	BDRF*	Battle Damage Repair Flight, *ground school, based at Abingdon,*
	BDRT*	Battle Damage Repair Training, *the art of patching up a shot up aircraft,*
	BDTF	Bomber Defence Training Flight, *air gunner familiarisation and training unit,*
	BDU	Bomber Development Unit, *trials and installations unit,*
	BEA	British European Airways, *now part of BA,*
	BFTS	Basic Flying Training School, *flying school,*
	BFWF*	Basic Fixed Wing Flight, *AAC training unit, based at Middle Wallop,*
	B&GS	Bombings & Gunnery School (RCAF), *flying training unit,*
	BOAC	British Overseas Airways Corporation, *airline, became BA,*
	BRNC*	Britannia Royal Naval College, *ground school, based at Dartmouth - see also FGF,*
C	C(A)	Controller (Aircraft), *body that 'owns' trials aircraft, also CS(A) - Controller, Services (Air),*
	CAA*	Civil Aviation Authority, *UK administrative authority,*
	CAACU	Civilian Anti-Aircraft Co-operation Unit, *gunnery facilities unit,*
	CAFU*	Civil Aviation Flying Unit, *calibration and standards unit, now at Stansted,*
	Cam Flt	Camouflage Flight, *flying unit for checking the effectiveness of camouflage,*
	CATCS*	Central Air Traffic Control School, *ground and flying unit, based at Shawbury,*
	CAW	College of Air Warfare, *weapons and tactics school, now part of RAFC,*
	CBE	Central Bombing Establishment, *trials unit, based at Marham,*
	CCAS	Civilian Craft Apprentices School, *ground school, became CTTS,*
	CCF*	Combined Cadet Force, *recruitment and education organisation,*
	CF	Communications Flight, *as suffix with other unit, or for an airfield,*
	CFE	Central Fighter Establishment, *trials unit, based West Raynham,*
	CFS*	Central Flying School, *instructor school, headquarters at Scampton with other bases,*
	CFCCU	Civilian Fighter Control and Co-operation Unit, *radar facilities flight,*
	C&TTS	Communications and Target Towing Squadron, *general duties flight,*
	CGS	Central Gunnery School, *gunnery and armament school,*
	CGS*	Central Gliding School, *instructor school, based at Syerston,*
	CIFAS*	Centre d'Instruction des Forces Aeriennes Strategiques, *French conversion unit,*
	CNCS	Central Navigation and Control School, *became CATCS,*
	CoA*	Certificate (or Permit) of Airworthiness, *generally quoted with expiry date,*
	Cott	Cottesmore, *in relation to V-Bomber wings,*
	CPF	Coastal Patrol Flight, anti-submarine unit, equipped with Hornet Moths and Tiger Moths,
	cr	crashed, *or other form of accident,*
	CRD	Controller, Research and Development, *Government purchasing and research body,*
	C&RS	Control and Reporting School, *procedures school,*
	CS	Communications Squadron, *as a suffix with other units, or for an airfield,*
	CS(A)*	Controller, Services (Air), *Government purchasing body, can also be given as CA,*
	CSE	Central Signals Establishment, *electronics and radio trials unit, Also major flying school and fixed-base operator at Oxford Airport,*
	CSF*	Canberra Servicing Flight, *based at Wyton,*
	CTTS*	Civilian Technical Training School, ground school, based at St Athan,
D	dbr	damaged beyond repair, *to distinguish an aircraft that was written off but did not crash,*
	del	delivered, *denotes an airframe that arrived by air,*
	DFLS	Day Fighter Leader School, *tactics and standards unit, based at West Raynham,*
E	ECTT*	Escadre de Chase Tous Temps, *French all weather conversion unit,*
	EFTS*	Elementary Flying Training School, *current example based at Swinderby,*
	ERS	Empire Radio School, *radio and telegraphy flying school,*
	Esc*	Escadre, *French squadron,*
	ETPS*	Empire Test Pilots School, *ground and flight school, now based at Boscombe Down,*
	ETS*	Engineering Training School, *ground school, based at Culdrose,*
	ETU	Experimental Trials Unit, *installations and trials unit,*
	EWE&TU*	Electronic Warfare Experimental and Training Unit, *based at Wyton,*

F FAA Fleet Air Arm.
FAAHAF* Fleet Air Arm Historic Aircraft Flight, *well known airshow attenders, based at Yeovilton.*
FCCS Fighter Command Communications Squadron, *communications unit.*
FC&RS Fighter Control and Reporting School, *procedures school.*
FEAF Far East Air Forces, *RAF 'owning' unit for any aircraft in South East Asia.*
FECS Far East Communications Flight, *communications unit.*
FF&SS* Fire Fighting and Safety School, *ground school, based at Catterick.*
FGF* Flying Grading Flight, *flying school, based at Plymouth Airport.*
FLS Fighter Leader School, *an element of DFLS.*
F* Flight, *see notes at header.*
FOAC Flag Officer, Aircraft Carriers, *naval officer, with communications aircraft.*
FP Ferry Pool, *ferry communications holding unit.*
FPP Ferry Pilots Pool, *ferry communications unit.*
FRADU* Fleet Requirements and Development Unit, *gunnery and facilities unit, based Yeovilton.*
FRL* Flight Refuelling Ltd, *fleet operating and trials company.*
FRS Flying Refresher School, *flying standards unit.*
FRU Fleet Requirements Unit, *became FRADU.*
FSS Ferry Support Squadron, *communications unit.*
FSS Flying Selection Squadron, *became EFTS.*
FTC Flying Training Command.
FTS* Flying Training School, *basic or advanced flying school.*
FU Ferry Unit, *communications and ferry unit.*
FWS Fighter Weapons Unit, *armament school.*
G GE* Groupement Ecole, *French Air Force training unit.*
GCF Group Communications Flight, *communications unit.*
GTS Glider Training School, *flying school.*
GS Glider School, *flying training school.*
GSU Ground Support Unit, *army co-operation unit.*
GU Glider Unit, *holding both assault gliders and aircraft.*
H HAB Hot air balloon.
HCCF/S Home Command Communications Flight/Squadron, *communications unit.*
HCEU Home Command Examining Unit, *standards unit.*
HCF Hornet Conversion Flight, *type conversion unit.*
HDU Helicopter Development Unit, *experimental and trials unit.*
HQ Headquarters.
HS Handling Squadron, *unit tasked with writing pilot's notes for a type.*
HTF Helicopter Training Flight, *training unit, based at Middle Wallop.*
I IAM* Institute of Aviation Medicine, *research unit, based at Farnborough.*
IWM Imperial War Museum, *based at South Lambeth and Duxford.*
J JEHU Joint Experimental Helicopter Unit, *trials unit.*
JMU Joint Maritime Unit, *experimental and trials unit.*
JASS Joint Anti-Submarine School, *inter-service school.*
JCU Javelin Conversion Unit, *type conversion school.*
JWE Joint Warfare Establishment, *trials unit, based at Old Sarum.*
L LTF Lightning Training Flight, *conversion unit.*
M MCS Metropolitan Communications Squadron, *communications unit.*
MEAF Middle East Air Force, *often used in an aircraft's history to denote transfer to that theatre, when specific units are not known.*
MECS Middle East Communications Squadron, *communications unit.*
MinTech Ministry of Technology, *government operating/research unit, more often than not denoting an aircraft used by RAE or manufacturer.*
MoA Ministry of Aviation, *see MinTech entry.*
MoS Ministry of Supply, *see MinTech entry.*
MOTU Maritime Operational Training Unit, *training unit, flying Shackletons, based St Mawgan.*
MPA Man powered aircraft.

M MU* Maintenance Unit, *overhaul, repair and storage facility. The following are mentioned in the main text ; 4 Stanmore Park (detachment); 5 Kemble; 6 Brize Norton, 7 Quedgeley; 8 Little Rissington; 9 Cosford; 10 Hullavington; 12 Kirkbride; 14 Carlisle; 15 Wroughton; 16 Stafford; 19 St Athan (also 32); 20 Aston Down; 22 Silloth; 23 Aldergrove; 27 Shawbury; 29 High Ercall; 32 St Athan (also 19); 39 Colerne; 44 Edzell; 46 Lossiemouth; 47 Sealand; 48 Hawarden; 54 Cambridge; 57 Wig Bay; 60 Leconfield; 71 Bicester; 431 Bruggen.*

N NACDS* Naval Air Command Driving School, *ground school, based at Culdrose.*

NASU* Naval Aircraft Servicing Unit, *maintenance and repair units, at Culdrose and Yeovilton.*

nea Non effective airframe, *downgrading of an aircraft to non-flying status for long term store.*

NCS Northern Communications Squadron, *communications unit, based at Topcliffe.*

NSF Northern Sector Flight, *general duties unit.*

O OCU* Operational Conversion Unit, *type conversion unit.*

OCTU Officer Cadet Training Unit, *experience school, based at Henlow and Jurby.*

OTU Operational Training Unit, *front line training unit.*

P (P)AFU (Pilot) Advanced Flying Unit, *flying school.*

PAX Passenger, *as used in Chipmunk PAX trainer, familiarisation trainer.*

PCSS Protectorate Communications and Support Squadron, *general duties flight, based Aden.*

PEE* Proof and Experimental Establishment, *research and trials facility, at Foulness Island.*

PFS Primary Flying School, *flying training unit.*

PP Pilot's Pool, *communications and ferry unit.*

PRDU Photo Reconnaissance Development Unit, *development and trials unit.*

PTF Phantom Training Flight, *conversion unit, based at Leuchars.*

PTS Primary Training School, flying training unit.

R RAAF* Royal Australian Air Force.

RAE* Royal Aircraft Establishment and renamed 4/88 the Royal Aerospace Establishment, research and development facility, bases at Aberporth, Bedford, Farnborough, Lasham, Llanbedr, West Freugh.

RAeS Royal Aeronautical Society.

RAF Royal Air Force.

RAFA Royal Air Force Association, *benevolent association.*

RAFC* Royal Air Force College, *graduate school, based at Cranwell.*

RAFEF* Royal Air Force Exhibition Flight, *recruitment display unit, based at Abingdon.*

RAFG* Royal Air Force Germany.

RAFGSA* Royal Air Force Gliding and Soaring Association, *regional gliding clubs.*

RAFHSF Royal Air Force High Speed Flight, *record breaking and trials unit.*

RAN* Royal Australian Navy.

RCAF Royal Canadian Air Force, *now Canadian Armed Forces.*

Regt Regiment, *Army unit, using Austers and/or helicopters.*

RNAY* Royal Naval Aircraft Yard, *naval equivalent of an MU, at Fleetlands and Wroughton.*

RNEC* Royal Naval Engineering College, *ground school, based Manadon.*

ROC* Royal Observer Corps, *part time observation and monitoring organisation.*

RPRE* Rocket Propulsion Research Establishment, *based at Spadeadam and Westcott.*

RRE Royal Radar Establishment, *experimental and trials unit, became RSRE.*

RRF Radar Reconnaissance Flight, *trials unit.*

RS Radio School, *ground and flying school.*

RSRE Radar and Signals Research Establishment, *was based at Pershore, absorbed by RAE.*

RTR* Royal Tank Regiment, *Auster and helicopters operator.*

S SAAF* South African Air Force.

SAC School of Army Co-operation, *flying school, based at Old Sarum.*

SAF School of Aerial Fighting, *flying school.*

SAH* School of Aircraft Handling, *ground school, based at Culdrose.*

SAR* Search and Rescue.

SAREW* Search and Rescue Engineering Wing, *maintenance unit, based at Finningley.*

SARTS* Search and Rescue Training Squadron, *flying school, based at Valley.*

Scamp Scampton, *to distinguish a V-Bomber wing.*

SCBS Strike Command Bombing School, *became part of the 230 OCU and then disbanded.*

SCS Southern Communications Squadron, *communications unit.*

S	SER	Static External Replica, *outwardly a replica of the aircraft in question, but using non-original construction techniques,*
	SF*	Station Flight, *general duties and communications unit, usual prefixed by an airfield name,*
	ShF*	Ship's Flight, *ship with aircraft detached, usually prefixed with a ship's name,*
	SFTS	Service Flying Training School, *basic flying school,*
	soc	Struck off charge, *removed from service inventory, written off,*
	SoRF	School of Refresher Training, *standards unit, absorbed into 3 FTS at Leeming,*
	SoTT*	School of Technical Training, *ground school. The following are mentioned in the main text ; 1 Halton (current); 2 Cosford (current); 4 St Athan; 8 Weeton; 9 Newton; 10 Kirkham; 12 Melksham,*
	SRCU	Short Range Conversion Unit, *conversion unit, flying Pioneers from Odiham,*
	SS	Signals Squadron, *radio and electronics unit,*
	SS	Support Squadron, *general duties and communications flight,*
	SU	Support Unit, *general duties flight,*
T	TAC	The Aeroplane Collection, *based in Manchester,*
	TAF	Tactical Air Force, *NATO component force in Europe,*
	TAW*	Tactical Airlift Wing, *USAF transport unit,*
	TCCF	Transport Command Communications Flight, *communications unit,*
	TEU	Tactical Exercise Unit, *training and co-operation unit,*
	TFF	Target Facilities Flight, *target interception training facility,*
	TFTAS*	Tactical Fighter Training Aggressor Squadron, *USAF tactics and training unit, 527th based at Alconbury,*
	TFW*	Tactical Fighter Wing, *USAF fighter unit,*
	Thum Flt	Temperature and HUMidity Flight, *weather monitoring flight, based Woodvale,*
	toc	Taken on charge, *date aircraft accepted into service,*
	TRE	Telecommunications Research Establishment, *based at Defford,*
	TS	Training Squadron, *training unit,*
	TTCCF	Technical Training Command Communications Flight, *communications unit,*
	TWU	Tactical Weapons Unit, *armament school, 1 TWU at Brawdy, 2 TWU at Chivenor,*
U	UAS*	University Air Squadron, *reservist flying training school. Prefixed with a university name, with the following abbreviations ; Abn - Aberdeen & St Andrews; Bir - Birmingham; Bri - Bristol; Cam - Cambridge; Dur - Durham; Edn - Edinburgh; Elo - East Lowlands; Ems - East Midlands; G&S - Glasgow & Strathcylde; Lee - Leeds; Liv - Liverpool; Lon - London; Man - Manchester & Salford; Nor - Northumbrian; Not - Nottingham; Oxf - Oxford; QUB - Queens University Belfast; Stn - Southampton; Wal - Wales; Yor - Yorkshire,*
	UNFICYP*	United Nations Forces In Cyprus, *international peace-keeping force,*
	USAF*	United States Air Force,
	USAAF	United States Army Air Force, *became USAF in 1948,*
	USMC*	United States Marine Corps,
	USN*	United States Navy,
W	Wadd	Waddington, *denoting a V-Bomber wing,*
	WCS	Western Communications Squadron, *communications unit,*
	Witt	Wittering, *denoting a V-bomber wing,*
	WSF	Western Sector Flight, *general duties unit,*

TYPE INDEX

C

D

E

T

LOCATIONS INDEX

European Wrecks & Relics

'Why can't there be a *Wrecks & Relics* for Europe?' the occasional sadistic reader will ask. The answer has normally been somewhat short, deeply philosophical and always in the negative.

But not anymore. It is planned to launch during the summer of 1989 a brother/sister companion to *Wrecks & Relics* that will span the whole of Europe, in the same style of coverage as the British version, both for civil and military. There have been several W&R-type books launched on the continent before now, specialising in one particular country and normally concentrating on the military side of things, but never a single comprehensive reference work.

As with the British version, *European Wrecks & Relics* will rely heavily on inputs from readers and contributions in the form of notes, up-dates, suggestions and photographs will all be welcomed by the editor. The editor of this tome is very pleased and at the same time relieved to say that someone has stepped forward to undertake this massive work - Mike Bursell, well known editor of the Foreign Military section of the excellent *Humberside Air Review.* Mike looks forward to hearing from you, via the address below.

Publishers will be Midland Counties Publications and announcements about publication date and price will be made via the aviation press and their mail-order catalogues.

Wrecks & Relics 10th Edition

Each edition of *Wrecks & Relics* relies heavily on the edition before it in order to paint an accurate picture of the two-year span of events at every location in the UK and Eire. If you have not got the 10th edition (which celebrated 25 years of publication of the title), you will be pleased to know that limited stocks of the work are still available from Midland Counties Publications, priced £8.50 (including post and packing).

Aviation & Military Books by Post

We stock many thousands of books from all over the world for world-wide mail order. Our quick turn-round and superb packing is unrivalled. Free informative and illustrated catalogue on request - write or 'phone –

Midland Counties Publications
24 The Hollow
Earl Shilton
Leicester
LE9 7NA

Telephone: 0455 - 47091/47256

WARBIRDS WORLDWIDE

The top quality journal on the restoration and operation of ex-military aircraft, published quarterly. Printed on glossy paper with laminated colour covers, each issue includes approx 120 b/w and six pages of colour photos. 48pp A4 Softback.

SUBSCRIPTIONS WELCOME

Issue 1: Project Vulcan; Corsair NX1337A; Blenheim experience; Australia's last Spitfire; Albatross HU-16 restoration; MiG-15 profile; Bearcat survivors; Tico.

Issue 2: Boeing B-17 G-FORT goes home; Benson's Me109; Hispano Ha.1112MIL survey; SAAF T-6s; Me109 survivors; Filming of 'Empire of the Sun'; Blenheim swansong; Baghdad Furies.

Issue 3: The Fighter Collection; Unlimited Race results; P-47 Thunderbolt pilot report; VAT's Vampire and Venom; SAAF Harvard flight; John Sandeberg's 'Tsunami' racer.

Issue 4: Texas Air Museum; Fw190F-8 rebuild; Mosquito to Miami; P-51 review; Mitchell round up; Liquid Cooled Hawks part 2; Gnats in the USA; Harvard display team.

Issue 5: Old Flying Machine Company; making of the 'Battle of Britain' film; Military Austers - minimum warbird; Ventura adventure pt.2; Bombertown, Florida; Wirraway rebuilders report.

Issue 6: Warbirds at Oshkosh '88; restoration of Yak F-AZNN; Bombertown, Florida pt.2; making of the 'Battle of Britain' film part 2; Douglas Skyraider;

Mustangs Worldwide A 'Warbirds' special, surveys the remaining P-51s around the world, plus special features on Dominican P-51s; Flying the P-51; the fall and rise of 'Silver Dollar'; cockpits and more.

Each issue **£3.95** *post free*
from the worldwide distributors
MIDLAND COUNTIES PUBLICATIONS
24 The Hollow, Earl Shilton, Leicester, LE9 7NA
Telephone: 0455 47091